S O N I C S

TECHNIQUES FOR THE USE OF
SOUND AND ULTRASOUND IN
ENGINEERING AND SCIENCE

SONICS

TECHNIQUES FOR THE USE OF SOUND AND ULTRASOUND IN ENGINEERING AND SCIENCE

THEODOR F. HUETER

Research Associate in Physics
Massachusetts Institute of Technology

RICHARD H. BOLT

Professor of Acoustics
Massachusetts Institute of Technology

JOHN WILEY & SONS, INC., NEW YORK

CHAPMAN & HALL, LIMITED, LONDON

Library of Congress Catalog Card Number: 55-6388

Printed in the United States of America

PREFACE

During the past few years we have received many inquiries regarding industrial uses of sound and ultrasound: metals testing, spot welding, drilling, gas analysis, medical diagnosis, aerosol agglomeration, fish location, clothes washing, degreasing—these and many other real or imaginary uses of sound have come up for discussion. In trying to solve some of these problems and in studying the expanding literature on these seemingly unrelated subjects, we began to see that a new area of technology was taking shape. The multiplicity of concepts and techniques could be designated by the name *sonics*, much as electronics and nucleonics connote particular areas of technical practice.

Sonics encompasses the analysis, testing, and processing of materials and products by the use of mechanical vibratory energy. The particular frequency that is best suited for a given task is determined by the special requirements and limitations of that task. All applications, however, are based on the same physical principles, and the relation of the frequency to the range of audibility for man's ear is irrelevant from this point of view.

The unity of *sonics* is, therefore, the keynote of this book. The common principles are presented in general form and then applied in many special ways to the design of sonic techniques for a particular medium or frequency range. The relevant fundamentals of vibration and sound are given in Chapters 2 and 3, and general aspects of transducers for sound generation and reception are presented in Chapters 4 and 5. The applications are divided into two branches: sonic processing, Chapters 6 and 7; and sonic analysis, Chapter 8. Molecular aspects of sound propagation in fluids, a topic of particular interest in modern physics, are discussed in the Appendix following Chapter 8.

The wide diversity in the possible applications of sonics and in the professional backgrounds of its potential users has posed our most challenging problem. A book that was understandable only to an advanced physicist would be of limited usefulness in many industrial developments. A purely practical discussion of devices and design formulas would not provide an adequate basis for the exploration of

v

entirely new applications. We have tried to find a middle ground. The underlying physics is presented as simply as possible, with plausibility arguments frequently used in place of rigorous derivations. The associated mathematical expressions are also given in simple form, but in many cases the implications of a fuller mathematical treatment are pointed out in a footnote or in small type, as in our discussion of the tensor notation for crystal transducers.

Wherever possible a discussion is concluded with simplified engineering formulas and with practical instructions for their use. We have deliberately not discussed, or even enumerated, all of the applications that have been mentioned in the literature. Instead, typical examples have been selected that illustrate the operating principles and that suggest other uses in many fields. We have tried to make this book understandable to anyone with college training or its equivalent in any branch of science or engineering. In particular, we have assumed that the reader has little or no specialized training in acoustics, but that he has some understanding of electronics.

The bibliography and the references to collateral reading have been selected with particular care. We have included only those that are most informative on a given subject or that give the most recent review of earlier developments along a particular line. Extensive bibliographies, to more than 5000 entries, are contained in other publications to which we refer.

Our attempts to systematize this subject started in 1950 when we prepared a series of lectures which one of us (R.H.B.) delivered during successive weeks to the Shell Development Company, San Francisco, and the California Research Corporation, La Habra, California. We are greatly indebted to these two organizations for their encouragement in the starting of this book. In 1951 we gave a special summer session course, "Industrial Applications of Acoustics," at the Massachusetts Institute of Technology. Stimulating discussions by the participants, who represented many different industries, led to a considerable expansion of our subject matter. In the spring of 1953 one of us (T.F.H.) initiated a full-term course in the Department of Physics at Massachusetts Institute of Technology, using a large segment of this book for class notes. Suggestions made by the students have helped us in the final reworking of the manuscript.

We are indebted to many colleagues and industrial organizations for making available much interesting and timely information as noted in specific acknowledgments throughout the text. We are grateful to S. J. Lukasik and M. S. Cohen for careful reading and assistance with some of the material; to C. Twardzik for skillful drawing of the illustrations; and especially to F. Massa for critical review and many helpful suggestions. We also express deepest appreciation to our wives, whose complaints during our protracted period of writing lay strictly outside the audible range.

T. F. HUETER

R. H. BOLT

Cambridge, Massachusetts
November, 1954

CONTENTS

CHAPTER 1

Introduction

1.1   A Definition of "Sonics"

The field of acoustics, viewed broadly, deals with mechanical waves at all frequencies in all substances. The branch of architectural acoustics, which aims to endow buildings and rooms with good hearing conditions and with adequate protection against noise, is widely known. Equally prominent are the subjects of communication acoustics and electroacoustic instrumentation. Scientists and engineers in these branches contribute to the improvement of speech transmission through telephone, radio, and intercommunication systems, and to the design of microphones, loudspeakers, and apparatus for measuring sound. Still other phases of acoustics encompass the science of musical sounds and instruments, the behavior of the ear and the properties of speech, and the control of noise and vibration in machines.

In these pursuits, and many others, we are concerned primarily with audible sounds as such, and with their relation to man's sense of hearing. But, quite apart from the fortuitous role of man's ear, the phenomenon of acoustic vibration can be utilized in many ways. With sound waves we can sonograph (as with light waves we photograph) the inner structure of bodies opaque to light. Sound waves can penetrate many solids and liquids more readily than X-rays or other forms of electromagnetic energy. Thus sound can expose a tiny crack imbedded many feet in metal, where detection by any other means might be commercially impracticable if not impossible.

By acoustic techniques we can measure elastic constants of solid materials, and non-isotropic stresses and inhomogenieties can be analyzed. The molecular structure of many organic liquids can be inferred from sound measurements. Rates of energy transfer among gas molecules and chemical affinity of gaseous mixtures can be determined by using sound waves.

As soon as we can measure a process we have within reach a means of controlling it. Indeed, acoustic instrumentation offers extensive but virtually unexplored opportunities in the automatic control of industrial processes. The geometry of metal parts; the quality of cast metals and laminated plastics; the presence of foreign bodies in sealed containers; the composition of compounds in liquid or gas phase; the flow velocity of liquids and gases—these and many other process variables throughout industry may, in time, come under the watchful ear of acoustics.

In all these applications the sound is used as a measuring stick or flashlight—the amounts of power are small and incidental. In another class of applications large amounts of acoustic power are employed to do useful work. As a potent microagitator, sound will emulsify "immiscible" liquids, homogenize and disperse, depolymerize, and in other ways affect liquid products. Acting on gas mixtures and aerosols, sound can speed up agglomeration and collection of particles, and can influence the separation of gases.

Thus we have a rapidly developing branch of acoustics that does not serve man's ear but, rather, provides many useful techniques for industrial purposes. *Sonics*, then, is *the technology of sound as applied to problems of measurement, control, and processing.*

1.2 Frequency Limits

From the point of view of sonics, the distinction between audible and inaudible frequencies is arbitrary. Sonic frequencies as low as a few hundred cycles per second (cps) have been used commercially for homogenization, and sonic techniques for measuring dynamic mechanical properties of viscoelastic materials have been extended considerably below 1 cps. The range from 1 to 10 megacycles per second (mcps) is used widely in flaw-detection equipment, and laboratory research in properties of metals and liquids has pushed the upper frequency limit to several hundred megacycles per second.

We might ask whether sonics is ever likely to span more than the 9 or 10 decades of frequency that have already been explored. The answer can be derived in part from the physical nature of matter. The relationship of sound velocity, frequency, and wavelength ($c = f\lambda$) is of particular importance, and is illustrated in a general way in Fig. 1.1. In this figure gases, liquids, and metals are each represented by three substances. Air, water, and steel are included as commonly encountered, typical examples. The other two substances of each class illustrate the highest and lowest values of sound velocity normally found in each class. We see that gases cover a ten-fold range of wavelengths at a given frequency, while liquids cover only a three-fold range.

As the frequency of sound increases, the wavelength correspondingly decreases and approaches the dimensions of the atomic or molecular structure. The relevant dimension in a crystalline solid is the inter-atomic spacing; in a gas we might take the mean free path. In any case, a wave in the usual sense cannot exist if it tries to move through a medium of discrete particles spaced widely in comparison with its own wavelength. Motions can be imparted to such a system—a group of billiard balls on a table, for example—but the resulting behavior of the system is more logically described by the kinetics of the individual particles than by a wave-theory formulation which assumes a "continuous" medium. The limit thus imposed by the structure of matter ranges from 10^8 or 10^9 cps for gases at normal temperature and pressure to 10^{13} or 10^{14} cps for solids.

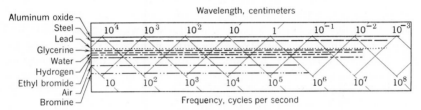

Fig. 1.1. Relation of wavelength to frequency of compressional acoustic waves in unbounded medium. Range covers maximum and minimum values for normal gases, liquids, and metals.

From a practical point of view, the useful limit will probably lie somewhat lower. At wavelengths even a few orders of magnitude greater than the structural dimensions, the attenuation of the sound becomes very high. The coherent acoustic energy is dissipated before it can go far enough to serve a useful purpose. From this consideration we can place the upper limits of industrial usefulness at about 10^6 cps in gases and 10^9 in liquids and solids.

A lower frequency limit of sonics must be set (if we must set one!) on a more arbitrary basis. The subject of vibration, a highly developed field of mechanical engineering, already covers a wide range of vibration rates, up to several hundred vibrations per second in some problems. Seismology deals with earth waves whose rates may fall in the lower range we are discussing. Waves of the order of $\frac{1}{10}$ cps are well known to the oceanographer and the mariner! Whether the waves are in liquids or solids, on the surface or inside the substance, whether longitudinal or flexural, whether of high or low frequency—they are all viewed alike (with minor variations) by the physicist.

Therefore the lower limit will be determined largely by engineering usage and convenience.

The field of acoustics in general has grown outward from the audible range. Within this range there have been developed certain characteristic methods of analysis and instrumentation. A notable example is the electroacoustic transducer which has been highly refined, in many forms, to facilitate sound generation and detection by convenient techniques of electronics. Some of this methodology can be extended several decades below the audible range to yield useful devices for industrial sonics.

1.3 Scope of Applications

We have sketched the boundaries of the field from the point of view of the physical phenomena involved. It is also interesting to outline the subject in terms of the branches of engineering to which sonics can be applied. These would include mechanical, electrical, and chemical engineering, biology and sanitation engineering, metallurgy, petroleum engineering, rubber technology, and food technology. Therefore, the techniques of sonics, like those of electronics, will be used by engineers and scientists of many different backgrounds. In few cases will it be expeditious for the specialist in the field of application to acquire a comprehensive training in acoustics. At the same time, his employment of sonics as a tool should be based on an adequate understanding of the principles, possibilities, and limitations of sonics. To fulfill this need is a primary purpose of this book.

Although the subject of sonics has not previously been synthesized into a working guide for the non-specialist in acoustics, there is a voluminous and diversified bibliography on the subject. Perhaps it is not surprising to find the literature from the formulative stage of a new field sprinkled with misconceptions, unjustified optimism, and speculations. The surging list of "amazing new uses of sound and ultrasound" might lead one to believe that sonics is a panacea for all the unsolved problems of industry. The many inevitable disappointments are apt to deter the exploitation of valid applications.

Even more important than the validity is the economic competitiveness of any proposed technique. Many processes that "work" in the laboratory must fall by the wayside simply because in full-scale application they cost too much. It is hoped that the material collected in this book will aid in evaluating the engineering economics of new uses on a rational basis.

A complete listing at this time of the hundreds of applications that have been suggested or explored would be misleading because very few of the cases have been investigated adequately for evaluating their technical and economic promise. The following outline will suggest to the reader the broad scope of problems to which sonics may be applied.

Analytical applications
  Geometrical analysis (dimensions, shape, flaw detection; see Sections 8.1 and 8.10).
  Dynamic analysis (moduli of elasticity and effects of viscosity; see Sections 8.2 and A.3).
  Molecular analysis (structure, composition, relaxation rates, etc.; see Appendix).
Power applications
  Mechanical effects (microagitation, cavitation, cutting, etc.; see Sections 6.5, 6.9, 7.4, and 7.5).
  Chemical effects (breaking of bonds, emulsification, electrokinetic effects; see Sections 6.9 and A.6).
  Biological effects (sterilizing, influencing growth, tissue heating; see Sections 6.9 and 7.3).
Instrumentation and control applications
  Process-control devices and systems (viscosimetry, gas analysis; see Sections 8.6 and A.4).
  Underwater signaling (see Sections 3.3, 4.11 and 5.9).
  Special devices (cavitometry, delay lines, flow meters, etc.; see Chapter 8).

The entire frequency range of sonic applications is shown in Table 1.1 with an indication of the parts of the spectrum that are most useful for each of the general classes of application. The ranges of usefulness of the basic types of sound generators are also shown. The limits shown in this table are inherently somewhat vague. They are determined to some extent by limitations in generating and detecting equipment, and these restrictions may in time be reduced by new developments. In relatively few applications have the basic physical limitations been fully explored to date. However, Table 1.1 is a useful guide to the frequency band and generating technique most likely to be appropriate for each type of problem.

1.4 The Choice of Units; The MKS System

The material covered in this book is drawn from many different domains. Although our approach will always be on the basis of simple reasoning, the final aim of our discussion is to present useful engineering knowledge to readers with various industrial backgrounds: to applied physicists, electrical engineers, mechanical engineers, chemical engineers, metallurgists, food technologists, and many others. This brings up the important question of terminology: which of the several systems of units will be most acceptable to the majority of readers.

Table 1.1. Ranges of Sonic Applications

Frequency, cps / Ranges:

10^{-2} 1 10^{2} 10^{4} 10^{6} 10^{8} 10^{10} 10^{12}

INFRAAUDIBLE ←——— AUDIBLE ——→ ← "Ultrasonic" ——— ULTRAAUDIBLE ———→ "Hypersonic"

Fields and Uses

- Crystal lattice vibrations
- Signaling in air
- Signaling in water
- Delay lines

Analysis

- Vibration engineering
- Geological exploration
- Seismology
- Ocean waves
- Viscosimetry
- Flaw detection
- Thickness gauging
- Analysis of molecular properties ..... Gases ..... Liquids..
- Measurement of dynamic elastic moduli

Processing

- Gas phase
- Liquid phase
- Mechanical power uses
- Drilling
- Medical applications

Generators

- Explosives
- Fluid-dynamic (whistles, sirens, etc.)
- Electrodynamic
- .... Mechanical vibrators →
- Magnetostrictive →
- Piezoelectric (BaTiO₃, ADP, Quartz, etc.)
- heat

Receivers

- Resistance strain gauges
- ——— Magnetic Vibration Pickups ———
- Piezoelectric receiving elements (mainly non-resonant ——— mainly resonant ——— harmonics)
- Radiation Pressure
- Optical Devices (Light Diffraction)
- x-rays

Frequency, cps:

10^{-2} 1 10^{2} 10^{4} 10^{6} 10^{8} 10^{10} 10^{12}

A survey of the literature reveals a great lack of uniformity. Usually the writer of a paper uses the units which are most common in his particular field of interest. Many of the existing books, however, which try to give a comprehensive account of acoustic phenomena and techniques, do not use the same units throughout; the metric system and the English system are intermingled, and an electromagnetic field quantity may occur in any one of four possible units. Such inconsistency reduces greatly the value of a book for engineering reference and basic teaching.

This predicament is not resolved easily, because the various professional groups are still divided over the choice of units which are preferable for practical work. It is generally recognized today, however, that the metric system has definite advantages over the English system. Furthermore, if the MKS (meter-kilogram-second) system is used, the resulting basic equations are simpler than if electrostatic or electromagnetic CGS units are used. These advantages are most apparent whenever equivalent circuits are employed for an analysis of mechanical or electromechanical networks in terms of the electric components capacity, inductance, and resistance.

For example, we shall relate the mechanical radiation impedance of a piezoelectric transducer to its electric input impedance by a simple formula $Z_{el} = Z_r/\alpha^2$, in which Z_r is the mechanical load impedance of the transducer and α is the turns ratio of a hypothetic ideal transformer between the mechanical and the electric terminals of the transducer. If we use mechanical CGS units for Z_r and electrostatic cgs units (esu) for α, the result has to be divided by 9×10^{11} in order to obtain Z_{el} in ohms. If MKS units are used for both Z_r and α, the equation yields Z_{el} in ohms, directly, and the power output is simply V^2/Z_{el} in watts, if V is the rms driving voltage of the crystal (see Chapter 4). Similar simple relationships evolve for magnetic drive mechanisms (see Chapter 5) if we express the field strength in those quantities which are directly measurable, that is, the current I (amperes) through a coil of N turns and of length l (meters): field strength $H = IN/l$ (amp-turns/m.).

It is hoped that the consistent use of the MKS system throughout this book will bring all its merits into light and will enable the reader to use this sytem to his advantage.[1] For the benefit of those who wish to continue using CGS units or English units, the information in many

---

[1] We shall use the MKS system in its *rationalized* form. This system was recommended in 1948 by the Ninth General Conference of Weights and Measures and the International Union of Pure and Applied Physics. At this conference the ampere was adopted as the fourth fundamental unit.

tables of the book is presented in the units of both systems. This practice, together with a conversion table (back end of book), will eliminate most of the difficulties of using data and equations in other units which appear in the literature.

Besides meters, kilograms, and seconds we shall use, as additional basic units, volts, amperes, and degrees Celsius (Centigrade). Also, the following secondary units will frequently occur:

For force: 1 newton = 1 kg·m/sec^2 = 10^5 dynes

For electric charge: 1 coulomb = 1 amp·sec = 3×10^9 esu

For magnetic induction: 1 weber = 1 volt·sec = 10^8 gauss

For power: 1 watt = 1 volt·amp = 1 kg·m^2/sec^3

$$= 10^7 \text{ ergs/sec}$$

Finally, we shall mention two basic equations by which the MKS system relates field strength (electric or magnetic) to either electric charge density (displacement) or magnetic flux density (induction):

Electric fields: $D = \epsilon\epsilon_0 E$ [coulombs/m^2]   (1.1)

Magnetic fields: $B = \mu\mu_0 H$ [webers/m^2]   (1.2)

In these equations two fundamental physical constants appear: the *rational* permittivity of free space:

$$\epsilon_0 = \frac{1}{4\pi \times 9 \times 10^9} \text{ farad/m} \tag{1.3}$$

and the *rational* permeability of free space:

$$\mu_0 = \frac{4\pi}{10^7} \text{ henry/m} \tag{1.4}$$

Both constants are related by

$$\mathbf{c}_0{}^2 = 1/\epsilon_0\mu_0 \tag{1.5}$$

in which $\mathbf{c}_0 = 3 \times 10^8$ (m/sec) is the velocity of light in free space. The constants ϵ and μ, on the other hand, have the same meaning as in the CGS system; that is, ϵ = permittivity of the medium relative to free space; μ = permeability of the medium relative to free space.[2]

---

[2] An excellent review of the basic definitions underlying the CGS and MKS systems is given by D. Williams, *Physics Today*, 7 (April, 1954), 8 (published by the American Institute of Physics, 51 East 55th Street, New York 22, N.Y.). This article is strongly recommended to those who have difficulty in following the modern trend of using rationalized MKS units in physics and engineering textbooks.

CHAPTER 2

Basic Principles

2.1 Fundamentals of Vibration

We have now blocked out the scope of the field in a general way, and are ready to consider the basic physical principles of sonics. First we shall review some fundamental concepts of vibration and wave motion, without regard to any particular medium or application. In this way we can sort out those characteristics of sound and vibration that are common to all uses of acoustics.

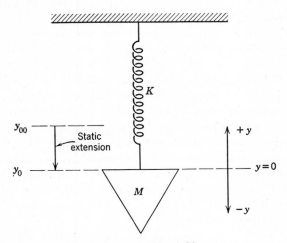

Fig. 2.1. A simple oscillator.

Let us start with a mass of M kg hanging on a spring of stiffness K newtons/m, as shown in Fig. 2.1.[1] At first the mass is at rest at its equilibrium position, which we shall designate y_0. Here the spring is extended somewhat in supporting the mass. In fact, the spring is extended to that point at which the stiffness-restoring force of

[1] Conversions from the MKS system of units to the CGS and English systems are given at the end of the book.

the spring just balances the gravitational force on the mass.   Let the original unextended position of the mass be y_{00}.   Then:

$$K(y_{00} - y_0) = Mg \qquad (2.1)$$

in which $g = 9.80$ m/sec^2 and displacement is measured in meters.

Linearity   Strictly speaking, the value of K is constant only as long as the spring is linear in behavior.   Then the spring obeys Hooke's law: the restoring force is proportional to the displacement. Most springs and elastic media are linear for very small displacements. This is true for air carrying audible sounds of moderate intensity; and air is simply a kind of spring, as we shall see in Section 2.8.

In most of the testing and analysis applications in industrial sonics, the elastic displacements of the medium are small enough to satisfy Hooke's law, and we can derive sufficiently accurate equations using only linear restoring forces.   In processing applications this is no longer so.   The high intensities required to influence the medium in some useful way are usually so great that the acoustic behavior becomes non-linear.   Then eq. 2.1 does not hold, and the more accurate stiffness laws we must use complicate the theory enormously.

It may sometimes be necessary only to add one or two terms, proportional to y^2, y^3, etc.   In other cases the spring has hysteresis, or permanent deformations at large amplitudes which completely change the properties of the spring.   A liquid medium may be ruptured by cavitation under intense acoustic radiation; or the thermodynamic properties of a gas may undergo drastic changes as the temperature or pressure becomes very high.   Under such conditions the simple picture of sound waves breaks down completely and we are faced with questions of turbulence, vorticity, and instability.   Mathematical analyses of these effects are being attacked from several fronts today, but the problems are imposing and are not likely to be completely understood in practical terms for some time.

We shall restrict the mathematical parts of this discussion to the linear range.   This at least lays the foundation for understanding the field in a general way, and this in itself will be adequate for many of our problems.

2.2   The Equations of Motion

Let us return to the mass on a spring—a simple oscillator.   Equation 2.1 specifies the static condition in which the spring force and the gravitational force on the mass just balance.   By use of this equation we can determine the value of K, by measuring the mass and the initial and final positions of the end of the spring. Beyond this, we are not really interested in the effect of gravity or in the unstretched length of the spring.

We now take y_0, the equilibrium position of the mass-loaded spring, as the y-coordinate origin, and measure all displacements from this origin. If we pull the mass down from its equilibrium position, the extended spring exerts a force upward; if we push the mass above the origin, the compressed spring pushes downward. In all cases the spring force is $-Ky$, the minus sign showing that the force is opposite to the displacement.

If we hold the mass at a displaced position Y from equilibrium and let it go, the spring starts to move the mass. The mass undergoes an acceleration a, which leads to an inertial force Ma. When the mass reaches the origin it is no longer accelerated by the spring, but it has momentum which carries it beyond. At all times the stiffness force and inertial force are exactly in balance:

$$-Ky = Ma \qquad (2.2)$$

This is the basic equation of all vibration. Every acoustic phenomenon involves the vibration of particles of a medium, moving back and forth under the combination of stiffness and inertial forces.

We can now progress more efficiently with the theory if we use some calculus and a simple differential equation. We should look on these expressions as shorthand notations for describing simple physical motions. Equation 2.2 can be written:

$$M \frac{d^2y}{dt^2} + Ky = 0 \qquad (2.3)$$

A particular solution of this equation is:

$$y = Y \cos (\omega t) \qquad (2.4)$$

which we differentiate twice and obtain:

$$\frac{d^2y}{dt^2} = -Y\omega^2 \cos (\omega t) = a \qquad (2.5)$$

Inserting this in eq. 2.3 we obtain:

$$MY\omega^2 \cos (\omega t) + KY \cos (\omega t) = 0$$

This last equation is satisfied if

$$\omega^2 = K/M = \omega_0{}^2 \qquad (2.6)$$

The subscript in ω_0 means that this is a particular value of ω, a "characteristic value" determined by M and K. The mass vibrates uniformly at the natural frequency $f_0 = \omega_0/2\pi$, which is determined only by the value of the mass and the spring constant. In each cycle the displacement reaches maximum values $\pm Y$, the *displacement amplitude* which is determined by the way the motion is started. The *velocity amplitude* $Y\omega_0 = U$, and *acceleration amplitude* $Y\omega_0^2$ are also determined by the initial conditions, but are related to Y in a definite manner determined by the properties of the oscillator.

The velocity at any instant is 90° out of phase with the displacement, and the acceleration is 180° out of phase, or in direct opposition to the displacement. The mass and the spring are always in dynamic equilibrium; the greater the displacement, the greater the restoring force which causes acceleration. These relationships are direct consequences of combining a linear stiffness force and an inertial force, and this combination is the basic requisite of a vibrating system.

Actual systems are never so simple. Some loss of energy is always present, owing to frictional and viscous forces. Some of the vibrational energy is converted into heat energy. If the damping is not too great, if the velocity of the mass is not too high, and if the surrounding medium is "usual," the damping force is proportional to the velocity. This force can be written as $R_m u$, in which the resistance R_m expresses the damping property of the system. Equation 2.3 becomes:

$$M \frac{d^2y}{dt^2} + R_m \frac{dy}{dt} + Ky = 0 \qquad (2.7)$$

or

$$M \frac{du}{dt} + R_m u + K \int u \, dt = 0$$

A particular solution is:

$$y = Y \cos (\omega_f t) e^{-\kappa t} \qquad (2.8)$$

in which $\kappa = R_m/2M$ is the damping constant, and $\omega_f = \sqrt{\omega_0^2 - \kappa^2}$. Now the system vibrates with a damped natural frequency $f_f = \omega_f/2\pi$, which is a little lower than the undamped natural frequency. The amplitude of motion is no longer constant but diminishes exponentially. The resistance R_m can be evaluated by measuring the rate of diminution of the vibration amplitude.

One further addition is needed to illustrate vibrating systems in general. Often the vibrator is driven, at least part of the time, by some externally applied force. An analysis of all possible driving forces is beyond the scope of this book.[2] Let us now consider a steady sinusoidal force expressed by $F = F_0 e^{j\omega t}$. The complete (differential) force equation then is

$$M \frac{d^2y}{dt^2} + R_m \frac{dy}{dt} + Ky = F_0 e^{j\omega t} \qquad (2.9a)$$

or

$$M \frac{du}{dt} + R_m u + K \int u \, dt = F$$

2.3 A Solution by Electric Circuit Analogy; Mechanical Impedance[3]

If we choose to use different symbols we can write this equation:

$$L \frac{d^2Q}{dt^2} + R \frac{dQ}{dt} + \frac{1}{C} Q = V_0 e^{j\omega t} \qquad (2.9b)$$

or

$$L \frac{di}{dt} + Ri + \frac{1}{C} \int i \, dt = V$$

This is the equation for an electric circuit with an inductance L, resistance R, and capacitance C, all in series and driven by an alternating voltage of amplitude V_0.

Pursuing this analogy, we see that velocity u of the mass is analogous to electric current $I = dQ/dt$, and that displacement y is analogous to charge Q. Here the mechanical resistance and mass are directly analogous to electric resistance R and inductance L, respectively. Stiffness constant K is inversely analogous to capacitance C; but this is purely circumstantial, for we could just as well deal with compliance $1/K$ of the spring or with electric stiffness $1/C$ of a condenser. This highly useful analogy is illustrated in Fig. 2.2a.

The displacement of the mass can be measured along a scale that is fixed with respect to the ground. The velocity of the mass is also measured with respect to the ground or fixed coordinate system. Furthermore, the effects of the spring and the resistance (drawn as a dashpot) depend on the motion of their free ends with respect to the ground, and the force is applied, essentially, by pushing against the ground. Thus all the elements acting on the mass are in *parallel*. In the analogous electric circuit, on the other hand, the current flows

[2] A complete discussion is given in P. M. Morse, *Vibration and Sound*, 2nd edition, McGraw-Hill, New York, 1948.

[3] For general reference see L. L. Beranek, *Acoustics*, McGraw-Hill, New York, 1954 and M. F. Gardner and S. C. Barnes, *Transients in Linear Systems*, Vol. 1, Chapter 2, John Wiley & Sons, New York, 1942.

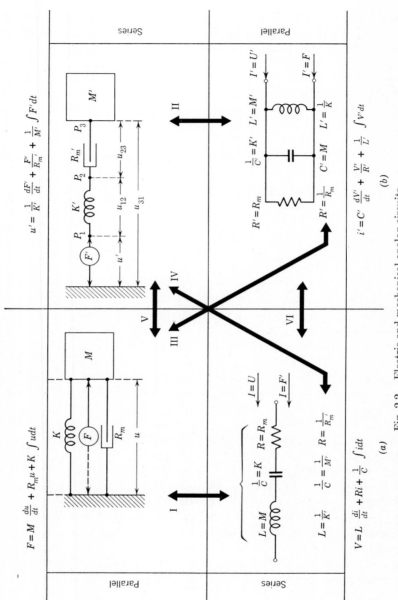

Fig. 2.2.   Electric and mechanical analog circuits.

through the several elements, and these elements are all in *series*. This inversion is a consequence of the particular way in which we selected the analogy. Another form of analogy is possible, as we shall see below.

By applying electric network analysis directly to eq. 2.9a we can write the equations for the simple vibrating system. As a matter of historical interest, this kind of "borrowing" has worked in both directions, for some of the early investigations in electromagnetism were visualized in terms of mechanical systems.

Let us take a familiar electrical solution, Ohm's law $I = E/Z$, in which the impedance Z is in general a complex quantity. The analogous *mechanical impedance* is, by direct substitution of variables,

$$Z_m = R_m + j(\omega M - K/\omega) \tag{2.10}$$

and the mechanical velocity of the mass (using Ohm's law) is

$$u = \frac{dy}{dt} = \frac{F_0 e^{j\omega t}}{R_m + j(\omega M - K/\omega)} \tag{2.11}$$

Since $u = dy/dt = j\omega y$ for simple harmonic motion, we can write the displacement:

$$y = F_0 e^{j\omega t}/j\omega Z_m \tag{2.12}$$

Thus, by using circuit analysis (whether we call it electric or mechanical) we can solve for the behavior of vibrating systems by simple algebraic expressions.

Let us now consider a mechanical system in which the elements are connected in series, as shown in Fig. 2.2b. We apply a force F' to point P_1 at one end of the spring of stiffness K', and wish to determine the resulting velocity $u' = u_{01}$ of Point P_1 with respect to ground. In other words, we are interested in finding the mechanical impedance Z' at the driving point P_1.

Whereas in Fig. 2.2a the total *force* was the sum of the forces on the three elements, in Fig. 2.2b the total velocity is the sum of the relative velocities across the three elements.[4] The velocity across

---

[4] For the mechanical network depicted in Fig. 2.2a we obtained $\sum\limits_{m}^{m} F_m = 0$, while the network of Fig. 2.2b leads to $\sum\limits_{m}^{m} u_m = 0$. Both forms correspond to Kirchhoff's laws in electric networks, in the first case for the currents in a mesh node, in the second case for the voltages around a mesh loop.

the spring is obtained from $F' = -K'y = K'(y_{P_1} - y_{P_2})$,

$$\frac{d}{dt}(y_{P_1} - y_{P_2}) = u_{12} = \frac{1}{K'}\frac{dF'}{dt}$$

Similarly, we obtain from the force laws for the resistance and the mass:

$$u_{23} = \frac{F'}{R_m'} \quad \text{and} \quad u_{30} = \frac{1}{M'}\int F'\,dt$$

The input velocity then is:

$$u_{01} = u_{12} + u_{23} + u_{30}$$

so the differential equation is:

$$u_{01} = u' = \frac{1}{K'}\frac{dF'}{dt} + \frac{F'}{R_m'} + \frac{1}{M'}\int F'\,dt \tag{2.13a}$$

The velocities in this system may be considered analogous to the currents in the branches of the parallel electric circuit shown in Fig. 2.2b. The equation for this circuit is

$$i' = C'\frac{dV}{dt} + \frac{V'}{R'} + \frac{1}{L'}\int V'\,dt \tag{2.13b}$$

Equations 2.13a and b are of similar form, just as eqs. 2.9a and b are similar. In the present case the mechanical resistance R_m', mass M', and compliance $1/K'$ are again directly analogous to electric resistance R', inductance L', and capacitance C'. However, these coefficients now appear reciprocally and at different places in the differential equations. The two pairs of equations also differ in that u and I are the independent variables in eqs. 2.9a and b, whereas F and V are the independent variables in eqs. 2.13a and b. However, we see that all four equations have the same form:

$$y = a\frac{dx}{dt} + bx + c\int x\,dt \tag{2.14}$$

which indicates a general relationship among them. It is therefore possible to represent either of the mechanical systems by either of the electric circuits, by proper substitutions, as indicated by the arrows in Fig. 2.2. Following the vertical arrows I or II the analogies of force to voltage and velocity to current are retained. In this case the following substitutions must be made in eq. 2.14:

	y	x	a	b	c
I	$F = V$	$u = I$	$M = L$	$R_m = R$	$K = 1/C$
II	$u' = I'$	$F' = V'$	$1/K' = C'$	$R_m' = R'$	$M' = L'$

On the other hand, conversion along the diagonal arrows III or IV leads to the reciprocal analogies[5] of velocity to voltage and force to current.

	y	x	a	b	c
III	$F = I'$	$u = V'$	$M = C'$	$R_m = 1/R'$	$K = 1/L'$
IV	$u' = V$	$F = I$	$1/K' = L$	$1/R_m' = R$	$1/M' = 1/C$

In operations III and IV, the impedance elements of the parallel mechanical system determine the magnitude of the admittance elements of the parallel electric circuit. Conversely, the mechanical series admittance converts to electric series impedance. This reciprocal behavior is readily confirmed by differentiating the associated differential equations with respect to time, and dividing each by its independent variable and by $j\omega$.

Duality In general, mechanical and electric networks can be represented either by the sum of impedance components (if velocity and current are the independent variables), or by the sum of admittance components (if force and voltage are the independent variables). Such behavior, which is called *dual*, has useful applications[6] in the analysis of the impedance or admittance of complex electromechanical systems.

Duality leads to two further operations:

	y	x	a	b	c
V	$u' = F$	$F' = u$	$1/K' = M$	$1/R_m' = R_m$	$1/M' = K$
VI	$I' = V$	$V' = I$	$C' = L$	$1/R' = R$	$L' = C$

[5] F. A. Firestone, *J. Acoust. Soc. Amer.*, *4* (1933), 249.

[6] F. S. Fischer, "Grundzüge der Elektroakustik," published by Schiele and Schön, Berlin, 1950; and P. Le Corbeiller and Ying-Wa Yeung, *J. Acoust. Soc. Amer.*, *24* (1952), 643. See also Chapter 5 of this book.

Two electric circuits that are dual with each other have the same resonance frequency and bandwidth. However, duality does not imply completely identical behavior. A series circuit has a maximum of admittance at resonance, and infinite impedance at zero or infinite frequency. On the other hand, a parallel circuit has a maximum of impedance at resonance, and infinite admittance at zero or infinite frequency.

2.4   General Behavior of Driven Damped Oscillator

Relations among driving force, displacement, velocity, and acceleration of a vibrating mass or particle are of practical importance and will be discussed briefly now. Let us start with eq. 2.12, insert all

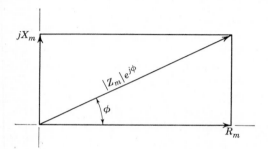

Fig. 2.3.   Phase angle of complex impedance.

the variables, and rationalize the expression in order to separate the real and imaginary parts.

$$y = \frac{F_0 e^{j\omega t}}{j\omega[R_m + j(\omega M - K/\omega)]} = \frac{-jF_0 e^{j\omega t}[R_m - j(\omega M - K/\omega)]}{\omega[R_m^2 + (\omega M - K/\omega)^2]} \quad (2.15)$$

We shorten the expression by introducing the mechanical reactance $X_m = (\omega M - K/\omega)$. The absolute magnitude of the impedance is $|Z_m| = \sqrt{R_m^2 + X_m^2}$. Putting these in eq. 2.15, and using $e^{\pm j\pi/2} = \pm j$, we get:

$$y = \frac{F_0 e^{j(\omega t - \pi/2)}}{\omega|Z_m|^2}[R_m - jX_m]$$

But $R_m - jX_m = |Z_m|e^{-j\phi}$

in which the phase angle is obtained from $\tan \phi = X_m/R_m$. These impedance relations are shown graphically in Fig. 2.3. From the equations

$$y = \frac{F_0 e^{j(\omega t - \pi/2 - \phi)}}{\omega Z_m}$$

$$u = \frac{F_0 e^{j(\omega t - \phi)}}{Z_m}$$

(2.16)

$$a = \frac{\omega F_0 e^{j(\omega t + \pi/2 - \phi)}}{Z_m}$$

we can describe all essential operating characteristics of a driven oscillator. We shall assume that the force amplitude F_0 is the same at all frequencies regardless of the reaction of the oscillator on the force generator. Such a force can be obtained, at least over some

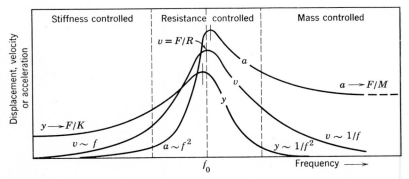

Fig. 2.4. Steady-state response of simple oscillator to constant driving force.

frequency range, by certain types of electroacoustic generators.[7] Other generators impress a constant velocity amplitude on the oscillator, or a constant acceleration amplitude. In many practical cases the generator does not fit any of these three specifications; and the output of the generator may be influenced in a complicated way by the reaction (impedance) of the oscillator. These points are of considerable importance in the design of acoustic transducers (see Chapter 4).

The response to a constant driving force is illustrated qualitatively in Fig. 2.4. Separate curves show the magnitudes of the displacement, velocity, and acceleration, respectively, as a function of frequency. (The relative heights of these three curves are purely arbitrary.)

There are three characteristic frequency ranges of operation of this

---

[7] Constant-voltage generators with piezoelectric transducers, constant-current generators with magnetic transducers; both below transducer resonance.

system.   At very low frequencies the oscillator is stiffness controlled: the force of the spring predominates over the inertia of the mass and the resistive force.   The displacement is in phase with the applied force, as can be calculated from eq. 2.16.   For $\omega \ll \omega_0$, X_m is negative and is much larger than R_m; tan ϕ approaches minus infinity where $\phi = -\pi/2$.   Therefore the exponent in the equation for y contains $(-\pi/2 + \pi/2)$, which cancels, leaving no phase shift between y and F_0.   This can also be predicted directly from Hooke's law; in the low-frequency stiffness-controlled region the vibrating system is, for all practical purposes, just a spring and an applied force.

In the middle frequency range the stiffness and inertial forces counteract each other; they exactly cancel each other at the resonance frequency given by eq. 2.6.   This middle range is the resistance-controlled region, for the value of R_m is larger than that of X_m, and R_m is the only force coefficient that has an effect at resonance.   At this frequency the velocity of the mass reaches a maximum value which is controlled by the resistance.   Near resonance the velocity is about in phase with the applied force, while the displacement leads the force and the acceleration lags the force by approximately 90° in each case.

Strictly speaking, only the velocity has its maximum value at the resonance frequency $f_0 = (K/M)^{1/2}/2\pi$.   The acceleration maximum occurs at a slightly higher frequency, and the displacement maximum at a lower frequency, owing to the extra ω in the expressions for y and a of eq. 2.16.   These differences are slight except for highly damped oscillators.   It is usual to consider the velocity maximum as the actual point of resonance, unless otherwise specified.

Bandwidth and Q   The influence of the amount of damping is shown qualitatively in Fig. 2.5.   Although the damping is supplied by the resistance, the effect of the damping depends on the relation between the resistance and the reactance.   In eq. 2.8 this effect is expressed by the damping constant[8] $\kappa = R_m/2M$; and this is convenient for specifying the rate of decay of a free oscillator.   Damping properties of driven and free oscillators are often specified by the *quality factor* Q which is (in analogy with electrical practice):

$$Q = \omega_0 M/R_m = \omega_0/2\kappa \tag{2.17}$$

Another convenient variable is the bandwidth, B, of a driven system.   This is the total width, in cycles per second, of the steady-state response curve between points at which the power is one-half the

_____

[8] In the literature one also finds the quantity $\kappa/f = \delta$, which is called the "logarithmic damping decrement."   In an electric series circuit, this is $\delta = \pi R \sqrt{C/L}$ and hence the quality factor becomes $Q = \pi/\delta$.

power at the resonance peak. Since power is proportional to the square of the velocity or displacement, the bandwidth is measured at amplitudes of $1/\sqrt{2}$ times the maximum resonant amplitude. If the oscillator is not heavily damped the bandwidth is approximately

$$B \simeq \omega_0/Q = R_m/M = 2\kappa \qquad (2.18)$$

A more accurate expression for large damping can be derived from eq. (2.15).

Far above resonance the system is mass controlled. The principle effect of the force is to accelerate the mass, and this acceleration is in

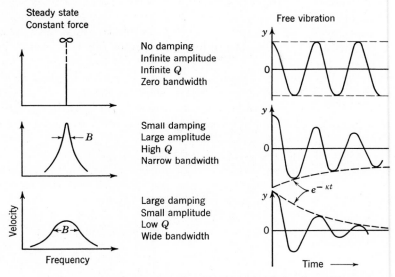

Fig. 2.5.   Influence of damping on response of simple oscillator.

phase with the force. The displacement now leads the force by about 180°, and the velocity leads by 90°. Both the displacement and the velocity decrease as the frequency is increased if the magnitude of the force is held constant.

This concludes our brief review of the behavior of a vibrating system. The relations have been derived for a particular system that is much simpler than those we usually meet in practice. There may be many masses—or even an infinite number of particles in a continuous medium. But each particle, or microscopic element of the medium, has its own inertia and is acted on by spring-like and resistive forces of the surrounding medium, and is set in motion by applied forces. All acoustic phenomena stem basically from these four types of forces, mutually interacting in the same general way as in the simple oscillator.

2.5 Some Properties of Wave Motion

We are now ready to consider the motion of waves in an extended medium. At this stage, waves on a flexible string will serve to illustrate simply and graphically some basic properties of interest. We can look at a wave as a simultaneous motion of an infinite number of particles or tiny masses, each one behaving like the mass in the simple oscillator. But every element interacts with every other element, through elastic and viscous forces, in a manner that is uniquely determined by the properties of the medium and its boundaries. Therefore it is more logical, as well as far simpler, to view the wave as a whole and to express it mathematically by a continuous function of position in the medium.

A string has only one position coordinate, which we call x, the distance along the string from some arbitrary origin. The wave function, then, will involve both x and t, whereas the vibration function of the simple oscillator involves only time, t, as its single independent variable.

The required function, at least for waves of small amplitude with linear forces of stiffness and damping, can be any relation in which x and t are combined in the form $(x - ct)$, in which c is the velocity of the wave. We must now distinguish carefully between the velocity of a particle, which we still designate u, and the velocity of the wave moving through the medium. One possible wave function is:

$$y = Y \cos\left(\omega t - \frac{\omega x}{c}\right) = Y \cos\left[-\frac{\omega}{c}(x - ct)\right] \qquad (2.19)$$

This may represent a continuous sinusoidal wave moving to the right. The displacement, y, is measured perpendicular to the string, so this is a *transverse* wave. In *longitudinal* waves the particles of the medium vibrate in the same direction as the wave propagates.

Now let us look at the wave motion in two different ways. First, let us take an instantaneous flash picture of a long section of the wave. The displacement along the wave varies as $\cos(\omega x/c)$. Next, let us pick just one particle on the string and follow its motion with time; we see a simple harmonic motion like that of a mass on a spring. If we still want to express its motion as $\cos(\omega t)$, with a plus sign for increasing time, the space wave must be given by $\cos(-\omega x/c)$ with a minus sign to designate a wave moving to the right. The values of y at successive positions to the right of any point P correspond to values of y at successively earlier times at point P. Conversely, we can predict all future displacements at P by looking at the present displacements along the negative direction to the left of P. In either case we must compare x with ct or $-ct$, which measures the distance the wave travels in time t.

The essential feature of simple one-dimensional wave motion is that the space shape is just the same as the time shape of the wave. The shape we have chosen to illustrate by eq. 2.19 is but a particular solution of a general wave equation, just as eq. 2.8 is a particular solution of eq. 2.7. We shall not derive the wave equation here; full mathematical details of its derivation are given in standard textbooks.[9] But we shall go through some manipulations in order to point out that the wave equation is simply a statement of the forces of distributed inertia and stiffness (plus damping and driving in the complete case) that give rise to particle vibration and wave motion.

The wave equation Let us start with eq. 2.19 and differentiate it with respect to time to obtain particle velocity and acceleration, and with respect to distance to obtain slope and curvature:

$$\frac{\partial y}{\partial t} = -Y\omega \sin \frac{\omega}{c}(ct - x) = \text{velocity of particle}$$

$$\frac{\partial^2 y}{\partial t^2} = -Y\omega^2 \cos \frac{\omega}{c}(ct - x) = \text{acceleration of particle}$$

$$\frac{\partial y}{\partial x} = -Y\frac{\omega}{c} \sin \frac{\omega}{c}(ct - x) = \text{slope of string}$$

$$\frac{\partial^2 y}{\partial x^2} = -Y\frac{\omega^2}{c^2} \cos \frac{\omega}{c}(ct - x) = \text{curvature of string}$$

Comparing the expressions for acceleration and curvature we see that:

$$\frac{\partial^2 y}{\partial x^2} = \frac{1}{c^2}\frac{\partial^2 y}{\partial t^2} \tag{2.20}$$

This is the general wave equation, not only for waves on a string but for one-dimensional waves in any medium. It can be derived directly from properties of the medium. However, since the behavior differences in different media are described only by the wave velocity c in this equation, we can bring out the essential physics by deriving c in a simple way.

[9] L. E. Kinsler and A. R. Frey, *Fundamentals of Acoustics*, John Wiley & Sons, New York, 1950.

2.6   Velocity of Waves on a String

In Fig. 2.6 is drawn a curved segment of a string carrying a wave. We assume that this is an "ideal" string, that is perfectly flexible. This string is stretched to a uniform tension T and it has a uniformly distributed mass ρ. Let s be the length of a small segment, curved so slightly that its shape is essentially an arc of a circle of radius r.[9a]

Since the segment is moving around a circle at this instant, its mass has an outward centrifugal reaction: $c^2\rho s/r$, where c m/sec is the velocity of the wave. This is also the velocity with which we would have to pull the string if we wanted the wave segment to stand still as shown in the figure; or we could make it appear stationary if we moved along with the wave at its own velocity. In any case, the

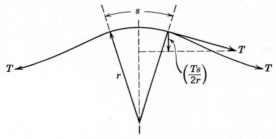

Fig. 2.6.   Derivation of string-wave velocity.

tangential velocity of the mass segment is c, and this segment can be constrained to move in a circular arc only if we supply an inward force equal to the centrifugal or outward inertial force of the segment.

The required inward force is supplied by the tension of the string. We can see from the geometry in Fig. 2.6 that the inward radial component of tension on one end of the segment is approximately $T(s/2r)$, and the total inward force is Ts/r. By equating the outward and inward forces we obtain:

$$c^2 = T/\rho \qquad (2.21a)$$

which we insert in eq. 2.20 and obtain:

$$T\frac{\partial^2 y}{\partial x^2} = \rho\frac{\partial^2 y}{\partial t^2} \qquad (2.21b)$$

This wave equation for a string expresses clearly the basic forces that give rise to wave motion. On the right is the mass of an elementary segment of the string times the acceleration of that segment. The

[9a] In the MKS system we express T in newtons, ρ in kg/m, s and r in meters.

required restoring force is proportional to the curvature, and the "stiffness constant" is simply the tension. This equation corresponds to eq. 2.3 for the mass on a spring. It may seem that the sign is reversed; we recall, however, that a positive curvature is concave upward, which corresponds to pulling the segment upward, whereas a positive upward displacement of a spring gives a downward restoring force.

Equations 2.19 through 2.21b are of considerable generality; with appropriate substitutions for the effective stiffness and the mass per unit element, these equations apply to compressional longitudinal waves in gases and liquids, and to longitudinal waves in wires and rods. If there is damping (as there always is to some extent), the stiffness modulus is a complex number with an imaginary part corresponding to the loss factor.

2.7 Vibrations in Solids

Waves in solid bodies are somewhat more complicated, for it is not possible to displace a section of the medium in one direction without causing displacements in other directions. Let us consider a solid bar which is compressed along its axis, x. Hooke's law then takes the form:

$$F_x = -SY_0 \frac{d\xi}{dx} \qquad (2.22)$$

where S is the cross section of the bar, $d\xi/dx$ is the longitudinal strain, and Y_0 is Young's modulus. This elastic modulus is specifically defined for slender bars whose lateral dimensions will not remain constant if a longitudinal stress is applied. Since the sides of such a bar are not constrained they will bulge out under longitudinal compression and draw inward under longitudinal dilation. The ratio of the change in diameter $\partial\eta$ to the change in length $\partial\xi$ is called *Poisson's* ratio $\sigma = \partial\eta/\partial\xi$. On the other hand, a bar-shaped section located within an infinite solid body will be laterally constrained. It is obvious that the effective stiffness modulus Y_B of such a constrained section will be higher than the Young's modulus Y_0 for a free bar. It follows from elastic theory that

$$Y_0/Y_B = 1 - b \qquad (2.23)$$

where b depends on Poisson's ratio: $b = 2\sigma^2/(1 - \sigma)$. For most hard solids σ is approximately 0.3, so that $b \simeq 0.257$. The highest values for σ occur in certain soft rubbers with $\sigma \simeq 0.45$ and $b \simeq 0.725$. A value of σ equal to 0.5 would lead to $b = 1$, and according to eq. 2.23 a free bar-shaped section of such a medium would have a vanishing stiffness modulus Y_0. This limiting case corresponds to a free mass of liquid which would change its shape, but not its volume, if a force were applied in one direction only (see Chapter 8, footnote 44a).

With these definitions we can derive the wave equation for a slender bar. A section of length dx, cross-sectional area S, and density ρ is illustrated in Fig. 2.7. The force at x is F_x, and the force at $x + dx$

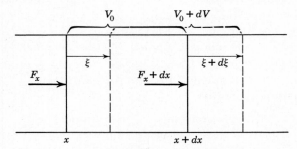

Fig. 2.7.   Balance of forces for compressional wave.

is $F_x + dF_x = F_x + (\partial F_x / \partial x)\, dx$. With the use of eq. 2.22 the net force will then be:

$$\frac{\partial F_x}{\partial x}\, dx = -SY_0 \frac{\partial^2 \xi}{\partial x^2}\, dx \qquad (2.24)$$

This elastic force will be in dynamic equilibrium with the inertial reaction of the mass element $\rho S\, dx$:

$$-SY_0 \frac{\partial^2 \xi}{\partial x^2}\, dx + \rho S\, dx \frac{\partial^2 \xi}{\partial t^2} = 0$$

which reduces to

$$\frac{Y_0}{\rho} \frac{\partial^2 \xi}{\partial x^2} + \frac{\partial^2 \xi}{\partial t^2} = 0 \qquad (2.25)$$

If we compare eq. 2.25 with eq. 2.20 we find for the longitudinal bar velocity:

$$c_l = \sqrt{\frac{Y_0}{\rho}} \qquad (2.26a)[10]$$

[10] The corresponding longitudinal velocity in thin plates is $c_p = c_l \sqrt{1/(1 - \sigma^2)}$.

Further, from eq. 2.23 we find the velocity for solid media in bulk:

$$c_B = \sqrt{\frac{Y_B}{\rho}} = \sqrt{\frac{Y_0}{\rho(1-b)}}$$

$$= c_l \sqrt{\frac{1-\sigma}{(1+\sigma)(1-2\sigma)}} \qquad (2.26b)$$

Both types of waves are compressional, but they are distinguished by the difference in effective stiffness resulting from the different elastic boundaries in the free bar and the infinite medium. A bar or rod can be considered "slender" only if its lateral dimensions are small compared with wavelength. As the frequency is increased for a bar of given dimensions, this condition will cease to be valid. As the wavelength approaches the value $\lambda = 2d$, where d is the rod diameter, c_l will no longer be constant, but will approach the velocity of shear waves:

$$c_s = c_l \sqrt{\frac{1}{2(1+\sigma)}} = \sqrt{\frac{\mu}{\rho}} \qquad (2.26c)$$

in which μ is the shear modulus of the solid.

Shear waves are characterized by particle motion transverse to the direction of propagation. They are, in a sense, polarized inasmuch as the displacement vectors in a shear wave are oriented within the plane normal to the direction of propagation at a specific angle. For shear waves *generated* at a boundary the angle of "polarization" is defined by the requirement that the displacement be also within a plane normal to the boundary. In some cases a special type of shear wave is encountered which is confined to a thin layer on the free boundary of a solid. These surface waves are called "Rayleigh waves" and propagate with a velocity about 2 per cent less than c_s.

Dispersion The transition from longitudinal waves to shear waves in a rod involves a continuous change of propagation velocity with frequency. This is an example of velocity dispersion, a phenomenon that is familiar in the propagation of light and other forms of electromagnetic energy. Dispersion also occurs in the propagation of flexural waves in bars and plates, whose velocity is

for bars:
(width $\simeq a$)
$$c_f = \left[\frac{Y_0 \kappa^2}{\rho}\right]^{1/4} \omega^{1/2} \qquad (2.26d)$$

for plates:
(width $\gg a$)
$$c_f = \left[\frac{Y_0 \kappa^2}{\rho(1-\sigma^2)}\right]^{1/4} \omega^{1/2} \qquad (2.26e)$$

in which κ is the radius of gyration about the axis of bending,[10a] and a is the thickness of the bar or plate.

The radius of gyration for typical cross sections is:

For a cylindrical rod of radius a: $\kappa = a/2$.
For a rectangular bar or a plate of thickness a: $\kappa = a/\sqrt{12}$
For a circular tube of wall thickness $(a - b)$: $\kappa = (a^2 + b^2)^{1/2}/2$, where a and b are the outer and inner radii, respectively.

We now see that solids can carry four basic types of waves, each of which propagates with a different velocity. The highest velocity is c_B, associated with bulk waves. The next highest is c_l, associated with longitudinal waves in a slender bar at low frequencies (wavelength much greater than diameter). Shear waves propagate with a still lower velocity, c_s. The lowest velocities occur with flexural waves. Both longitudinal waves and flexural waves in bars and plates are dispersive. As the frequency increases, the values of c_l and c_f asymptotically approach the value of the shear velocity.[11] In this transition region there is coupling among the different types of motion: shear, compression, and transverse displacement. These related phenomena of coupling and dispersion have some interesting practical consequences which are discussed in Chapter 8. The strain-stress relationship is not the same for shear waves as for longitudinal waves, and becomes quite complicated in non-isotropic bodies. But, in general, it is possible to express the effective stiffness for any type of wave by some combination of characteristic constants of the medium such as Poisson's ratio, Young's modulus or the Lamé constants.

2.8   Sound Waves in Fluids

It will be instructive to study the velocity of sound waves in gases and liquids, as related to properties of the medium. When a sound wave passes through a fluid there is a small alternating increase and decrease in pressure superimposed on the static pressure. These pressure variations are accompanied by small changes in the volume occupied by a given group of molecules. Alternations in density and temperature also occur. All these small variations are interrelated in a manner determined by the equation of state of the fluid and by the type of thermodynamic process that takes place.

[10a] Equations 2.26 are derived from a fourth-order differential wave equation; see P. M. Morse, *Vibration and Sound*, 2nd edition, McGraw-Hill, New York, 1948, pp. 154 and 209.

[11] Actually, the limiting velocity has the value of Rayleigh waves.

Sound velocity in an ideal gas   The equation of state for an ideal gas is

$$P_0 V_0 = P_0 M/\rho = RT_0 \qquad (2.27a)$$

in which P_0, V_0 are the undisturbed values of pressure in newtons/m^2 and volume in m^3, respectively, for 1 mole of the gas; T_0 is the absolute temperature (Kelvin); M is the molecular weight of the gas; and R is the gas constant.[12]

Under most conditions, sound variations in a gas are adiabatic, for the alternations are so rapid that there is not time for the temperature to equalize itself throughout a region that is compressed or expanded. There are exceptions to this, and some of these exceptions may be of practical use.   For example, if the gas is contained within the inter-communicating pores of a fine metal wool or granular structure, the heat conductivity of the surrounding substance can equalize the temperature during sound pulsations at very low frequencies, and the sound process becomes isothermal.   But most regions containing air or other gases obey the adiabatic condition:

$$P_0 V_0{}^\gamma = \text{constant} \qquad (2.27b)$$

in which $\gamma = C_p/C_v$ is the ratio of specific heats at constant pressure (C_p) and constant volume (C_v).   Taking the total differential of this equation we obtain:

$$\gamma P_0 V_0{}^{\gamma-1}\, dV + V_0{}^\gamma\, dP = 0$$

and
$$\frac{dP}{P_0} = -\gamma \frac{dV}{V_0} \qquad (2.28a)$$

Equation 2.28a says that the fractional change in pressure is proportional to the fractional change in volume, but of opposite sign, and γ is the proportionality constant.   This statement is somewhat analogous to that for the force of a spring: $F = -Kx$, from which we see that γ is a kind of stiffness constant.   Actually, the role of γ is more like that of Young's modulus in the spring; the spring constant involves the geometry of the spring in addition.   The more significant analogy appears when we direct our attention to the differential change in pressure, which is simply the sound pressure $p = dP$:

$$p = -\gamma P_0 \,(dV/V_0) \qquad (2.28b)$$

In this form, the quantity γP_0 is the constant of proportionality between the sound pressure and the differential volume strain, and is called the *stiffness constant* for sound motion in a gas.

[12] In MKS units, $R = 8.31436$ joules/mole degree.

The strain can also be expressed in terms of displacements of the molecules. Let us assume that Fig. 2.7 now represents a section of a plane wave in a gas. The vertical line at x designates a plane in which a certain group of molecules is located in the absence of displacement by sound. This plane moves to $x + \xi$ under the influence of sound pressure. Another plane at $x + dx$ is moved, in general, by some different amount and then is located at $x + dx + \xi + d\xi$.

All the molecules contained in the undisturbed volume V_0, between the solid lines, are still contained in the disturbed volume $V_0 + dV$, between the dashed lines. The change in volume can be calculated directly from the geometry of Fig. 2.7 and turns out to be: $dV = V_0 \, \partial\xi/\partial x$. Combining this with eq. 2.28b we get:

$$p = -\gamma P_0 \frac{\partial \xi}{\partial x} \tag{2.28c}$$

This equation relates the excess (sound) pressure of the gas to the displacement strain in compression or expansion. If the displacement ξ from equilibrium varies with x then the volume has been changed from its equilibrium value and the disturbed gas exerts an elastic restoring pressure.

If the pressure on the right side of a small volume dV of gas is greater than the pressure on the left side by $dp = (\partial p/\partial x) \, dx$, there will be a net force to the left equal to $-(\partial p/\partial x) \, dx$ over a unit area. This force will accelerate the mass of gas according to Newton's second law; therefore

$$-\frac{\partial p}{\partial x} dx = \rho_0 \frac{\partial^2 \xi}{\partial t^2} dx \tag{2.29}$$

in which ρ_0 kg/m is the (static) density of the gas. By partial differentiations we can combine all eqs. 2.28 and 2.29 in two different ways:

$$\gamma P_0 \frac{\partial^2 \xi}{\partial x^2} = \rho_0 \frac{\partial^2 \xi}{\partial t^2} \quad \text{and} \quad \gamma P_0 \frac{\partial^2 p}{\partial x^2} = \rho_0 \frac{\partial^2 p}{\partial t^2} \tag{2.30}$$

These equations correspond to eq. 2.21b for the string. Corresponding to eq. 2.21a is the velocity of sound in a gas:

$$c^2 = \gamma P_0/\rho_0 \tag{2.31}$$

The static pressure P_0 and the density ρ_0 are controllable experimental variables—at least within limits. But the ratio of specific heats γ is determined by the molecular properties of the gas itself. This quantity will be discussed in connection with molecular analysis of gases (see Appendix).

The sound velocity in a liquid can be derived in a similar way, using the appropriate equation of state and thermodynamic relations. The result is:

$$c^2 = K/\rho$$

in which K is the bulk stiffness modulus for the liquid, or the reciprocal of the bulk compressibility.[13]   Special properties of sound propagation in liquids are discussed in the Appendix.

Temperature dependence of sound velocity   It is important to note that eq. 2.31 is only a first-order approximation for infinitesimal sound-pressure amplitudes.   For large amplitudes the density ρ can no longer be assumed to be a constant.   One consequence of the variation of density with pressure is radiation pressure, which will be discussed later in this chapter.   Other high-amplitude phenomena in gases are mentioned in Chapter 6.   In explosion phenomena the sound velocity reaches values which are much higher than eq. 2.31 would predict.   However, the dependence of c on temperature can easily be obtained by combining eq. 2.31 with eq. 2.27a:

$$c = \left(\gamma \frac{R}{M} T\right)^{\frac{1}{2}} \tag{2.31a}$$

Let c_0 be the sound velocity at 0°C ($T = 273°K$): $c_0 = (273 \cdot \gamma R/M)^{\frac{1}{2}}$ and $t = T - 273$, the temperature in Centigrade.   Equation 2.31a then takes the form:

$$c = c_0(1 + t/273)^{\frac{1}{2}}$$
$$\simeq c_0 + c_0 t/546 \tag{2.31b}$$

We find that the sound velocity in a gas increases with temperature; for instance, in air near room temperature this increase amounts to about 0.6 m/sec/°C.

We have noted that sound waves are accompanied by alternations in particle velocity, particle acceleration, temperature, and density, as well as the variations in particle displacement and excess pressure which appear in eq. 2.30.   The same wave equation applies to all these variables.   Experimentally, the two most important field variables are the sound pressure p and the particle velocity u.   Analytically, also, these two variables suffice to determine power transfer, reflection, absorption, and essentially all relevant properties.

The particle velocity can be obtained directly from the pressure (we should not forget that we are talking about small amplitude,

---

[13] This is the adiabatic compressibility $\beta_{ad} = 1/K$.

linear sound behavior) by using eq. 2.29. For simple harmonic motion, $\partial/\partial t = j\omega$, so

$$\frac{\partial^2 \xi}{\cdot \, dt^2} = j\omega \frac{\partial \xi}{\partial t} = j\omega u$$

Therefore
$$u_x = -\frac{1}{j\omega\rho_0} \frac{\partial p}{\partial x} \qquad (2.32)$$

The subscript in u_x signifies the particle velocity in the x direction; and we see that this is proportional to the pressure gradient in the x direction. Gradients in other directions are involved in general three-dimensional waves, but we are still considering only one-dimensional plane waves.

2.9 Acoustic Impedance and Plane-Wave Transmission

We have seen that the cosine function for waves on a string, eq. 2.19, satisfies the wave equation (2.20). Likewise, the wave equation for sound in a gas, eq. 2.30, is satisfied by: $p = P \cos(\omega t - kx)$, in which P is the sound-pressure amplitude, and

$$k = \omega/c = 2\pi f/c = 2\pi/\lambda \qquad (2.33)$$

is the *wave number*, which plays the same role in the space coordinate as ω does in the time coordinate. The wavelength λ measures the length of one wave cycle in space just as the period T measures one cycle in time.

Most waves must be represented by functions that are more complicated, or at least more general, than the single cosine function used above. Complex exponential functions are convenient and have the required generality. From: $e^{\pm jz} = \cos z \pm j \sin z$, we see that the cosine solution is simply the real part of an exponential solution. Let us develop the subsequent theory from the more general solution:[14]

$$p = P_+ e^{j(\omega t - kx)} + P_- e^{j(\omega t + kx)} = P e^{j\omega t} \qquad (2.34)$$

[14] These exponential functions contain more information than we usually need to analyze acoustic phenomena. Equation 2.34 can be expanded into:

$$p = P_+\{\cos(\omega t - kx) + j \sin(\omega t - kx)\} + P_-\{\cos(\omega t + kx) + j \sin(\omega t + kx)\}$$

$$= \{P_+ \cos(\omega t - kx) + P_- \cos(\omega t + kx)\}$$
$$+ j\{P_+ \sin(\omega t - kx) + P_- \sin(\omega t + kx)\}$$

The first term is the *real part* of the complex function, and we shall use this part to represent the *physical quantity*—sound pressure in this particular equation. We could just as well adopt the convention by which the imaginary part represents the physical quantities, but we must use only one convention consistently throughout the analysis.

The first term represents a wave going to the right with a pressure amplitude P_+, and the other gives a wave going to the left with amplitude P_-. These two pressure amplitudes are not generally equal, and they may be complex quantities. These amplitudes are determined by the way the wave is driven or started, and by the influence of any boundaries that may confine the wave.

The particle velocity is obtained by applying eq. 2.32 to eq. 2.34, which yields, after using eq. 2.33:

$$u_x = \frac{1}{\rho_0 c}[P_+ e^{j(\omega t - kx)} - P_- e^{j(\omega t + kx)}] = U_x e^{j\omega t} \qquad (2.35)$$

We are now ready to introduce the concept of impedance which is of considerable usefulness in sonics measurement and analysis.

The *specific acoustic impedance* $Z_{sp} = P/U$ is the complex ratio of the sound pressure to the particle velocity at a given point in a wave field. If there is a uniform pressure over an area S, such as the cross-sectional area of a tube with a plane wave in it, the product PS is the total force exerted by the sound across that area. The ratio PS/U is thus force divided by velocity, which is equal to *mechanical impedance* Z_m as defined in connection with the mechanical oscillator. Therefore, *specific acoustic impedance* is *mechanical impedance* per unit area.

On the other hand, we define *acoustic impedance* Z_{ac} as the ratio of sound pressure to volume velocity:

$$Z_{ac} = P/US = Z_{sp}/S = Z_m/S^2$$

The concept of acoustic impedance is useful in the analysis of lumped systems, such as cavity resonators, sirens, jets, etc. The unit of acoustic impedance is the "acoustic ohm" with the dimension $g/cm^4/$ sec (**CGS** acoustic ohm), or $kg/m^4/sec$ (**MKS** acoustic ohm).

From eq. 2.34 and 2.35 we obtain a general expression for specific acoustic impedance of plane waves:

$$Z_{sp} = \rho_0 c \left[\frac{P_+ e^{-jkx} + P_- e^{jkx}}{P_+ e^{-jkx} - P_- e^{jkx}}\right] = \rho_0 c[\phi] \qquad (2.36)$$

The impedance function ϕ is determined by boundary conditions and by the point in the wave at which the impedance is designated.

In a free plane wave (*no* boundaries) propagating in one direction, there is no returning wave, so $P_- = 0$. Then $\phi = 1$ and the specific acoustic impedance is equal to $\rho_0 c$. This is called the *characteristic impedance*[15] of the medium. It is a pure resistance, for there is no imaginary part in the expression. This says, as we would expect with free waves, that energy is continually drained away into a radiation resistance and there is no reactive component in the "circuit." In air at room temperature and sea-level pressure, the characteristic impedance is about 420 MKS units (newton·sec/m³).

Complete reflection and standing waves Next consider plane waves in an ideal rigid tube of uniform cross-sectional dimensions small compared with the wavelength, and terminated rigidly at $x = L$. At this rigid boundary there can be no particle velocity normal to the boundary, so $u_{x=L} = 0$. Putting this into eq. 2.35 yields the relation:

$$u_L = \frac{e^{j\omega t}}{\rho_0 c}[P_+ e^{-jkL} - P_- e^{jkL}] = 0$$

With this we can express P_- in terms of P_+, insert into eq. 2.36, and cancel the P_+ coefficients in the numerator and denominator, giving:[16]

$$\phi = \frac{e^{jk(L-x)} + e^{-jk(L-x)}}{e^{jk(L-x)} - e^{-jk(L-x)}} = -j \cot [k(L - x)] \qquad (2.37)$$

The impedance $Z = -j\rho_0 c \cot (kd)$ is purely reactive, at all distances $d = L - x$ from a perfectly rigid boundary. Since $kd = 2\pi d/\lambda$, the phase angle kd equals $\pi, 2\pi, 3\pi, \cdots$ when $d = \lambda/2, 2\lambda/2, 3\lambda/2, \cdots$. The impedance runs through all values from $-j\infty$ to $+j\infty$ each time the distance d is increased by a half wavelength. Within a quarter wavelength of the rigid termination the impedance is a negative reactance, which corresponds to a capacitative reactance in an electric circuit and to a stiffness in a mechanical circuit. Right at the boundary ($d = 0$) the sound wave feels an infinite stiffness, and as d is increased out to $\lambda/4$ the stiffness diminishes to zero. In the range $\lambda/4 < d < \lambda/2$, the acoustic impedance is an inertial reactance, analogous to electric inductive reactance. Where d is almost $\lambda/2$ the mass-like impedance is very large. Right at $\lambda/2$ the impedance is infinite and can be considered as either an infinite mass or an infinite stiffness. Each subsequent half wavelength the impedance sequence repeats itself exactly.

Ideally, this rigid tube would drain no energy from a source, and the smallest amount of sound started in the tube would continue forever. In actual cases there is at least some resistance, introduced

---

[15] The CGS unit for characteristic impedance is the "rayl" (g/cm²/sec). To obtain the MKS unit for $\rho_0 c$, multiply the number of rayls by 10.

[16] $e^{jz} + e^{-jz} = 2 \cos z;$ $\qquad e^{jz} - e^{-jz} = 2j \sin z$

by viscous drag at the walls or by motion of the boundaries. In many important cases in acoustics[17] the resistive loss takes place mainly at the termination, and losses along the line can be neglected.

Transmission line with arbitrary termination impedance The influence of the termination can be specified conveniently by a complex input impedance which we shall call the normal specific acoustic impedance of the surface. This is the ratio of the sound pressure at the surface to the particle velocity into the surface at normal incidence. Associated with this particle motion into the surface is generally some transfer of energy into the termination. There is also a partial reflection of energy, except for the special case of a perfectly absorptive (matched) boundary.

The pressure amplitude of the reflected wave can be expressed as some fraction of the amplitude of the incident wave. For mathematical convenience we choose for this fraction:[18] $P_-/P_+ = e^{-2\alpha_0}$. If $\alpha_0 = 0$ the reflected pressure is undiminished in amplitude, and as α_0 increases toward an infinite value the reflected pressure diminishes toward zero. In general there may also be a change in phase of the reflected wave relative to the incident, and this phase change can be expressed by: $-e^{-j2\beta}$. The complete relation between P_+ and P_- at a boundary at $x = L$, then, is (see eq. 2.34, and note that $e^{j\omega t}$ cancels):

$$P_- e^{jkL} = -P_+ e^{-jkL} e^{-2j\beta} e^{-2\alpha_0} \qquad (2.38)$$

With this we express P_- in terms of P_+, insert into eq. 2.36, cancel the P_+ coefficients, and regroup the exponentials to give:[19]

$$\Phi = \frac{e^{\alpha_0 + j\beta + jk(L-x)} - e^{-\alpha_0 - j\beta - jk(L-x)}}{e^{\alpha_0 + j\beta + jk(L-x)} + e^{-\alpha_0 - j\beta - jk(L-x)}}$$

$$= \tanh \left[\alpha_0 + j\left(\beta + \frac{2\pi d}{\lambda}\right)\right] = \frac{R}{\rho_0 c} + j\frac{X}{\rho_0 c} \qquad (2.39)$$

in which $k = 2\pi/\lambda$, and $d = L - x$ is the distance from the termination.

The line variables α_0 and β are related to properties of the standing wave as follows:

[17] L. L. Beranek, *Acoustic Measurements*, John Wiley & Sons, New York, 1949, Chapter 7, p. 317.

[18] In some references, e.g., P. M. Morse, *Vibration and Sound*, the quantities $\pi\alpha_0$ and $\pi\beta_0$ are used where we use α_0 and β. This difference should be noted in using published charts for eq. 2.39.

[19] $(e^z - e^{-z})/(e^z + e^{-z}) = \sinh z/\cosh z = \tanh z$

$$\frac{P_+ + P_-}{P_+ - P_-} = \frac{p_{max}}{p_{min}} = \text{SWR} \qquad (2.40)$$

$$= \coth \alpha_0 = 1/\tanh \alpha_0$$

$$\frac{d_{min}}{\lambda} = +\frac{n}{2} - \frac{\beta}{2\pi} \qquad (n = 1, 2, 3 \cdots)$$

in which p_{max} and p_{min} are the sound pressures at pressure maximum and minimum, respectively, d_{min} is the distance from the termination to a minimum in the standing wave, and SWR is the *standing-wave ratio*.

This is a complex transformation between the pair of impedance variables $(R/\rho_0 c)$, $(X/\rho_0 c)$, and the pair of line variables (α_0), $(\beta + kd)$. If specific values are assigned to either pair, the other pair is uniquely determined (except for periodic identities in phase which are physically indistinguishable). Often the easiest way to use this equation is to employ a chart in which one pair of variables is plotted continuously as a function of the other; several forms of such charts have been developed.[20]

We shall discuss only the "Smith chart," which is commercially available as a circular slide-rule calculator and is reproduced in simplified form in Fig. 2.8.

Equation 2.39 and Fig. 2.8 express all the ways in which the impedance seen by a plane sinusoidal wave can be affected by an oppositely traveling wave of arbitrary amplitude and phase.

When $\alpha_0 = \infty$, $\tanh \alpha_0 = 0$, the opposing wave has zero amplitude $(P_- = P_+ e^{-\infty} = 0)$, its phase is immaterial, and the outward wave sees the (real) characteristic impedance $\rho_0 c$. This condition is represented by the center of the circular chart, Fig. 2.8.

When $\alpha_0 = 0$, $\tanh [j(\beta + kd)] = -j \tan (\beta + kd)$, the opposing wave has the same amplitude as the outward wave but the relative phase shifts continuously with the distance d from the boundary at which the opposing wave is reflected. The relative phase is additionally influenced by the boundary which can reflect either with zero phase change $(\beta = \pi/2,$ "hard wall") or with 180° phase reversal $(\beta = 0,$ "soft wall"). These conditions arising from complete reflection are represented around the circumference of the chart, along a scale marked in fractions of a wavelength from 0 to 0.5, rotating

[20] P. M. Morse, *Vibration and Sound*, 2nd edition, McGraw-Hill, New York, 1948, p. 453. L. L. Beranek, *Acoustic Measurements*, John Wiley & Sons, New York, 1949, p. 319.

clockwise.   This scale measures the total phase angle $\left(\beta + \dfrac{2\pi d}{\lambda}\right)$, in d/λ units, with the origin at $\beta = 0$ and $d/\lambda = 0$ corresponding to a location of a pressure minimum in the standing wave.   One such minimum occurs at the termination if the boundary impedance is lower than the line impedance.   At $d/\lambda = 0.25$ from this termination

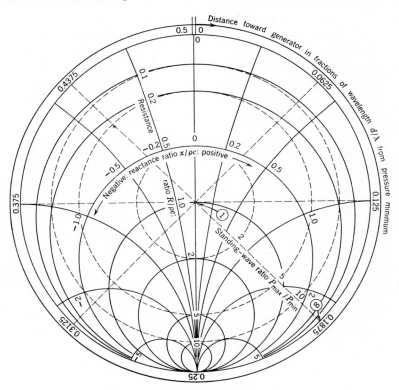

Fig. 2.8.   "Smith" impedance chart.

there is a pressure maximum, and at $d/\lambda = 0.5$ there is again a minimum.   Successive rotations around the chart represent successive half wavelengths away from the termination and toward the generator.

If α_0 lies between 0 and ∞, as it usually does in practice, positions along the standing wave are represented by points around a circle of radius less than the maximum radius of the chart.   This radius diminishes as the termination impedance more nearly matches the characteristic impedance of the line.   The resistance and reactance at any point in the line can be read from the set of orthogonal contours so indicated. These values are given as ratios to the characteristic impedance ρc. Thus the center of the chart gives $R/\rho_0 c = 1$, $X/\rho_0 c = 0$. At every point along a transmission line there is a particular value of impedance $R + jX$, related to the line variables α_0, $\beta + kd$, which in turn are determined uniquely by the terminating impedance (through α_0 and β) and by the position of the point in the line (through d).

In the above analysis we have assumed that energy is lost only in the termination. This results in circles of constant α or SWR. If there is dissipation along the line, α_0 increases with increasing distance from the termination. The α_0 contour (SWR contour) is no longer a circle, but a spiral of decreasing radius, approaching the center. At large distances the impedance in the line is not influenced by the termination, because a wave is completely absorbed before it can make a round trip to the termination.

2.10 Pressure Reflectivity and Transmissivity

We have seen that when a wave of amplitude P_+ strikes a boundary there is, in general, a reflected wave of amplitude P_-. Let us compute the ratio P_-/P_+, which we call the pressure reflectivity. A certain fraction of the incident pressure will also be transmitted into the medium on the other side of the boundary. This fraction is the pressure transmissivity.

The waves at either side of the boundary must satisfy two boundary conditions: (1) the total pressure must be the same on both sides, and (2) the particle velocity into the boundary must equal the particle velocity out of the boundary on the other side. For convenience, we take the boundary at $x = 0$, so the exponentials $e^{\pm jkx}$ equal unity. We designate quantities in the first and second media by subscripts 1 and 2, respectively, and obtain from eq. 2.34 the pressure amplitudes:

$$P_1 = (P_{1+} + P_{1-})$$
$$P_2 = (P_{2+} + P_{2-})$$

and from eq. 2.35 the particle velocity amplitudes:

$$u_{x1} = \frac{1}{Z_1}(P_{1+} - P_{1-})$$

$$u_{x2} = \frac{1}{Z_2}(P_{2+} - P_{2-})$$

in which $Z_1 = \rho_1 c_1$ and $Z_2 = \rho_2 c_2$ are the characteristic impedances of the first and second medium, respectively. Since we are considering waves originating in the first medium only, and assuming that the waves transmitted into the second medium travel away to infinity without reflection, we must set $P_{2-} = 0$. From the above specified boundary conditions we then obtain:

$$P_{1+} + P_{1-} = P_{2+}$$

$$Z_2(P_{1+} - P_{1-}) = Z_1 P_{2+}$$

These two equations can be solved simultaneously to yield:

$$\frac{P_{1-}}{P_{1+}} = \frac{r-1}{r+1} \qquad \text{(normal incidence pressure reflectivity)}$$

$$\frac{P_{2+}}{P_{1+}} = \frac{2r}{r+1} \qquad \text{(normal incidence pressure transmissivity)}$$

$$(2.41)$$

in which $r = Z_2/Z_1$ is the *impedance ratio* at the boundary.

If the two media have nearly the same impedance ($Z_2 \approx Z_1$, $r \approx 1$), the reflectivity is nearly zero and the transmissivity is nearly unity, as we should expect. If $Z_2 \gg Z_1$ ($r \gg 1$), there is almost complete reflection and very little power transmission. If $Z_2 \ll Z_1$ ($r \ll 1$), there is again almost complete reflection, but with a reversal in phase as indicated by the minus sign in the reflectivity for this case. Obviously the impedance ratio r is the important quantity for determining the nature of reflection and transmission at a boundary. In general, r, Z_1, Z_2, and the reflectivity and transmissivity are complex quantities, though in many practical problems they are real.

Let us examine the relation between reflectivity and the transmission-line behavior discussed above. We consider a boundary between two different media, with substantially plane waves entering and leaving the boundary. These conditions are found, for example, in a tube of small diameter ($d \ll \lambda$) containing two fluids separated by a thin membrane, or in a crystal transducer of large diameter ($d \gg \lambda$) radiating compressional waves into a large body of solid or liquid. Let us assume that both media are lossless (not highly viscous) so that their characteristic impedances are real. We send a plane wave of pressure amplitude P_{1+} to the right in a medium of impedance $\rho_1 c_1$, and observe a wave P_{1-} reflected from a boundary beyond which the impedance is $\rho_2 c_2$.

The two waves, to the left of the boundary, combine into a standing wave with pressure maxima of amplitude $P_{\max}$ spaced at half-wavelength intervals, and minima $P_{\min}$ midway between. At a maximum, the two component waves combine exactly in phase and their pressures

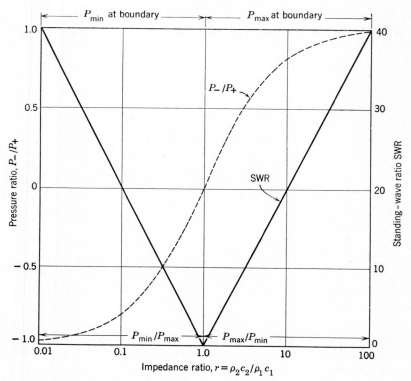

Fig. 2.9.   Reflectivity and standing-wave ratio for boundary with real impedance.

simply add: $P_{max} = P_{1+} + P_{1-}$. At a minimum, the components are opposite in phase; so $P_{min} = P_{1+} - P_{1-}$. The standing-wave ratio is:

$$\frac{P_{max}}{P_{min}} = \frac{P_{1+} + P_{1-}}{P_{1+} - P_{1-}}$$

which can be transformed to:

$$\frac{P_{1+}}{P_{1-}} = \frac{P_{max} + P_{min}}{P_{max} - P_{min}} = \frac{(P_{max}/P_{min}) + 1}{(P_{max}/P_{min}) - 1}$$

A comparison of this result with eq. 2.41 might lead us to conclude that $(P_{max}/P_{min}) = r = \rho_2 c_2 / \rho_1 c_1$. Actually, this is correct if $\rho_2 c_2 > \rho_1 c_1$. Conversely, if $\rho_2 c_2 < \rho_1 c_1$, then $(P_{max}/P_{min}) = 1/r$. The complete relation is:

$$\frac{P_{\max}}{P_{\min}} = \mathrm{SWR} \begin{cases} = r & \text{if} \quad \dfrac{d_{\min}}{\lambda} = \dfrac{1}{4}, \dfrac{3}{4}, \cdots \\[2ex] = \dfrac{1}{r} & \text{if} \quad \dfrac{d_{\min}}{\lambda} = 0, \dfrac{1}{2}, 1, \cdots \end{cases} \qquad (2.42)$$

These relations among SWR, reflectivity, and r are shown graphically in Fig. 2.9. We recall that the horizontal diameter of the Smith chart is a scale of r values from zero to infinity, and that the impedance is a pure resistance along this diameter. Exactly the same physical meaning is attached to the abscissa of Fig. 2.9, but the values of r on its (logarithmic) scale cover only the range from 0.01 to 100.

2.11 Energy, Intensity, and Power

Up to this point we have ignored the energy that is associated with a sonic disturbance. The sound pressure and particle velocity, taken together, are sufficient to specify completely the nature of the sound field. But in many applications we are more interested in the intensity of radiation or in the power that is transferred from one part of a system to another. We are now ready to obtain these and related quantities quite simply by using some of the foregoing results.

Let us start with the very useful equation $p = uZ$. We recall that mechanical power is equal to the time-average product of force and velocity. The total alternating force exerted over an area $S(m^2)$ by a sound of pressure p (newtons/m^2) is pS, and the alternating particle velocity is u (m/sec); so the *sound power* is:

$$W = \overline{up}S \text{ (watts)} \qquad (2.43)^{[21]}$$

in which the bar over u and p indicates a time average. If the pressure and particle velocity are in phase with each other, their time averages can be taken separately. These are the root-mean-square values p_{rms} and u_{rms}, which for simple harmonic waves or components are related to the respective amplitude values by: $p_{\mathrm{rms}} = P/2$, $u_{\mathrm{rms}} = U/2$.

We now notice that $p = uZ$ can also be written as $p_{\mathrm{rms}} = u_{\mathrm{rms}}Z$, or $P = UZ$, by performing an identical operation on both sides of the equation. Using these results we can write:

$$W = u_{\mathrm{rms}}p_{\mathrm{rms}}S = UPS/2 = U^2ZS/2 = P^2S/2Z \qquad (2.44)$$

subject to the "in-phase" restriction. This restriction is fully satisfied by free plane waves in a lossless medium, for then Z is a real quantity, the characteristic impedance. In other cases we must use just the

[21] If CGS units are used, namely, u (cm/sec), p (dynes/cm^2) and S (cm^2), the power is obtained in ergs/sec. The conversion is: 1 erg/sec = 10^{-7} watt.

real part of Z to compute the power radiated. Furthermore, eq. 2.43 and 2.44 are valid only if p and u are constant over the entire area S; in other cases the power must be computed for each element of area and integrated.

Sound intensity Most sound fields in practice are not uniformly distributed, so it is useful to consider the power that is transmitted through a unit area, which is called the *sound intensity:*

$$\mathcal{I} = W/S = \overline{up} \ (\text{watt/m}^2)$$
$$= u_{rms}p_{rms} = U^2Z/2 = P^2/2Z = p^2/Z \qquad (2.45)^{22}$$

($p = p_{rms}$ throughout this book unless otherwise specified.)

Intensity is a space vector, a measure of the power flowing at normal incidence to the specified unit area. Thus, in a free plane wave the intensity vector is zero in a direction parallel to the wave fronts.

In a perfect standing wave the intensity is zero because there is no net flow of energy; yet there is energy stored at every point along the standing wave. In fact, there is always energy associated with the particle motions that make up a sound wave. Each particle of mass m carries kinetic energy in the amount $\frac{1}{2}mu^2$, and the amount is $\frac{1}{2}\rho_0u^2$ for all the particles in unit volume. The kinetic energy has a maximum value $\frac{1}{2}\rho_0U^2$ at an instant of maximum velocity. At the same instant, the potential energy of the particles is zero, but at an instant of zero velocity all the energy is in potential form and the kinetic energy is zero.

The total energy per unit volume remains constant during the cycle (as with a mass on a lossless spring), therefore its value, the *energy density*, is:

$$E_0 = \rho_0U^2/2 = P^2/2\rho_0c^2 \ (\text{joule/m}^3) \qquad (2.46)^{23}$$

in which we have used eq. 2.45, together with $Z = \rho_0c$ for the characteristic impedance. We also see that the intensity in a free plane wave has the value

$$\mathcal{I} = E_0c \qquad (2.47)$$

This equation states that the intensity is equal to the amount of energy in a "tube" of unit cross-sectional area, and length equal to the distance that sound travels in 1 sec. In other words, intensity is energy flow per unit time through unit area (watt/m^2 = joule/m^2/sec).

---

[22] In CGS units $\overline{up}$ has the dimension erg/cm^2/sec; 10^7 ergs/cm^2/sec = 1 watt/cm^2.

[23] 1 joule/m^3 = 10 erg/cm^3.

Intensity reflection and transmission coefficients We frequently deal with a system of two or more different substances carrying sonic energy. In eq. 2.41 we found expressions for the reflectivity and transmissivity to sound pressure at an interface. We can now readily find the intensity change on reflection and transmission. The incident intensity is: $\mathcal{I}_{1+} = P_{1+}{}^2/2Z_1$; the reflected intensity is: $\mathcal{I}_{1-} = P_{1-}{}^2/2Z_1$; and the transmitted intensity is: $\mathcal{I}_{2+} = P_{2+}{}^2/2Z_2$; and $r = Z_2/Z_1$ as before.

The *reflection coefficient* is:

$$\alpha_r = \frac{\mathcal{I}_{1-}}{\mathcal{I}_{1+}} = \frac{P_{1-}{}^2}{P_{2-}{}^2} = \left(\frac{r-1}{r+1}\right)^2 \tag{2.48}$$

the *transmission coefficient* is:

$$\alpha_t = \frac{\mathcal{I}_{2+}}{\mathcal{I}_{1+}} = \frac{p_2{}^2 + z_1}{p_1{}^2 + z_2} = \frac{4r}{(r+1)^2} \tag{2.49}$$

In the limits of large mismatch at the boundary the transmission coefficient becomes:

$$\alpha_t \simeq 4r, \qquad r \ll 1$$
$$\alpha_t \simeq 4/r, \qquad r \gg 1 \tag{2.50}$$

2.12 Radiation Pressure[24]

In Section 2.2 we discussed linearity of elastic media, and we have been developing relations for sound waves under the implicit assumption that the medium is a linear, compressible fluid. In a sense this is a contradiction of terms. If the medium is compressed, its change in dimensions alters its internal properties, such as the acoustic impedance, which we have been considering truly constant.

If we pass an alternating electric current through an element whose resistance varies with the magnitude of the current, we produce not only an alternating voltage but also a steady (d-c) component. This is simply rectification, and the non-linear element is a rectifier. Similarly, if a moving piston drives a fluid with a particle velocity u, the resulting sound pressure $p = \rho c u$ will have a d-c component if the resistance ρc varies periodically with the motion. We see that this steady component, the *radiation pressure*, adds to the static pressure

[24] The derivation of radiation pressure given in this section is restricted to elementary reasoning which conveys a simple physical picture. For a rigorous justification of the final result (eq. 2.51) see C. Schaefer, *Ann. Phys.*, Leipzig, *35* (1939), 473; R. E. Beyer, *Am. J. Phys.*, *18* (1950), 25; and F. E. Borgnis, "Theory of Acoustic Radiation Pressure," *Tech. Rept.* 1, Calif. Inst. of Tech., July 25, 1951.

within the beam. The radiation pressure can produce forces on interfaces between media of different acoustic properties and within absorptive media. On the other hand, radiation pressure does not produce measurable effects in a plane progressive wave of infinite extent in a lossless fluid.

When a small element of volume V_0 is enlarged by an amount dV in the presence of a sound wave (see Fig. 2.7), the molecules spread out and the density is decreased by an amount $d\rho = -\rho_0 \, dV/V_0$. Using this in eq. 2.28a we obtain:

$$p = \gamma P_0 \frac{d\rho}{\rho_0}$$

The modified density can be written as:

$$\rho = \rho_0 + d\rho = \rho_0 \left(1 + \frac{p}{\gamma P_0}\right)$$

The impressed sound pressure p slightly increases the density, so the relation between p and u should be written:

$$p = \rho_0 \left(1 + \frac{p}{\gamma P_0}\right) cu$$

Since the p on the right side appears in a small correction term it can be expressed by the uncorrected value of pressure.[25] For a plane progressive wave we then have:

$$p = \rho_0 \left(1 + \frac{\rho_0 c U_+ \cos (\omega t - kx)}{\gamma P_0}\right) c U_+ \cos (\omega t - kx)$$

$$= \rho_0 c U_+ \cos (\omega t - kx) + \frac{\rho_0^2 c^2 U_+^2 \cos^2 (\omega t - kx)}{\gamma P_0}$$

The time average of the first term is zero since

$$\int_0^{2\pi} \cos (\omega t - kx) \, d(\omega t) = 0$$

But the average of $\cos^2$ over one cycle is $\frac{1}{2}$, so the second term yields a static pressure:

$$\Pi = \frac{1}{2} \frac{\rho_0^2 c^2 U_+^2}{\gamma P_0} = \frac{\rho_0 U_+^2}{2} = \frac{P_+^2}{2\rho_0 c^2} = \frac{\mathcal{G}}{c} = E_0 \; (\text{newton/m}^2) \quad (2.51)$$

In this equation we have used the substitution $\gamma P_0 = \rho_0 c^2$ from eq. 2.31. The quantity Π is the *radiation pressure*, which is equal in

[25] We are simply making a first-order perturbation calculation.

value to the energy density E_0.[26] The product of sound pressure and particle velocity (average over time) is the acoustic power per unit area: $\overline{pu} = W/S = \mathcal{I} = Ec$. We see that the intensity is also equal to the product of radiation pressure and sound velocity. Therefore, in a free plane wave:

$$\Pi/p = \bar{u}/c \qquad (2.52)$$

Thus the sound pressure and radiation pressure are two related phenomena associated with the transport of energy in a sound field. But if energy is transported there will be a flow of momentum, whether the wave is acoustic, electromagnetic, or any other type. The radiation pressure is equal to the rate of change of momentum through unit area. At any instant, the rate at which the mass of fluid flows through unit area normal to the beam is equal to $dm/dt = \rho u$, the density of the fluid times the particle velocity. Since u changes sign and magnitude periodically, there is no net flow of mass. However, there is a transfer of momentum at a rate equal to:

$$u(dm/dt) = d(mu)/dt = \rho u^2 \qquad (2.53)$$

This quantity does have a net value because the time average of u^2 is not zero but $U_+^2/2$. Comparing eq. 2.53 with 2.51 we see that the radiation pressure is simply equal to the rate of flow of momentum through unit area, as required by Newton's law: force = rate of change of momentum.

The manifestations of radiation pressure most usually encountered are summarized in Table 2.1. In this table a drag coefficient D is defined as the force F per unit cross-sectional area S of the obstacle in a sound field of unit energy density E_0:

$$D = F/SE_0$$

The net forces exerted on a perfect absorber or on a perfect reflector are often utilized for a measurement of the power radiated in a sound field. In order to yield easily interpreted results, the intercepting area S of the device should be much greater than wavelength. Figure 2.10 shows schematically a commercial ultrasonic power meter using a movable absorber consisting of a multiple array of cones of absorbing rubber. The absorber is supported by one arm (2) of a balance; the other arm (3) actuates a pointer (4) by means of a string (5) wound on a drum (6) which is attached to the pointer axle in the fashion of

[26] We can see that this result is dimensionally correct: joules = newtons $\times$ meters, and energy density is measured in joules/m^3 = newtons/m^2. The conversion to CGS units is: 1 newton/m^2 = 10 dynes/cm^2.

a hot-wire ammeter. The whole assembly is enclosed in a box (7) filled completely with water, which has a sound-transparent window (8) opposite the absorber. The membrane of this window also stops the streaming that may be set up by the presence of absorption in the coupling liquid which fills the cup-shaped space (9) above the sound window.

Devices using perfect reflectors are more sensitive because of the doubling of energy density that occurs in this case.[27] But care must be taken that the standing-wave system set up in front of a reflector does not act back on the transducer. One way to achieve this is shown in Fig. 2.11, where a plane-wave sound beam of cross-sectional

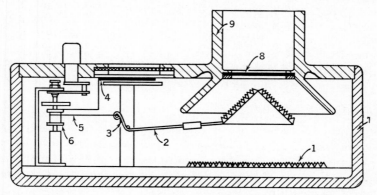

Fig. 2.10. Ultrasonic power meter, using small absorbing rubber cones. Courtesy of Altlas-Werke, Bremen, Germany.

area S strikes a reflector that is bent to a 90° angle. Perfect reflection is easily obtained from two overlaying thin metal sheets ($t < 0.03\lambda$) that are separated by a thin piece of dry paper and that are sealed from the surrounding liquid by having their edges soldered. If the reflector points symmetrically into the sound beam, the radiation is split into two equal beams deflected oppositely at 90° to the incident

[27] Right at a perfectly reflecting rigid surface the sound pressure is doubled, so one might expect the energy density to be increased by a factor of 4 over that in the free wave. Actually, the reflector sets up a standing wave in which the pressure amplitude varies, from $2P_+$ at the surface and at pressure maxima every $\lambda/2$ from the surface, to zero at the nodes $\lambda/4$, $3\lambda/4$, $5\lambda/4 \cdots$ from the surface. The energy density is the average over time and *space* of:

$$E_i = \frac{1}{2} (\rho u^2 + p^2/\rho_0 c^2).$$

The space averaging introduces an additional factor of $\frac{1}{2}$ in the standing wave.

Table 2.1   Manifestations of Radiation Pressure for Plane Progressive Sound Waves with Energy Density E_0

Physical Situation	Energy at Interface	D = drag coefficient (Net Force, $F = DE_0S$)
Perfect absorber $(r = 1)$ of area S, normal to sound beam.	In front of absorber: $E_1 = E_0$ In back of absorber: $E_2 = 0$	$D = 1$
Perfect reflector $(r = 0$ or $\infty)$ of area S, normal to sound beam.	Front: $E_1 = 2E_0$ Back: $E_2 = 0$	$D = 2$
Perfect reflector $(r = 0$ or $\infty)$ of area S at angle θ to sound beam.	Front: $E_1 = 2E_0$ Back: $E_2 = 0$	$D = 2\cos^2\theta$
Partially reflecting interface $(r \neq 1)$ of area S, normal to sound beam.	Front: $E_1 = 2E_0\left[\dfrac{r^2+1}{(r+1)^2}\right]$ Back: $E_2 = E_0\left[\dfrac{4r}{(r+1)^2}\right]$	$E_1 - E_2 = E_0 \cdot D$ $D = 2\left[\dfrac{(r-1)^2}{(r+1)^2}\right]$
Non-reflecting interface between two media $(r = 1; c_1 \neq c_2)$ of area S, normal to sound beam.	Front: $E_1 = E_0$ Back: $E_2 = E_0(1 - D)$	$D = 1 - c_1/c_2$ for $c_1 < c_2$ force away from source; for $c_1 > c_2$ force toward source
Absorbing medium, no interface. $\mathcal{I}_x = \mathcal{I}_0 e^{-2\alpha x}$ $\mathcal{I}_0 = \mathcal{I}_{x=0}$	$\left(\dfrac{dE}{dx}\right)_x = \dfrac{1}{c}\dfrac{d\mathcal{I}_x}{dx}$	Differential pressure causes streaming: $-\dfrac{dE}{dx} = E_x \cdot D$ $D = 2\alpha$
Scattering particle $(a \ll \lambda)$ of density $\rho \gg \rho_0$.	$E_\vartheta \sim (1 - A\cos\vartheta)^2$ cylinder: $A = 2$ sphere: $A = 3$	cylinder: $D = \frac{5}{8}\pi^2\,(ka)^3$ sphere: $D = \frac{11}{9}(ka)^4$

$r = \rho_2 c_2/\rho_1 c_1$, the impedance ratio at an interface.   The area S is taken to be smaller than the cross-sectional area of the sound beam.

beam. This reflected radiation is then absorbed, as, for example, by a pair of brushes. The lateral thrusts of the deflected beams cancel each other, but a net force of IIS is exerted on the reflector in the direction of the incident radiation. The magnitude of this force can be measured by a scale balance. For instance, a reflector that intercepts a sound radiation of 10 watts will be acted upon by a force of 0.67 g.

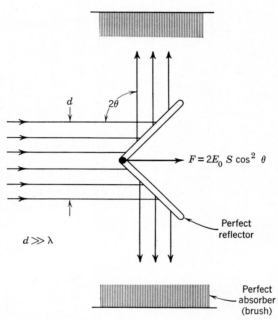

$$F = 2E_0 S \cos^2 \theta$$

Fig. 2.11.   Measurement of radiation pressure in liquids by means of a 90° reflector.

Figure 2.12 gives an exploded view of a commercial ultrasonic power meter[28] which is self-contained and usable in any desired position. This instrument measures sonic power up to 50 watts in the frequency range between 50 kcps and 5 mcps with an error of $\pm 2\%$ full scale. It uses a 90° reflector suspended on four torsional ribbons and a pair of absorbing brushes.

2.13   The Decibel Notation

"Decibels" (db) is one of the most frequently used words in the language of acoustics. Unfortunately, it is sometimes used loosely or inaccurately; and its meaning varies somewhat among different

[28] Siemens-Sonotest, U.S. Pat. 2,531,844, Nov. 28, 1950, by G. Fiedler.

branches of acoustics.   Because *sonics* encompasses a wide range of
subjects, frequencies, and media, we must be particularly careful
to define and use "decibels" in a precise and consistent manner.

Qualitatively, the decibel is a *logarithmic expression of the ratio of
two values.*   The logarithmic scale is used mainly for its convenience
in expressing numbers that extend over many orders of magnitude

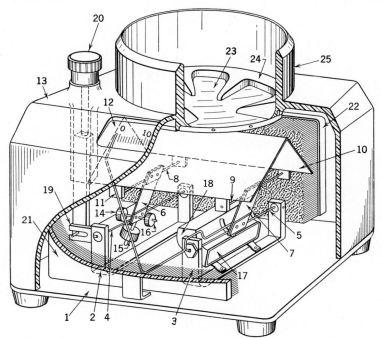

Fig. 2.12.   Ultrasonic power meter with 90° reflector ("Sonotest").   Courtesy of
Siemens-Reiniger Company, Erlangen, Germany.

(e.g., we hear sounds over an intensity range of some 10^{12}).   A logarithmic scale is convenient in other ways.   Products become sums.
Experimental accuracy is often a constant ratio, rather than a constant
absolute value, which can be expressed as "x db."   The attenuation
of sound is generally an exponential function of distance.

The decibel was first used to express the ratio of two powers (electrical or acoustical):

$$\text{power level} = 10 \log \ (W/W_0) \ \text{db}$$

in which W_0 is the *reference power.*   The selection of a reference power
is entirely an arbitrary matter; but appropriate or convenient reference

levels may become standardized for common usage in a field. We shall use decibels most often in connection with the following two quantities:

Intensity level

$$IL = 10 \log (\mathcal{I}/\mathcal{I}_{ref}) \text{ db}$$

in which:

$$\mathcal{I} = \text{intensity in watt/m}^2 \text{ (watt/cm}^2) \qquad (2.54)$$

and according to standards:

$$\mathcal{I}_{ref} = 10^{-12} \text{ watt/m}^2 \text{ (} 10^{-16} \text{ watt/cm}^2)$$

Pressure level

$$PL = 20 \log (p/p_{ref}) \text{ db}$$

in which:

$$p = \text{rms sound pressure in newton/m}^2 \text{ (dyne/cm}^2)$$

and according to standards:

$$p_{ref} = 2 \times 10^{-5} \text{ newton/m}^2 \text{ (} 2 \times 10^{-4} \text{ dyne/cm}^2) \qquad (2.55)[29]$$

A complete and unambiguous statement of these quantities must include the name of the quantity and the reference value, e.g., "IL = 90 db ref 10^{-12} watt/m^2."

These two quantities, IL and PL, are interrelated by eq. 2.45, from which we can write:

$$10 \log \mathcal{I} = 20 \log P - 10 \log Z$$

Equations 2.54 and 2.55 can be written:

$$IL = 10 \log \mathcal{I} + \begin{cases} 120 \text{ if } \mathcal{I} \text{ is in watt/m}^2 \\ 160 \text{ if } \mathcal{I} \text{ is in watt/cm}^2 \end{cases}$$

$$PL = 20 \log p + \begin{cases} 94 \text{ if } p \text{ is in newton/m}^2 \\ 74 \text{ if } p \text{ is in dyne/cm}^2 \end{cases}$$

Therefore IL = PL if:

$$20 \log p - 10 \log Z + 120 = 20 \log p + 94$$

using MKS units; whence:

$$10 \log Z = 120 - 94 = 26$$

and

$$Z = 400$$

---

[29] In underwater sound a pressure of 1 dyne/cm^2 = 1 microbar is sometimes taken as the reference level.

The characteristic impedance ($\rho_0 c$) of *free plane waves in air* is just 400 MKS units at barometric pressure 760 mm Hg, and temperature 40°C. At the more normal temperature of 20°C the impedance is about 415. Therefore, the intensity level is exactly equal to the pressure level for plane sound waves in air at 760 mm, 40°C; and the two quantities are within a fraction of a decibel of each other over the range of normal atmospheric conditions.

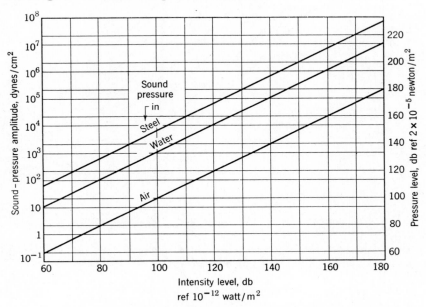

Fig. 2.13. **PL** $= f(\textbf{IL})$ for air, water, steel, using standard reference levels.

Since the standard reference pressure of 2×10^{-5} newtons/m^2 was chosen to yield IL = PL for air under the above-mentioned conditions, the intensity level is not equal to the pressure level in other media, but is given by:

$$\text{IL} = \text{PL} + 26 - 10 \log Z \qquad (2.56)$$

Corresponding values in air, water,[30] and steel are plotted in Fig. 2.13.

The microphones most commonly in use today measure sound pressure directly. Their output can be processed and presented on a meter that reads pressure level in decibels ref 2×10^{-5} newton/m^2 (as in

---

[30] In air-free water ($Z = 1.436 \times 10^6$) the pressure associated with 10^{-12} watts/m^2 is $P = 1.2 \times 10^{-3}$ newtons/m^2. Using this pressure as reference one would obtain IL = PL. If 1 dyne/cm^2 = 1 microbar is used for reference, one obtains IL = PL + 10 − 10 log Z.

the American standard sound level meter). Although this reading is *not* equal to the intensity level except under the particular conditions noted above, it can be converted to IL by eq. 2.56 if we know the acoustic impedance at the point of measurement.

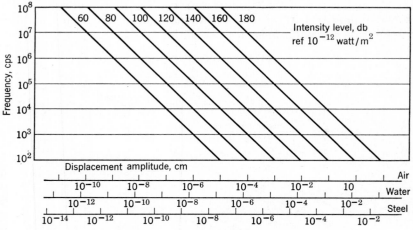

Fig. 2.14. Displacement amplitudes in air, water, and steel.

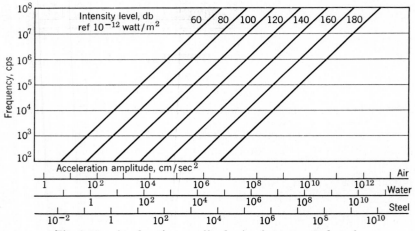

Fig. 2.15. Acceleration amplitudes in air, water, and steel.

In some applications it is useful to know the displacement amplitude Y or the acceleration amplitude A in the sound field. These also can be determined from the sound pressure and the impedance Z through the relations (for simple harmonic motion):

$$\mathscr{I} = p^2/Z = P^2/2Z = ZU^2/2 = 2\omega^2 Y^2/2 = ZA^2/2\omega^2 \quad (2.57)$$

The corresponding values of IL and displacement amplitude for free plane waves in air, water, and steel are shown in Fig. 2.14. Similar relations for acceleration amplitude are given in Fig. 2.15.

The above relations between IL and PL are correct for free plane waves, in which $\mathscr{I} = Ec = p^2/\rho_0 c$, and $Z = \rho_0 c$ is a real quantity. We have noted that $\mathscr{I} = 0$ in a perfect standing wave, so IL is also zero; but there is a sound pressure (and PL) that varies from zero to a maximum value every half wavelength. In a diffuse sound field the intensity level is somewhat lower than the pressure level. In some cases the sound field may be quite complicated, a mixture of several standing waves or a radiation pattern near a sound generator. Some of these questions are taken up in Chapter 3, where we will see how the acoustic impedance depends on the curvature of the waves.

CHAPTER 3

Radiation

The basic principles of sonics are developed in Chapter 2 in terms of a single space variable. By thus restricting our attention to one-dimensional wave motion we could depict the essential physics without undue geometrical complications. At the same time we obtained results that are directly applicable to many practical situations in which sound waves are plane or nearly plane. Now we shall see how these results are extended to encompass waves of arbitrary shape in space. Strictly speaking, we are interested in the shape of the *wave front*, a surface over which the motion is everywhere in phase. Sometimes the wave fronts retain the same shape throughout space and vary only in a scale factor. In other instances the wave fronts vary in shape also, and produce a more complicated form of *radiation field*.

3.1 Spherical Waves

The simplest non-planar wave is a spherical wave. Consider a *simple source:* a radially pulsating sphere of diameter much smaller than the wavelength of the radiated waves. Such a source radiates sound uniformly in all directions. A long tube of small diameter conducting sound from a speaker unit will also radiate approximately spherical waves from its open end. Let us locate the simple source in a free field, outdoors or in an anechoic chamber, so that no waves are reflected back into the radiated sound field. Under these conditions the energy will be spread uniformly over a complete spherical surface at any radius r from the source. Therefore the intensity $\mathcal{I}$ (watts/m^2) will be related to the source power W (watts) by:

$$\mathcal{I} = W/4\pi r^2 \tag{3.1}$$

At a radial distance r that is much larger than the wavelength or the source diameter a $(r \gg a)$ the wave front is essentially plane over distances comparable with the wavelength. In this limit the sound radiates into the plane wave characteristic impedance $\rho_0 c$, and the intensity is proportional to the square of the sound pressure. We

54

therefore write for the peak pressure: $P = [\mathscr{g}2\rho_0 c]^{\frac{1}{2}}$ and with the use of eq. 3.1 for the instantaneous sound pressure:[1]

$$p = (\rho_0 c W/2\pi)^{\frac{1}{2}} \frac{e^{j(\omega t - kr)}}{r} \qquad (3.2a)$$

With the use of $W = P_a^2 S/2\rho_0 c$, where $S = 4\pi a^2$ is the radiating surface of the source, eq. 3.2a can be rewritten as:

$$p = P_a a \frac{e^{j(\omega t - kr)}}{r} \qquad (3.2b)$$

The pressure amplitude P_a is given correctly by eq. 3.2a only if W is taken as the total power actually radiated. This will be less than the power fed to the source (transducer) if the radiation efficiency is less than unity, as it usually is.

We can take the radial gradient of the pressure and use eq. 2.32 to obtain the radial particle velocity:

$$u_r = \frac{j}{\omega \rho_0} \frac{\partial p}{\partial r} = \frac{P_a a}{\rho_0 c} \frac{e^{j(\omega t - kr)}}{r} [1 + 1/jkr] \qquad (3.3)$$

in which $k = \omega/c = 2\pi/\lambda$. The specific acoustic impedance then is:

$$Z_r = \frac{\rho_0 c}{1 + (1/jkr)} = \frac{1}{(1/\rho_0 c) + (1/j\omega\rho_0 r)} \qquad (3.4)$$

If $kr \gg 1$, i.e., $r \gg \lambda$, the *spherical wave correction* term containing jkr vanishes. Then u_r and Z_r take on the plane-wave values, which is the condition assumed above for relating intensity to pressure. At a distance of 50 m and a frequency of 1000 cps, the impedance given by eq. 3.4 is within 1 per cent of the plane-wave value. At smaller distances the spherical correction becomes increasingly important.

3.2   Radiation Impedance

We noted in Chapter 2 that the loading of a sound source is determined by the impedance at the radiating surface. Since the surface of a pulsating sphere exactly fits a spherical wave front (at $r = a$) the

---

[1] Although this result is derived here from eq. 3.1 carried to its plane-wave limit, eq. 3.2a gives the correct dependence of p on r for *all* distances from a simple source; a rigorous derivation from the wave equation in spherical coordinates:

$$\frac{\partial^2 (r\xi)}{\partial t^2} = c^2 \frac{\partial^2 (r\xi)}{\partial r^2}$$

is given by P. M. Morse in *Vibration and Sound*, 2nd edition, McGraw-Hill, New York, 1948 Chapter VII.

specific radiation impedance Z_a of a sphere is obtained directly from eq. 3.4, and is:

$$Z_a = \frac{\rho_0 c}{1 + (1/ka)^2} + j\,\frac{\rho_0 c/ka}{1 + (1/ka)^2} = R_a + jX_a \qquad (3.5)$$

in which a is the radius of the sphere.

This equation is plotted in Fig. 3.1, with $R_a/\rho_0 c$ and $X_a/\rho_0 c$ as functions of ka. The total (mechanical) impedance is the specific impedance Z_a times the area of the sphere.

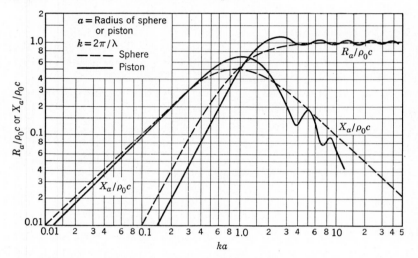

Fig. 3.1.   Radiation impedance of a sphere and a circular piston.

At very small values of ka, the resistance and reactance are:

$$R_a/\rho_0 c = (ka)^2 \qquad X_a/\rho_0 c = ka \qquad (ka \ll 1) \qquad (3.6)$$

These values are fairly close to those in eq. 3.5 up to $ka = 0.5$, at which the circumference of the sphere equals a half wavelength. Below this, the radiation efficiency, which is proportional to the resistance, drops off rapidly and the source works into a highly reactive load. Using eq. 3.6 we obtain the mechanical reactance:

$$4\pi a^2 X_a = \omega\rho_0 4\pi a^3 = 3\omega\rho_0 V$$

where $\rho_0 V$ is the mass of the medium in a volume equal to that of the sphere. The source exerts an alternating force which is expended mainly in moving this mass. As shown in Fig. 3.2a, the motion is primarily tangential, providing the expansion and contraction of the spherical "shell" of the medium around the source.

At very large ka the reactance drops to a negligible value, and the resistance approaches the constant value $\rho_0 c$, as it should in the plane-wave limit. In the intermediate region $(ka \simeq 1)$, where the circumference of the sphere is about a wavelength, the resistance and reactance are of the same order of magnitude. All aspects of this behavior can be predicted from an equivalent electric circuit. Equation 3.5 leads to the series combination of jX_a and R_a shown in Fig. 3.2b, and eq. 3.4 to the parallel combination of a resistance $R \simeq X_a^2/R_a$

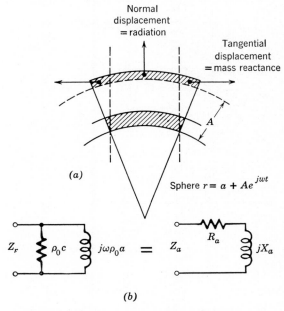

(a)

Normal
displacement
= radiation

Tangential
displacement
= mass reactance

Sphere $r = a + Ae^{jwt}$

Z_r $\rho_0 c$ $j\omega\rho_0 a$ = Z_a R_a jX_a

(b)

Fig. 3.2. (a) Tangential motion, the cause of mass reactance. (b) Equivalent circuits for radiation impedance.

$= \rho_0 c$ and a reactance $jX \simeq jX_a = j\omega\rho_0 a$ (using $a = r$) which is also illustrated in Fig. 3.2b. At very low frequencies the inductance $j\omega\rho_0 a$ in Fig. 3.2b shunts out the resistance $\rho_0 c$; at intermediate frequencies the inductive reactance is about equal to the resistance; and at high frequencies the reactance is so large that practically all the "current" flows through the resistance. The power factor can also be derived from this circuit:

$$\cos \phi = X/(R^2 + X^2)^{1/2}$$

The power factor is nearly zero at low frequencies, about 0.7 near $ka = 1$, and unity at very high frequencies.

   Cylindrical waves constitute another simple form of nonplanar
radiation.   They are generated in a free field by an infinitely long
cylindrical pulsating radially.   The intensity diminishes as the inverse
first power of the radial distance, instead of inverse square as for
spherical waves.   The expression for pressure is similar to eq. 3.2b,
but with $r^{1/2}$ in the denominator.   The velocity and wave impedance

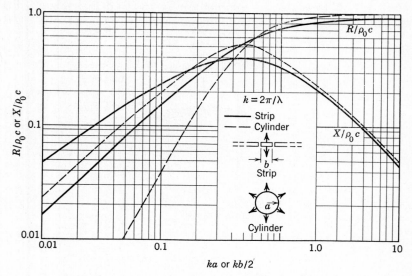

Fig. 3.3.   Radiation impedance of a cylinder and a long strip.

can be obtained exactly as before, and the resulting equation for the
radiation impedance of an infinite pulsating cylinder is:

$$Z_c = \frac{\rho_0 c}{1 + (1/2ka)^2} + j\,\frac{\rho_0 c/2ka}{1 + (1/2ka)^2} = R_c + jX_c \qquad (3.7)$$

in which a is the radius of the cylinder.   The low-frequency values are:

$$R_c/\rho_0 c = (2ka)^2 \qquad X_c/\rho_0 c = 2ka \qquad (ka \ll 1) \qquad (3.8)$$

Equation 3.7 is plotted in Fig. 3.3, and the result is strikingly similar
to the plot of eq. 3.5 in Fig. 3.1.   In fact, the only difference is a
downward shift of the curves to $\frac{1}{2}$ the corresponding values of ka.
If we differentiate the expression for X_c with respect to ka, and equate
this to zero, we find that the maximum occurs at $ka = \frac{1}{2}$, and that
the maximum value is $X_m/\rho_0 c = \frac{1}{2}$.   A similar operation on eq. 3.5
yields $ka = 1$ at the maximum, and the maximum value $X/\rho_0 c = \frac{1}{2}$.
This factor of 2 is a direct consequence of the essential dimensional

difference between spherical and cylindrical waves, the difference between inverse square and inverse first-power radiation.

We now recognize a very important and useful generalization: the basic properties of radiation impedance discussed above are characteristic of all forms of radiating devices. The impedance for a circular piston in an infinite flat baffle is shown in Fig. 3.1 and is seen to parallel closely the impedance for a sphere.[2] There are small ripples in the resistance and reactance for the piston, arising from detailed interference effects, which are discussed below. But the two cases have the same values within a factor of about 2 over the entire frequency range. The exact shape of a generator is much less important than its average dimension in determining radiation efficiency.[3] Impedance curves for an infinite flat strip in a baffle are shown in Fig. 3.3.

Accurate calculation of the impedance for a piston or a strip is very difficult, and few other shapes have been analyzed at all. It is possible, in principle, to calculate the impedance of any shape of radiator using numerical computations. But many engineering problems can be solved adequately on the basis of estimates made from the information in Fig. 3.1 and 3.3.

3.3 Directivity; The Far Field

Next we examine the radiation field around two simple sources placed a distance d apart, vibrating exactly in phase and with equal amplitudes. The sound pressure from each source is given by eq. 3.2b with the same value of P_a for each. In Fig. 3.4, we show a field point B at a distance r_1 from source S_1 and r_2 from S_2. The position of B is also specified by the distance r from the midpoint between the sources and the angle θ between r and the normal to the line S_1-S_2. We now consider only the *far field* (the *near field* will be analyzed subsequently), so we restrict r to values much greater than d. This simplifies the geometry and allows us to make the approximations $r_2 - r = r - r_1 = \delta = (d/2) \sin \theta$. The combined pressure at B then is:

---

[2] The specific resistance and reactance for a circular piston of radius a, in an infinite baffle, at low frequencies, are given approximately by:

$$R/\rho_0 c \simeq (0.7 \, ka)^2 \qquad X/\rho_0 c \simeq 0.7 \, ka \qquad (ka \ll 1)$$

corresponding to eq. 3.6 for a sphere. See P. M. Morse, *Vibration and Sound,* 2nd edition, McGraw-Hill, New York, 1948, p. 333, for a derivation and the general result.

[3] I. B. Crandall, *Theory of Vibrating Systems and Sound*, Van Nostrand, New York, 1926.

$$p_B = \frac{P_a a e^{j(\omega t - kr)}}{r} [e^{jk\delta} + e^{-jk\delta}]$$

$$= \frac{2P_a a e^{j(\omega t - kr)}}{r} \cos\left[\frac{kd}{2} \sin \theta\right] \qquad (r \gg d) \qquad (3.9)$$

In this approximation we have used $r_1 = r_2 = r$ in the denominator, because the small differences in distance have a negligible effect on the pressure amplitudes. But these differences have an important effect on the relative phase of the two contributions, expressed by the trigonometric function in eq. 3.9.

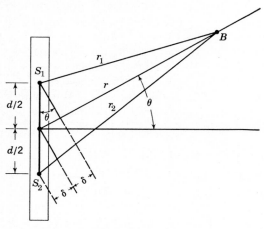

Fig. 3.4.   Far field of two simple sources.

The dipole *directivity function* $\cos\left[(\pi d/\lambda) \sin \theta\right]$ is plotted in Fig. 3.5 for several cases.[4] If $d/\lambda = 0$ the pattern is a circle and the dipole pattern is indistinguishable from that of a single simple source. The two source amplitudes add together (these sources are in phase) and give a double value of pressure in the field. At $d/\lambda = \frac{1}{4}$ the pattern is pulled in somewhat at 90° from the axis, and at $d/\lambda = \frac{1}{2}$ the pressure goes to zero at 90°. In these plots the radius vector is proportional to the sound pressure in the far field, and the angular coordinate corresponds to actual angles in space. The full pattern is a three-dimensional form, symmetrical around the line through the sources.

At $d/\lambda = \frac{3}{4}$ there are *side lobes* at 90°, but these are lower in pressure than the *main lobes* along the dipole axis. The directions of zero pressure in this case are about 42° off the axis. The width of the main

[4] For any phase difference φ between the two sources, the directivity function is $\cos\left[(\pi d/\lambda) \sin \theta - \varphi/2\right]$.

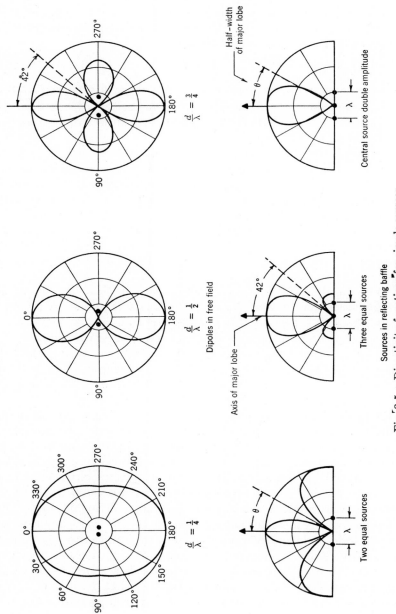

Fig. 3.5.   Directivity functions for simple sources.

lobe, or simply the *beam width*, is often specified by the angle θ between the axis and the first zero. The first zero in eq. 3.9 occurs when $(kd/2) \sin \theta = \pi/2$, from which we get:

$$\theta = \sin^{-1} (\lambda/2d) \qquad \text{half-beam width for dipole} \qquad (3.10)$$

In some cases it is more useful to specify the width of the beam at points where the pressure is $\frac{1}{2}$ (6 db down) or $\sqrt{\frac{1}{2}}$ (3 db down) of the pressure on axis. Formulas for these widths can be obtained directly from eq. 3.9.

Let us now place the simple sources against (or "in") a perfectly reflecting plane baffle of infinite extent. More specifically, we assume that the impedance of the baffle is very much greater than that of the medium. In this case each source will have an image source in the plane which will add its pressure to that from the actual source.[5] In front of the plane the radiation field will have the same shape as that from the dipole in free field, but the pressure everywhere will be doubled. Of course, there will be no field behind the plane. Some directivity patterns for this case are also shown in Fig. 3.5.

First is a dipole of $d/\lambda = 1$. The pressure in the side lobes at 90° is equal to that on the axis. This result is easy to predict by reference to Fig. 3.4. When point B is on axis it is equidistant from the two sources, so their contributions add in phase. At 90°, B is in line with the sources, but is at a distance λ further from one source than the other. Again the two add in phase. In between, at an angle of 30° (see eq. 3.10), one source is exactly $\lambda/2$ further from B than the other, so their pressures cancel.

Huyghens' principle This elementary bit of reasoning is fundamental to the entire subject of radiation. *Huyghens' principle* states that any wave phenomenon can be analyzed by the addition of contributions from some distribution of simple sources, properly selected in phase and amplitude to represent the physical situation. Each "Huyghens wave" can be expressed in the form of eq. 3.2*b*.

We can take a radiator of any size and shape, divide its surface into a number of areas each small enough to satisfy the simple source assumptions, and sum their contributions transmitted to any point in space. In a sense, the dipole is the first approximation to a *line source* of finite length. The possible outline of such a source is shown by light lines in Fig. 3.4; each source is centrally located in each half of the line and is taken to represent the behavior of its half. The next

---

[5] If the impedance of the baffle is much less than that of the medium there will also be an image of the same strength as the source, but in this case the image will be out of phase and therefore will cancel the source if the two are right at the plane.

better approximation would be three simple sources centered in equal thirds of the line.   Repeating the procedure of eq. 3.9 we obtain:

$$p_B = \frac{P_a a e^{j(\omega t - kr)}}{r} \left[1 + 2 \cos\left(kd \sin\theta\right) \right] \qquad (3.11)$$

in which d is the (equal) spacing between the sources.   The half-beam width is then:

$$\theta = \sin^{-1}\left(\lambda/3d\right) \qquad (3.12)$$

A radiation pattern for three equal sources at $d/\lambda = \frac{1}{2}$ is shown in Fig. 3.5.   The pattern has small side lobes at 90°, somewhat like those in the dipole pattern for $d/\lambda = \frac{3}{4}$, but of lower amplitude.   The beam width is the same, but this is reasonable because the equivalent line source length is $3\lambda/2$ for both cases.   As we take more and more points we approach the performance of the continuous line with

Table 3.1   Directivity Functions

Source Geometry	x_θ	P_θ/P_0
1. Series of N point sources of equal strength, in phase, uniformly spaced along a line.	$\dfrac{\pi d}{\lambda} \sin\theta$	$\dfrac{\sin(N x_\theta)}{N \sin x_\theta}$
2. Straight-line source $(1/d \to \infty)$ of uniform strength and phase.	$\dfrac{\pi l}{\lambda} \sin\theta$	$\dfrac{\sin x_\theta}{x_\theta}$
3. Tapered straight-line source strength decreasing linearly to zero at either end, uniform phase.	$\dfrac{\pi l}{\lambda} \sin\theta$	$\dfrac{\sin^2 x_\theta}{x_\theta{}^2}$
4. Circular ring source, uniform strength and phase.	$\dfrac{2\pi a}{\lambda} \sin\theta$	$J_0(x_\theta)$
5. Plane circular piston source, uniform strength and phase.	$\dfrac{2\pi a}{\lambda} \sin\theta$	$\dfrac{2J_1(x_\theta)}{x_\theta}$
6. Plane rectangular piston source, uniform strength and phase.	$x_\theta = \dfrac{\pi l_a}{\lambda} \sin\theta$ $x_\varphi = \dfrac{\pi l_b}{\lambda} \sin\varphi$	$\dfrac{\sin x_\theta}{x_\theta} \cdot \dfrac{\sin x_\varphi}{x_\varphi}$

λ = wavelength.
θ = angle to normal on source (in case 6, within plane parallel to l_a).
d = spacing between individual sources.
l = length of line source.
a = radius of ring or circular piston.
$\left.\begin{matrix} l_a \\ l_b \end{matrix}\right\}$ = sides of rectangular piston.
φ = angle to normal within plane parallel to l_b.

increasing accuracy; but the procedure rapidly becomes very tedious.[6] In Table 3.1 are summarized the radiation directivity functions for several of the commonest cases encountered in practice.

Some forms of sources are amenable to analytical solutions in a closed form. One starts with Huyghens' principle, but expresses the contributions in differential elements and integrates over the surface. The result for the far field of a circular piston of radius a, vibrating uniformly in an infinite baffle (see Table 3.1, case 5) is:

$$p_B = \frac{P_r e^{j(\omega t - kr)}}{r} \left[\frac{2J_1(ka\sin\theta)}{ka\sin\theta} \right] = \frac{P_r e^{j(\omega t - kr)}}{r} [D_s] \qquad (3.13)$$

in which J_1 is the Bessel function of the first kind.[7]

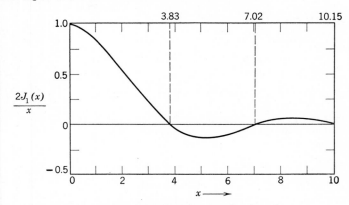

Fig. 3.6. Directivity function for circular piston.

Fraunhofer diffraction The directivity function D_s in the brackets in eq. 3.13 is plotted in Fig. 3.6. We note that the function becomes zero for arguments equal to 3.83, 7.02, 10.15, etc. The main

[6] The reader is referred to the work of H. Stenzel, *Leitfaden zur Berechnung von Schallvorgaengen*, Julius Springer, Berlin, 1939 (English translation: NAVSHIPS 250–940). See also J. Wolff and L. Malter, *J. Acoust. Soc. Amer.*, *2* (1930), 201.

[7] In general, the Bessel function $J_m(x)$ is the solution of the differential equation

$$\frac{d^2 y}{dx^2} + \frac{1}{x}\frac{dy}{dx} + \left(1 - \frac{m^2}{x^2}\right)y = 0$$

A derivation of eq. 3.13 is given by P. M. Morse in *Vibration and Sound*. For small arguments the directivity function can be approximated by:

$$\frac{2J_1(x)}{x} \simeq \frac{16 - x^2}{16 + x^2}$$

See E. M. J. Herrey, *J. Acoust. Soc. Amer.*, *25* (1953), 154.

lobe therefore is confined between the angles $\pm\,\theta$, which are determined by

$$\sin\theta = 3.83/ka = 0.61\lambda/a \qquad (3.14a)$$

This is the well-known *Fraunhofer* formula determining the sharpness of the main beam produced by a circular piston source. For a square source we obtain from Table 3.1, case 6:

$$\sin\theta = \lambda/l \qquad (3.14b)$$

where l is the width of the square piston. Some calculated patterns for the circular piston are shown in Fig. 3.7 (diameter $d = 2a$). It is instructive to compare these with the patterns in Fig. 3.5.

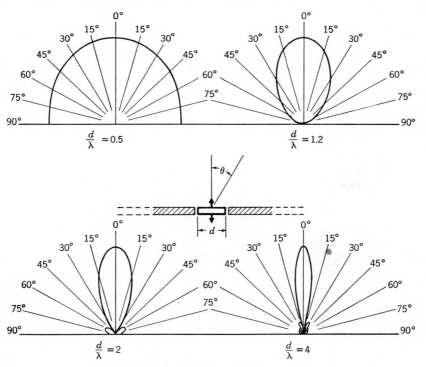

Fig. 3.7. Beam patterns for circular piston.

So far we have assumed that sound waves are radiated from an active source of specified geometry. The same considerations apply to receivers exposed to plane waves impinging under varying angles θ. If a system employs both a transmitter and a receiver whose individual functions are D_s and D_r, the overall directivity is determined

by the product $D = D_s D_r$. If the same transducer serves both for
sending and receiving, as in some pulse-reflection systems, the directivity is determined by $D_s{}^2$. The strength of an echo received from
a target will further depend on its scattering function. The angular
distribution of sound scattered from cylinders and spheres is discussed
in Section 3.6.

In all the foregoing cases the sources or surface were vibrating with
uniform amplitude. It is possible to alter the directivity pattern by
shading the transducer, that is, by modifying the amplitude distribution in some particular way. Let us illustrate this principle on the
line array of three sources, by giving the center source twice the
amplitude of the outer sources. The directivity function in eq. 3.11
then becomes $[2 + 2 \cos (kd \sin \theta)]$. When the cosine factor becomes
minus unity, the pressure drops to zero; this occurs, for example, at
$d/\lambda = \frac{1}{2}$, which case is also shown in Fig. 3.5. Comparing it with
the corresponding case of the unshaded line we see that shading has
reduced the side lobes to zero in this case. Most cases in practice
will be more complicated than this example; but it has illustrated the
possible use of shading to control side-lobe amplitudes.[8]

The sharpness of the main beam is determined primarily by the
ratio of the wavelength to the average dimension of the sound source.
But the smaller this ratio the greater is the number of side lobes, as
can be seen from the argument of the Bessel function in eq. 3.13.
Although shading reduces the amplitude of the side lobes it increases
the width of the main beam. The sharpness of the main beam is also
influenced by the shape of the source and by the manner in which the
vibration amplitude is distributed over the source surface.[9]

3.4 The Near Field (Fresnel Diffraction)

We have used Huyghens' principle to determine the far field (Fraunhofer region) by superposition of the radiation from arrays of simple
sources. We now analyze the near field (Fresnel diffraction region)
by assuming that a plane wave itself can be made up of an infinite
number of Huyghens waves. These combine in phase to form a plane-
wave front normal to the direction of propagation, but cancel in all
other directions. In turn, the elimination of one or more Huyghens
waves from an originally plane-wave front, as by a number of parallel
opaque strips, will lead to imperfect cancellation at certain angles.
We see from Fig. 3.8 that a regular array of such strips will produce
plane fronts of equal phase at certain specific angles defined by $\sin \theta$

[8] For some practical examples see Chapter 5, Section 9.
[9] H. Stenzel, *loc. cit.* (see footnote 6).

$= nd/\lambda$, where d is the distance between centers of the baffling strips
and $\pm n = 0, 1, 2, 3 \cdot \cdot \cdot$ We also notice that the system of Fig.
3.8 corresponds to an optical diffraction grating.

The same considerations lead to similar diffraction effects whenever
a plane wave is bounded in directions normal to the direction of propagation; at the boundary the Huyghens waves become manifest because
here the angular components are not completely canceled by neighboring Huyghens waves.

Let us now consider a plane wave bounded by two parallel opaque
edges.   This is equivalent to a rectangular piston source whose length

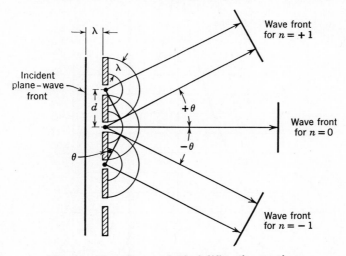

Fig. 3.8.   Interference field of diffraction grating.

is much larger than its width $(l \gg D)$.   A cross-sectional plane (x, y)
parallel to D and normal to l is represented in Fig. 3.9.   We approximate the radiation from the piston by a train of plane waves bounded
at $x = \pm D/2$ and two sets of cylindrical Huyghens' waves originating
at the boundaries $x = +D/2$ and $x = -D/2$.   The instantaneous
positions of pressure maxima of the plane wave and the two sets of
cylindrical waves are indicated by solid lines and circles spaced a
distance λ apart.   At the intersections of the circles and solid lines
the plane wave and the Huyghens waves are in phase and the sound
pressures add.   There is another set of intersections where the
cylindrical wave and the plane wave have opposite phase and therefore
cancel each other.   The loci of the points of addition (maxima) and
cancellation (minima) are represented by parabolas which focus at
$x = \pm D/2$ and $y = 0$.   In Figure 3.9, one such parabola is indicated

for each of the two conditions; for the maxima by a solid line, for the minima by a broken line.

We note that a first set of maxima results from the intersection of the nth circle with $(n - 1)$th line, a second set from the combination

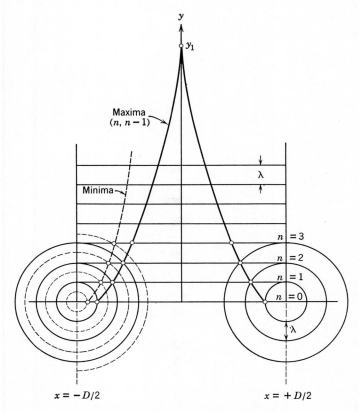

Fig. 3.9. Graphic construction of near field.

$[n, (n - 2)]$, etc. The parabola $[n, (n - 1)]$ is then obtained by combining the equations for the Huyghens circles $(x \pm D/2)^2 + y^2 = (n\lambda)^2$ and the straight lines $y = (n - 1)\lambda$, which yields:

$$(x \pm D/2)^2 = 2y\lambda + \lambda^2$$

If we set x equal to zero we obtain the position of that interference maximum which is located right on the beam axis, which, in this case, $[n, (n - 1)]$, is the first maximum encountered if the piston source is approached from infinity. For this first maximum we obtain:

$$y_1 = \frac{D^2 - 4\lambda^2}{8\lambda} \tag{3.15}$$

There will, of course, be additional maxima, closer to the source, corresponding to the parabolas resulting from the combinations $[n, (n - m)]$.

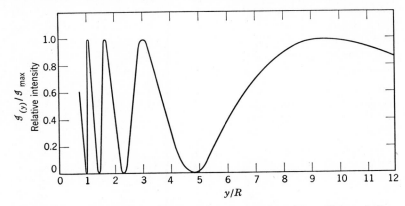

Fig. 3.10.   Axial intensity distribution of circular piston ($R/\lambda = 9.5$).

In general, we obtain for the positions of the maxima on the beam axis.

$$\text{Maxima:} \qquad y_+ = \frac{D^2 - (2m\lambda)^2}{8m\lambda} \qquad m = 1, 2, 3 \cdots \tag{3.15a}$$

The positions of the minima on the beam axis are derived from parabolas resulting from the combinations $[n, (n - m/2)]$ and hence:

$$\text{Minima:} \qquad y_- = \frac{D^2 - (m\lambda)^2}{4m\lambda} \qquad m = 1, 2, 3 \cdots \tag{3.15b}$$

The above equations were derived for a long radiating strip ($D \ll l$). For a circular piston one obtains similar expressions,[10] namely:

$$\text{for the maxima:} \qquad y_+ = \frac{4R^2 - \lambda^2(2m + 1)^2}{4\lambda(2m + 1)} \qquad m = 0, 1, 2 \cdots \tag{3.16a}$$

$$\text{for the minima:} \qquad y_- = \frac{R^2 - \lambda^2 m^2}{2m\lambda} \qquad m = 1, 2, 3 \cdots \tag{3.16b}$$

where R is the piston radius.   The axial intensity distribution in the near field can then be described simply by:

[10] H. Backhaus and F. Trendelenburg, *Z. tech. Phys.*, *7* (1926), 630.   See also K. Osterhammel, *Akust. Z.*, *6* (1941), 73.

$$\mathcal{g}_{(y)}/\mathcal{g}_{\max} = \sin^2 \frac{k}{2}\left[\sqrt{\frac{D^2}{4} + y^2} - y\right] \qquad (3.17)$$

which yields eqs. 3.16a and 3.16b for the extrema.

The axial intensity distributions for a circular piston of $R/\lambda = 9.5$ (for example, at 700 kcps and a source diameter of 4 cm) is illustrated in Fig. 3.10, in which the relative intensity $\mathcal{g}_{(y)}/\mathcal{g}_{\max}$ is plotted versus relative distance y/R. Beyond the last maximum at $y/R = 9$ (for $m = 0$), the Fraunhofer region (far field) begins, and the intensity drops uniformly with y^{-2} according to the inverse square law. If

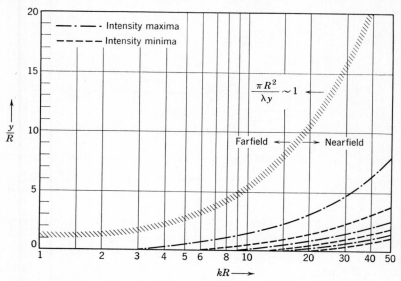

Fig. 3.11.   Near-field structure; transition to far field at $y \sim \pi R^2/\lambda$.

$m = 0$ and $R/\lambda \gg 1$ in eq. 3.16a, then $y/R \simeq R/\lambda$. We see, therefore, that a very sharp main beam, obtained when $R \gg \lambda$, also has a large extension of the near field. This relationship is illustrated in Fig. 3.11.

The ratio $2R/\lambda = kR/\pi$ also gives a measure of the number of pressure maxima along one diameter immediately in front of a circular piston. This is shown in Fig. 3.12, where the lateral pressure (in arbitrary units) for constant source velocity is plotted as a function of r/R for three values of kR. We see that for $kR = 10$ the ratio $2R/\lambda = 3.2$ corresponds to three lateral maxima. Similarly we obtain for $kR = 6$ two lateral maxima and for all values of kR smaller than π only one maximum. The total number of the side lobes appearing

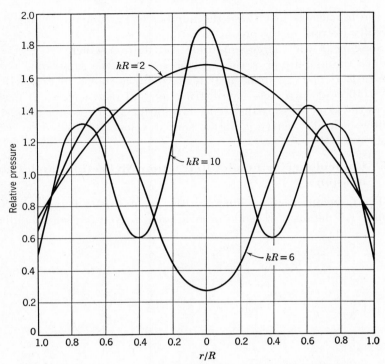

Fig. 3.12. Lateral pressure distribution at face of circular piston.

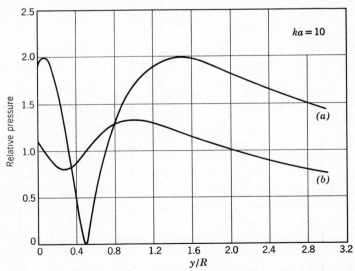

Fig. 3.13. Effect of shading on the axial pressure distribution in the near field.

in the far field is just twice the number of the maxima which occur
directly in front of the piston.

Shading of the source-amplitude distribution which was shown to
reduce the amplitude of the side lobes will at the same time reduce
the ratio P_{max}/P_{min} in the near field.   This is shown in Fig. 3.13 for
$ka = 10$ and two velocity distributions at the source.   Curve a
gives the axial pressure distribution (in arbitrary units) for a constant
source velocity; curve b for a source velocity distribution $U_v =
U_0(1 - r^2/R^2)$.

3.5   Coincidence Principle; Refraction, Reflection, and Transmission

The foregoing sections illustrate the generality of Huyghens' principle.   All details of a radiation field, near to and far from a radiator

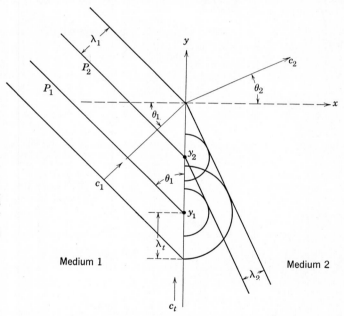

Fig. 3.14.   Refraction governed by coincidence principle.

of any shape or size, can be deduced from a properly selected distribution of elementary Huyghens waves.   When sound passes from
one region into another, the boundary acts simply as a radiator for
the second region.   Therefore the boundary can be replaced by a
distribution of Huyghens' sources.

In Fig. 3.14, we represent plane waves of infinite extent, traveling from medium 1 on the left into medium 2 on the right. The boundary at $x = 0$ runs from $y = -\infty$ to $y = +\infty$ and from $z = -\infty$ to $z = +\infty$ in the direction normal to the paper's plane. The incident waves have a velocity c_1, and their fronts form an angle θ_1 with the boundary. Let us consider the wave front P_1 in Fig. 3.14 which intercepts the boundary at point y_1. This point is the source of a cylindrical Huyghens wave, which propagates with a velocity c_2 into medium 2. At a time of 1 period $(T = 1/f)$ later, the wave front has moved to the position P_2 and now intercepts at y_2 while the succeeding wave front of the same phase has moved up to y_1. Since the distance $y_1 - y_2$ on the boundary separates points of equal phase it represents 1 wavelength λ_t of the velocity c_t with which the incident wave fronts trace along the boundary. From the geometry of the figure we see that

$$\sin \theta_1 = \lambda_1/\lambda_t = c_1/c_t \qquad (3.18a)$$

The tracing incident wave fronts are continuously producing Huyghens waves, which propagate into region 2 with successive pressure maxima spaced at a distance $\lambda_2 = c_2/f$. These Huyghens waves cancel each other, by destructive interference, in all directions but one. This direction is specified, as was shown in Fig. 3.8b, by the condition:

$$\sin \theta_2 = \frac{\lambda_2}{\lambda_t} = \frac{c_2}{c_t} \qquad (3.18b)$$

Combining eq. 3.18a and 3.18b we can eliminate the common trace velocity c_t. The result is Snell's law of refraction:

$$\frac{\sin \theta_1}{c_1} = \frac{\sin \theta_2}{c_2} \qquad (3.19a)$$

A similar set of Huyghens waves is reradiated into medium 1 to form a reflected wave. The velocity of the reflected wave is the same as that of the incident wave, c_1; hence the angle of the reflected wave must be equal to θ_1 to satisfy the condition of a common trace velocity.

We have not specified the *type* of waves in the above discussion. They may be compressional waves or shear waves or any other type which the particular medium can support. Suppose region 1 in Fig. 3.14 is a liquid and region 2 is a solid. If the front of a compressional wave in the liquid traces along the interface, the trace wave will in general produce Huyghens' sources for both compressional and shear waves in the solid. Since the velocities of these two types are not the same, the corresponding angles of refraction will also be different. Suppose, conversely, that a compressional wave propagates toward the interface from within the solid. Its trace sends compressional waves into the liquid. But both compressional and shear waves are, in general, reflected back into the solid. The conversion of part of the incident energy from a compressional wave into a shear wave is attributable to the nature of the boundary condition.

In Fig. 3.15a the vector F_θ represents the force associated with a compressional wave in a solid. This force can be resolved into two components F_x and F_y, which compress a small volume element located at the intersection of the lines A-A and B-B within the solid. These two components are balanced by internal elastic forces F_x'

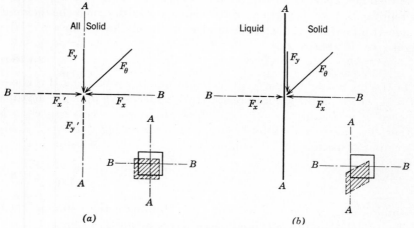

Fig. 3.15.   Generation of shear strain at a boundary.

and F_y', respectively. If the same force F_θ acts on a liquid-solid interface at A-A and parallel to F_y, as in Fig. 3.15b, the component F_x is balanced in part by the compressional force of the liquid and in part by the elastic force in the solid. The component F_y, on the other hand, must be balanced entirely by a shear force within the solid because the liquid (assumed to be non-viscous) cannot support a tangential stress. A small volume element located on the interface at the intersection of A-A and B-B now suffers a shear strain in addition to the compressional strain.

This distorted volume element at the interface becomes a source of both compressional and shear types of Huyghens waves. The shear-wave velocity is lower than the compressional-wave velocity, so the shear waves are reflected at a smaller angle. When the incident wave is at normal incidence the shear wave vanishes because there is no longer an unbalanced shear strain at the boundary.

An incident shear wave will also generate both types of waves at the boundary, but only if the angle of incidence is less than the *critical angle*. This is the angle at which the reflected compressional wave is propagated parallel to the interface (angle of reflection of 90°). At greater than critical angles all the energy is reflected in a shear wave. There is also a special angle for incident compressional waves at which all the energy is reflected in a shear wave. This is not strictly a critical angle, for neither of the waves has moved parallel to the surface. In this case the boundary strains are balanced in such a way that only Huyghens sources for shear waves are produced and the compressional sources are canceled. These several properties of wave reflection in solids find practical applications in systems for materials testing, in delay lines and in related instruments (see Chapter 8).

We have discussed a number of situations in which a boundary radiates Huyghens waves whose initial phase along the boundary depends on the trace velocity of the incident wave. All phenomena of this kind have one common feature: The angles involved are always such that the trace velocity of the incident wave and the trace velocities of the reflected, refracted, and transmitted waves are equal; i.e., there must be *coincidence* of the phases of all waves tracing the boundary. This is the *coincidence principle*.

Transmission through plates With the help of the coincidence principle we can easily determine the angles of maximum transmission of sound waves through plates. Consider a plate of infinite breadth and of thickness d smaller than wavelength, with a fluid on both sides. Figure 3.16 shows such a plate vibrating in flexure. The incident wave at the left side of the plate is in phase with the flexural wave in the plate only if there is coincidence between the trace velocity c_t and the flexural plate velocity c_f:

$$c_f = c_t = c_1/\sin \theta_1 = c_2/\sin \theta_2 \qquad (3.19b)$$

This relation is valid for any combination of fluids on the two sides of the plate; Fig. 3.16 shows the special case: $c_1 = c_2$, $\theta_1 = \theta_2$.

When the coincidence principle is thus satisfied on both sides of the plate there is a special condition that is called "space resonance."[11] At every point along the plate, and at every instant of time, the plate moves exactly in phase with the fluid on both sides. Where the incident wave has an instantaneous pressure of maximum positive value, the plate is forced to bulge away with maximum displacement. The plate therefore presents zero reactance to the incident wave, just as any oscillator at its "time resonance" presents zero reactance to its

[11] L. Cremer, *Arch. elek. Uebertragungs-tech.*, *1* (1947), 28.

driving force. There is perfect transmission through the plate, except for the internal losses associated with the bending of the plate.

Coincidence phenomena occur not only with flexural waves in thin plates but also with shear, compressional, and combination waves in plates of any thickness. The velocities of all types of waves in plates can be determined by analyzing measurements of sound transmission through the plates as a function of angle of incidence. We can show

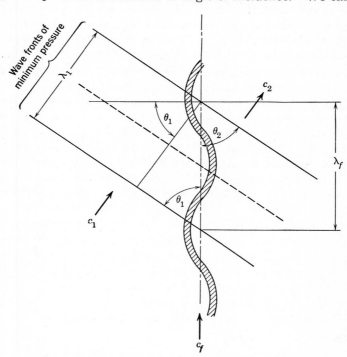

Fig. 3.16. Sound transmission through bending plates.

by transmission-line theory that compressional waves at normal incidence are transmitted through a plate without loss (except for internal damping) if the plate is exactly an integral number of half wavelengths thick. This half-wave resonance is simply the condition for a 1:1 transformation of the resistive impedance $\rho_0 c$ of the loading medium through the line.

In terms of the coincidence principle, a half-wave resonance corresponds to an infinite trace velocity. Each parallel face of the plate then has equal phase over its entire extent in all directions, at any instant of time. The frequencies at which the infinite phase velocities occur are associated with cut-off points in a velocity-frequency diagram. Analogous cut-off frequencies are encountered in electromagnetic wave guides. Above the cut-off the waves are transmitted with velocity dispersion. Such dispersion in solid plates and rods is discussed briefly in Section 2.7, and similar dispersion is found in liquid-filled tubes.[12]

Mach angle and moving sources Let us now consider some special characteristics of radiation from sources that are moving through a medium with a velocity that is greater than the propagation velocity in the medium. This situation exists, for example, if longitudinal waves are transmitted along a thin (compared with wavelength) rod or plate immersed in a liquid. We have noted that such waves produce periodic variations in the thickness of the rod or plate, except in the limiting case, not realized in practice, in which Poisson's ratio is zero. These periodic thickness variations, in turn, constitute a moving array of Huyghens sources that radiate waves into the surrounding medium. The longitudinal velocity $c_l = Y_0/\rho$ in the solid is generally greater than the velocity c_c of sound in a liquid.[13] The angle θ between the radiated wave fronts and the interface is given directly by the coincidence principle:

$$\sin \theta = c_c/c_l = 1/M \tag{3.20}$$

The ratio $M = c_l/c_c$ is called the *Mach number*, which has the same meaning for moving sound sources as it does for moving aircraft and projectiles. In fact, any object moving at $M > 1$, i.e., at supersonic speed, produces a Mach wave which is alternatively called a bow wave or a shock wave. In all such cases, the velocity of the object or the velocity of the Huyghens sources along the boundary is identically equal to the trace velocity of the radiated waves.

The bow wave from a ship is an interesting example. If the water is very deep compared with the wavelength of the surface waves, the velocity of the surface waves is given by:

$$c_W = (g/k + k\sigma/\rho)^{\frac{1}{2}}$$

in which g is the acceleration of gravity, σ is the surface tension, ρ is the density of the water, and $k = \omega/c_W$ is the wave number. For

---

[12] This type of dispersion associated with the crossmodes between boundaries must not be confused with the dispersion due to intramolecular phenomena. For reference, see G. S. Field, *Can. J. Research*, *17* (1939), 197. J. Goetz, *Akust. Z.*, *8* (1943), 145. R. D. Fay and O. V. Fortier, *J. Acoust. Soc. Amer.*, *23* (1951), 339.

[13] An exception would be a lead rod with longitudinal velocity 1200 m/sec immersed in glycerin with sound velocity 1900 m/sec.

large wavelengths ($\lambda > 5$ cm in the case of water), the velocity of surface waves in a deep layer reduces to: $c_W = g/\omega$. These waves are dispersive: the velocity increases as the frequency decreases. Below some frequency at which the depth equals the wavelength, the velocity of the surface waves approaches the constant value: $c_W = (gh)^{1/2}$, in which h is the depth of the water. In any case, if the velocity of the ship is greater than the surface wave velocity there is continuously produced a bow wave at an angle θ given by eq. 3.20.

The explosive charges used in geophysical prospecting also lead to Mach waves at the interfaces between stratified media. This is illustrated in Fig. 3.17 in which an explosive source is located at the boundary between medium 1 and medium 2. Spherical waves of velocity

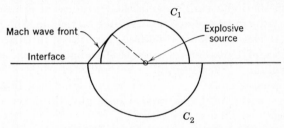

Fig. 3.17. Mach-wave generation at an interface.

c_1 and c_2 are radiated into the two media, respectively. In addition, there is produced a Mach wave in medium 1 by the trace of the wave in medium 2 ($c_2 > c_1$ in this case). If the source is not located at the interface the geometry of the waves is more complicated, but it can be derived directly from the coincidence principle.

3.6 The Doppler Effect

We have seen that the angles of refraction and reflection at interfaces, the angles of transmission through plates, and the angles of Mach waves are all predictable from an analysis of moving sources of Huyghens waves. This analysis is simply an application of the coincidence principle, which describes wave phenomena in the space domain. Related phenomena in the time domain can be similarly systematized in terms of the Doppler effect.

The Doppler effect is a shift in frequency or in wavelength, depending on the conditions of observation, caused by relative motions among sources, receivers, and the medium. Let us first consider a fixed receiver in a stationary medium, with a simple source moving at a velocity $v = |\mathbf{v}_s| \cos \theta_s$ relative to the receiver. The angle θ_s is taken between the velocity vector $\mathbf{v}_s$ of the moving source and the radius vector from the source to the receiver.   During one period $T = 1/f_s$, a wave front moves vT toward the receiver if $\theta_s < \pi/2$.   Thus two successive wave fronts are emitted a distance $(c_0 - v)T = \lambda_m$ apart, which is therefore the wavelength in the medium.   The wavelength is decreased from the fixed-source value $\lambda_0 = c_0 T$; it would be increased if the source were moving away from the receiver $(\theta_s > \pi/2)$.

The frequency observed by the receiver is equal to the velocity c_0 in the medium, divided by the wavelength in the medium, or:

$$f_r = \frac{c_0}{(c_0 - v)T} = f_s \frac{c_0}{c_0 - |\mathbf{v}_s| \cos \theta_s} \qquad (3.21a)$$

If the source is fixed and the receiver is moving away from it with the velocity $\mathbf{v}_r$, the wavelength in the medium is unchanged; but the wave fronts are intercepted by the receiver at the decreased frequency

$$f_r = f_s \frac{c_0 - |\mathbf{v}_r| \cos \theta_r}{c_0}, \qquad (3.21b)$$

in which θ_r is the angle between the velocity vector of the receiver and the radius vector from the source to the receiver.   Both cases are covered by the formula

$$f_r = f_s \frac{(c_0 - |\mathbf{v}_r| \cos \theta_r)}{(c_0 - |\mathbf{v}_s| \cos \theta_s)} \qquad (3.21c)$$

It is interesting that equal values of either source velocity or receiver velocity do not give equal values of Doppler shift.   A moving medium, on the other hand, does not cause a Doppler effect if the distance between source and receiver remains constant.[14]

In echo-ranging systems a signal which completes a round trip between a moving transducer $(\mathbf{v}_s)$ and a moving target $(\mathbf{v}_t)$ is received with a frequency

$$f_r = f_s \left[1 + \frac{2}{c_0} (|\mathbf{v}_s| \cos \theta_s - |\mathbf{v}_t| \cos \theta_t) \right] \qquad (3.22)$$

in which θ_s and θ_t are the instantaneous angles between the velocity vectors and the radius vector from the source to the target.   Moving-target indicators based on the Doppler effect are used in modern sonar and radar equipment, as well as in burglar alarm systems.[14a]

[14] If there is relative motion between receiver and source, the state of motion of the medium influences the received frequency.
[14a] S. Bagno et al. *J. R. E. Convention Record* (1954) Part 6, p. 49.

3.7 Scattering

In the preceding sections we have shown that the interaction between a sound wave and a boundary can be explained by suitable distributions of Huyghens waves. If the boundary has dimensions which are large compared with wavelength one obtains the simple laws of reflection and refraction by application of the coincidence principle. We have also discussed some cases in which the Huyghens sources were confined to finite regions (see Figs. 3.4 and 3.8b). This condition generally leads to diffraction phenomena. Beam formation and near-field structure are specific consequences of diffraction from Huyghens sources distributed over a finite area.

Let us now consider the converse case of a rigid obstacle placed in the course of an infinite plane wave. If this obstacle is a circular disc or a long flat strip it will interact with the sound wave in a way very similar to the one depicted in Fig. 3.9. The edges of a strip, for example, will radiate cylindrical Huyghens waves. Their interference with the incident plane waves leads to maxima and minima located in a set of parabolae, which are focused at the strip edges. The resulting diffraction pattern differs from the near field of a radiating strip in a baffle in only one but important point: There is no plane wave component directly behind the diffracting obstacle. If the obstacle is large compared with wavelength a shadow zone is found. This case corresponds to geometrical optics where the amount of energy diffracted into the regions behind the obstacle is so small that it can be neglected. The shadow zone behind a large obstacle is generally associated with a reflection zone in front of the obstacle.

The total disturbance of the sound wave by the obstacle is obtained by a particular set of Huyghens waves. The distribution of these Huyghens waves must be such that their radiation pattern produces all the field characteristics (reflection, diffraction, and shadow formation) by interference with the undisturbed sound wave. This interfering radiation pattern of the obstacle is called the "scattered wave." We note that a true shadow is formed behind the obstacle only if the scattered wave in this region is of equal strength and opposite phase compared with the undisturbed sound wave. The required set of Huyghens waves is determined from the boundary condition at the surface of the obstacle. For a rigid scatterer, for example, the sum of the particle velocities in the undisturbed wave and in the scattered wave must vanish at each point of the surface. In the general case this condition leads to cumbersome mathematical expressions.[15] We

[15] P. M. Morse, *Vibration and Sound*, 2nd edition, McGraw-Hill, New York, 1948, pp. 246–255.

shall demonstrate qualitatively for long wavelengths and thin rigid cylinders ($ka \ll 1$) how the scattering function can be obtained from simple physical reasoning. General results for cylindrical and spherical scatterers will be given without derivation.

Scattering from a thin rigid cylinder   The cross section of a cylindrical scatterer of diameter $d = 2b$ is shown in Fig. 3.18. To describe the effect of a rigid cylinder on a long sound wave ($\lambda \gg d$) we assume two pairs of Huygens sources (dipole sources). One pair (S_1 and S_2) represents the sound radiated from an equivalent image

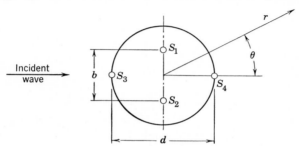

Fig. 3.18.   Equivalent dipoles of a cylindrical scatterer.

dipole of width $b = d/2$; they vibrate in phase and have the directivity function of eq. 3.9:

$$D_{12} = 2 \cos\left(\frac{kd}{2} \sin \theta\right) \simeq 2 \qquad (3.23a)$$

The other pair (S_3 and S_4) represents the sound reflected in front and screened off in back of the obstacle. Source S_3 represents a surface element vibrating in phase with the incident sound wave to give reflection. Source S_4, on the other hand, vibrates 180° out of phase to produce cancellation behind the obstacle. Since this **pair** is located at right angles to the image dipole (S_1, S_2) and operates with a phase shift of π, its directivity function becomes:

$$D_{34} = 2 \sin (kd \cos \theta) \simeq 2 \, kd \cos \theta \qquad (3.23b)$$

Let us now determine the particle-velocity amplitude of the scattered radiation at a distance $r > b$ from the scatterer. For the long-wave case considered here, D_{12} varies little with θ and can be approximated by $D_{12} \simeq 2$. Equation 3.23b, however, has zeros at $\theta = \pi/2$ and $\theta = \frac{3}{2}\pi$ and reduces to $D_{34} \simeq 2kd \cos \theta$.

Physically speaking, the incident sound wave interacts with the small cylinder in two ways: an image is formed of the surrounding Huyghens components of the incident wave which is equivalent to a radially pulsating source. At the same time the cylinder oscillates relative to the surrounding medium. The first component corresponds to a simple source of diameter $b = d/2$ whose source velocity amplitude is $U_{12}^* = (2\mathcal{g}^*/\rho_0 c)^{1/2}$, where $\mathcal{g}^*$ is that fraction of $\mathcal{g}_0$, the incident energy per unit area per second, which is used to drive the pulsating source. The particle velocity of a plane incident sound wave at the location of the scatterer is $U_0 = (2\mathcal{g}_0/\rho_0 c)^{1/2}$. The radiation resistance of the simple source according to eq. 3.8 is $R_c \simeq \rho_0 c(2ka)^2 = \rho_0 c(kb)^2$, and hence the image source energy per unit area per second is $\mathcal{g}^* = \dfrac{U_0^2}{2} R_c \simeq \mathcal{g}_0(kb)^2$. We thus obtain for the source velocity of the first component:

$$U_{12}^* \simeq \left(\frac{2\mathcal{g}_0}{\rho_0 c}\right)^{1/2} kb = U_0 kb \qquad (3.24)$$

For the second component of the scattered wave from a very small cylinder we can assume that in a first approximation the cylinder oscillates with the same velocity amplitude as the particles in the surrounding medium but in opposite phase: $U_{34}^* \simeq -U_0$.

We are now ready to determine the total particle velocity of the scattered wave at distance r from the obstacle. From eqs. 3.23a, 3.23b and 3.24 and allowing for a decrease of amplitude with distance of cylindrical waves proportional to $(b/r)^{1/2}$ we obtain:

$$U_{r,\theta} = [U_{12}^* D_{12} + U_{34}^* D_{34}] \cdot (b/r)^{1/2}$$

$$\simeq U_0 \left(\frac{b}{r}\right)^{1/2} [2kb - 2kd \cos \theta]$$

With $d = 2b$ this becomes:

$$U_{r,\theta} \simeq 2U_0 (b/r)^{1/2} kb[1 - 2 \cos \theta] \qquad (3.25)$$

In order to determine the intensity of the scattered wave we must consider the phase angle between the particle velocity and pressure due to the complex radiation impedance of the scatterer:

$$\mathcal{g}_{r,\theta} = \frac{U_{r,\theta}^2}{2} \rho_0 c \cos \varphi$$

We have demonstrated previously (see Fig. 3.2) that the power factor of a small radiating source is proportional to the wave number: $\cos \varphi = \psi kb$. The intensity of the scattered wave in the long-wave approximation ($kb \ll 1$) then is:

$$g_{r,\theta} \simeq 2\psi U_0{}^2 c(b/r)k^3b^3[1 - 2\cos\,\theta]^2$$

$$\simeq 4\psi\,\frac{g_0}{r/b}\,(kb)^3[1 - 2\cos\,\theta]^2 = 4\psi\Sigma \qquad (3.26)$$

This result has been obtained from the simple physical approach adopted throughout this chapter. A rigorous derivation[16] leads to the identical scattering function Σ and establishes the value of ψ, which in the long-range approximation becomes $\psi = \pi/32 \simeq 0.1$.

As kb approaches larger valves the number of Huyghens sources required to meet the boundary conditions increases and an increasing number of terms must be added to eq. 3.26, each term having a different phase angle and source strength. A further complication is that actual scatterers are not perfectly rigid, and their internal elastic properties cannot be neglected.[17] Some experimental results on brass and steel cylinders obtained at a frequency of 1 mcps are presented in Fig. 3.19, which also gives the corresponding patterns computed for absolutely rigid cylinders. Similar patterns are obtained from scattering air bubbles in liquids and from certain types of inhomogeneities in solids.

Often one is interested in the total power scattered rather than in the details of the angular distribution of intensity. The power that is scattered per unit length from a cylinder much thinner than wavelength is

$$W_s \simeq 7.5(kb)^3 b g_0 \qquad (kb \ll 1) \qquad (3.27a)$$

For a cylinder much larger than wavelength we have

$$W_s \simeq 4b g_0 \qquad (kb \gg 1) \qquad (3.27b)$$

Scattering from rigid spheres Similar expressions can be found for spherical obstacles. In the long-wave approximation the scattering function is

$$g_{r,\theta} \simeq 0.11\,\frac{g_0}{(r/a)^2}\,(ka)^4[1 - 3\cos\,\theta]^2 \qquad (ka \ll 1) \qquad (3.28)$$

where a is the radius of the sphere.

The directivity function $(1 - 3\cos\,\theta)$ goes to zero near $\theta = 70°$ and $290°$; it has a maximum value of 16 in the backward direction $(\theta = 180°)$, and it reaches a value of 4 in the forward direction $(\theta = 0°)$. The lack of shadow formation by small objects therefore is a result

---

[16] P. M. Morse, *Vibration and Sound*, 2nd edition, McGraw-Hill, New York, 1948, p. 350.

[17] J. A. Faran, *J. Acoust. Soc. Amer.*, *23* (1951), 405.

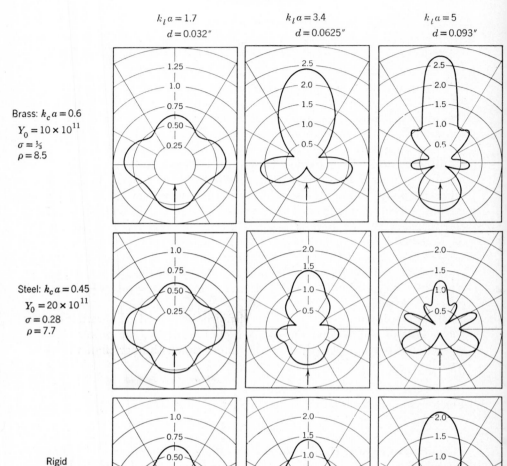

Fig. 3.19. Scattering distributions of metal cylinders (J. A. Faran). The diameter of the cylinders is $d = 2a$; the wave numbers k_c and k_e refer to the cylinders and the surrounding liquid, respectively.

of the fact that the intensity scattered forward is small compared with the back-scattered intensity. The converse is true for large objects $(ka \gg 1)$ which scatter most of the energy in the forward direction, thus producing a shadow by destructive interference.

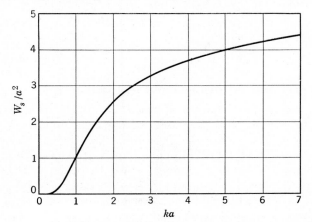

Fig. 3.20.   Total power per unit incident intensity scattered from a rigid sphere.

The dependence of the total power scattered from a sphere on ka is demonstrated in Fig. 3.20, in which $W_s/a^2\mathscr{I}_0$ is plotted as ordinate.   For small values of ka the scattered power increases with the fourth power:

$$W_s \simeq 5.6(ka)^4 a^2 \mathscr{I}_0 \qquad (ka \ll 1) \qquad\qquad (3.29a)$$

In the short-wave limit, on the other hand, the scattering depends only on the object size but is independent of wavelength:

$$W_s \simeq 2\pi a^2 \mathscr{I}_0 = 2S\mathscr{I}_0 \qquad (ka \gg 1) \qquad\qquad (3.29b)$$

in which S is the cross-sectional area of the sphere.[18]

The non-uniform distribution of the intensity around small scattering particles in a sound wave leads to radiation forces on the obstacle. Some important aspects of these forces are discussed in Chapter 6, Section 6. Scattering of sound in liquids containing gas bubbles may cause great losses of the energy in a sound beam transmitted through the medium, and scattering at the grain boundaries is one important cause for the absorption of ultrasonic waves in metals (see Chapter 8, Section 8).

[18] If the intensity is measured in watts per square meter, the quantities a and S must be expressed in meters and square meters, respectively.

CHAPTER 4

Piezoelectric Transducers

4.1 General Aspects of Electric Field Drive

Electric energy can be transformed into mechanical energy by several different physical processes, all of which involve interactions between electric or magnetic fields and matter, as described by Maxwell's equations. The present chapter is concerned only with the mechanical forces that produce or are produced by *electric* fields.

One familiar form of interaction is described by Coulomb's law: $F = k(Q_1 \cdot Q_2)/r^2$, which determines the force F between two charges Q_1 and Q_2 that are r meters apart. These charges, whether free on the electrodes of a condenser or bound into the ionic lattice of a crystal, interact with electric fields. The resulting electromechanical effects are classified as electrostatic, electrostrictive, and piezoelectric. The piezoelectric effect is utilized widely in the field of sonics, in the form of crystal transducers. Electrostriction is used to a comparable extent, in special polarizable ceramics, where it can be treated as a special case of piezoelectricity. Electrostatic devices are not yet widely used in industrial applications of sonics, although they are familiar in audio communication equipment.

The devices based on any of the three physical effects follow the same general laws. We shall restrict this chapter essentially to a treatment of the theory and practice of *piezoelectric transducers*. The discussion will serve to illustrate the general principles of all types of electroacoustic transduction. A comparative chart (Table 4.8) of constants and conversions for other transducer mechanisms, given at the end of this chapter, will facilitate the application of the principles given here.

4.2 Piezoelectric Properties

A piezoelectric (pressure-electric) substance possesses a useful combination of electrical and mechanical properties. A suitably cut piece with conducting electrodes on one pair of faces behaves like an electric condenser. For example, a simple rectangular slab of thickness l

86

(meters) between electroded surfaces of area S (meters^2) has a capacitance C (farads) given by the familiar equation:

$$C = \epsilon\epsilon_0 \frac{S}{l} = \frac{Q}{V} \tag{4.1}$$

in which ϵ_0 (farads/meter) is the dielectric constant of free space[1] and ϵ (dimensionless) is the ratio of the dielectric constant of the condenser substance to that of free space. This capacitance is by definition equal to the charge Q (coulombs) divided by the potential V (volts) across the condenser.

At the same time, this piece of material behaves like a mechanical spring with an internal stiffness that opposes an applied force. If the force and the resulting change in length are not too great, the spring is linear and obeys Hooke's law. Thus, if a force F (newtons) is applied uniformly to the surfaces S in such a way as to compress the slab by an amount ξ (meters), the stiffness constant c_{hk} (newtons/m^2) is given by:

$$c_{hk} = Fl/S\xi = X_h/x_k \qquad \text{(Hooke's law)} \tag{4.2}$$

which is simply the force per unit area ($X_h = F/S$) divided by the compression (or elongation) per unit length ($x_k = \xi/l$).

The subscripts hk allow for elastic anisotropy; a crystal generally has different stiffness constants for different orientations of the stress within the crystal lattice. Also a distinction between compressional stiffness ($h = k$) and shear stiffness ($h \neq k$) must be made.

Equation 4.2 contains only mechanical quantities, and eq. 4.1 contains only electrical. Piezoelectric materials possess, in addition, a special interlocking behavior in which electric charges are produced by straining the material and internal forces are produced by subjecting the material to an electric field. Figure 4.1 illustrates this behavior by a simplified model of the crystal structure in quartz. In general, the charges produced by a strain will develop a voltage across the material, owing to its condenser property.

If the two electrodes (of our suitably cut piece) are short circuited, thereby equalizing the potential, the charge developed per unit cross-sectional area, i.e., the polarization $P_i = Q/S$, is given by:

$$P_i = e_{ik}x_k \qquad \text{(short circuited)} \tag{4.3}$$

in which $x_k = \xi/l$ is the strain, the elongation or compression, per unit length. The subscripts ik indicate that in a cubic block of the crystal

---

[1] $\epsilon_0 = \dfrac{1}{4\pi \times 9 \times 10^9}$ farads/m.

one of three pairs of opposite faces (i) can be charged up by any one of the six possible strains (k). If the piece is firmly clamped so that it cannot change in length (very difficult to do practically!), the internal force developed per unit area, i.e., the stress X_h, is given by:

$$X_h = e_{hj}E_j \quad \text{(clamped)} \tag{4.4}$$

in which E_j is the field strength in volts/meter. In both eqs. 4.3 and 4.4 e_{hj} and e_{ik} represent the *piezoelectric stress constant*, relating a given

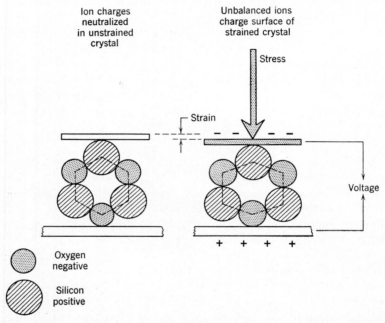

Fig. 4.1. Schematic representation of the interaction between force and field in piezoelectric crystals.

field strength vector (j) to a particular stress component (h), or a given strain component (k) to a particular polarisation vector (i).

Interrelation of constants Using subscripts in the manner shown above we can rewrite eq. 4.1 in the form

$$P_i = \epsilon_{ij}E_j \tag{4.5}$$

in which[2] $\epsilon_{ij} = \epsilon\epsilon_0$ is the effective dielectric constant; and eq. 4.2 in

[2] The subscripts ij allow for anisotropy of the dielectric permittivity, which exists in some crystals. In this book, however, ϵ will be assumed to be independent of the crystal cut.

the form

$$X_h = c_{hk}x_k \qquad (4.6)$$

These last four equations are interrelated in a manner that can be represented schematically by the following diagram.

$$
\begin{array}{ll}
X_h = c_{hk} \ \cdot \ x_k & \text{mechanical quantities} \\
\quad \cdot \ \diagdown \qquad \cdot \ \| \\
d_{ih} \quad e_{ik,hj} \ \ d_{kj} & \text{electromechanical quantities} \\
\| \ \diagup \qquad \cdot \ \cdot \\
P_i = \epsilon_{ij} \ \cdot \ E_j & \text{electrical quantities}
\end{array}
$$

This scheme contains an additional quantity, the *piezoelectric strain constant* d_{kj} or d_{ih}, which appears in the equations

$$x_k = d_{kj}E_j \qquad (4.7)$$

$$P_i = d_{ih}X_h \qquad (4.8)$$

The two piezoelectric constants e and d are not independent of each other but are related through eq. 4.6. We can obtain the stress X produced by a field E from the single eq. 4.4, or we can first obtain the strain by eq. 4.7 and then the stress by eq. 4.6. The equivalence of these two methods leads to a relationship

$$e_{ik} = \sum_h c_{kh}d_{ih}$$

where h goes from 1 to 6 for any given pair ik, i from 1 to 3, and k from 1 to 6.

Tensor relationship The subscript notation above indicates a tensor relationship. When a crystal is exposed to a field in a specific direction (a field vector), strains generally occur in other directions also. The additional strains, caused by internal coupling, will all contribute to produce the stress which is finally developed in the field direction. We see that the sequence from field to strain to stress is actually a three-dimensional problem involving several of the constants d and c for the equivalent of one constant e. The special rules required for obtaining any one of these constants from the remaining ones are generally expressed by tensor notation. This involves mathematical expressions which are lengthy but which for many practical cases can be reduced to simple linear equations such as those given above.

We now demonstrate briefly how the linear equations that are used in this chapter are related to certain tensors. We use Voigt's notation,[3] which is found widely in the literature. Conversion into other notations can be made as explained in the "Standards on Piezoelectric Crystals, 1949."[4]

[3] W. Voigt, "Theorie der piezoelektrischen Erscheinungen," *Abhandl. Ges. Wiss. Goettingen, 36* (1890), 1.

[4] *Proc. I.R.E., 37* (1949), 1378.

In the most general case the required quantities expressed in Cartesian coordinates are:

the 3 components of the electric field vector $\quad\quad\quad E_x \quad E_y \quad E_z$

the 3 components of the electric polarization vector $\quad\quad\quad P_x \quad P_y \quad P_z$

the 6 elastic stress components T_k
compressional $\quad\quad\quad X_x \quad Y_y \quad Z_z$
shear $\quad\quad\quad Y_z \quad Z_x \quad X_y$

the 6 elastic strain components S_h
compressional $\quad\quad\quad x_x \quad y_y \quad z_z$
shear $\quad\quad\quad y_z \quad z_x \quad x_y$

the 36 elastic stiffness constants $\quad\quad\quad c_{hk}$

the 36 elastic compliance constants $\quad\quad\quad s_{hk}$

the 18 piezoelectric stress constants $\quad\quad\quad e_{ik}$

the 18 piezoelectric strain constants $\quad\quad\quad d_{ih}$

where h and k go from 1 to 6 and i from 1 to 3.

The elastic response of a piezoelectric crystal to an electric field is commonly expressed by

$$S_h = \sum_i d_{ih}E_i$$

This is equivalent to writing:

(strain tensor) = (d tensor) · (electric field vector)

In general, each of the three components of the electric field vector produces both compressional and shear strain in each of the three coordinate axes.

The amount of strain produced is determined by the particular set of piezoelectric strain constants, as can be seen from the expansions:

for compression:
$$\begin{cases} x_x = d_{11}E_x + d_{21}E_y + d_{31}E_z \\ y_y = d_{12}E_x + d_{22}E_y + d_{32}E_z \\ z_z = d_{13}E_x + d_{23}E_y + d_{33}E_z \end{cases} \quad (4.9a)$$

for shear:
$$\begin{cases} y_z = d_{14}E_x + d_{24}E_y + d_{34}E_z \\ z_x = d_{15}E_x + d_{25}E_y + d_{35}E_z \\ x_y = d_{16}E_x + d_{26}E_y + d_{36}E_z \end{cases} \quad (4.9b)$$

Fortunately the analysis is usually simplified considerably because many of the 18 piezoelectric constants d_{ih} are equal to zero in actual crystals, and the remaining number of constants is further reduced by symmetry. Table 4.1 gives the constants that have significant values for the most important transducer crystals.

In the case of quartz, which we treat here as a typical example, only d_{11}, d_{12}, d_{14}, d_{25}, and d_{26} have non-vanishing values; and by symmetry:

$$d_{12} = -d_{11}, \quad\quad d_{25} = -d_{14}, \quad\quad d_{26} = -2d_{11}$$

so that eqs. 4.9 are reduced to the much simpler form:

$$x_x = d_{11}E_x$$
$$y_y = -d_{11}E_x$$
$$y_z = d_{14}E_x \qquad (4.10)$$
$$z_x = -d_{14}E_y$$
$$x_y = -2d_{11}E_y$$

These equations show that a field E_x across an X-cut[5] quartz plate produces dilation along x, compression along y, and shear in the yz plane.

Table 4.1   Main Piezoelectric Strain Constants of Several Crystals at Room Temperature (T = 20°C)

Crystal System	Substance	d_{11}	d_{14}	d_{15}	d_{24}	d_{25}	d_{31}	d_{32}	d_{33}	d_{36}
Monoclinic	Ammonium tartrate $(NH_4)_2C_4H_4O_6$		5.65	−14	−8.5	9.3	1.8	17.6	−26.2	−5.9
	Lithium sulfate $Li_2SO_4 + H_2O$		11.3	−12	−7.6	−2.9	−4.0		48.6	19.8
Rhombic	Rochelle salt $NaKC_4H_4O_6 + 4H_2O$		1000			−138				35.6
	Sodium-ammonium tartrate $NaNH_4C_4H_4O_6 + 4H_2O$	56				−150				28.3
Trigonal	Quartz SiO_2	−6.9	1.7							
	Tourmaline			−11			−0.74		−5.77	
Tetragonal	Potassium phosphate KH_2PO_4		3.85							−62.8
	Ammonium dihydrogen phosphate $NH_4H_2PO_4$		4.35							−137
	Barium titanate $BaTiO_3$ polarized			750			−235		570	
Regular	Hexamethyltetramine $C_6H_{12}N_4$		−52.4							
	Zinc sulfide ZnS		−9.8							

For CGS units: multiply numbers in this table by 10^{-8}.
For MKS units: multiply numbers in this table by $(\frac{1}{3})10^{-12}$.
(1 coulomb/newton = 3×10^4 cm/stat volt.)

[5] Applications of different crystal cuts are given later in this chapter. A discussion of their specific orientation within the various crystal classes is omitted here since in practice suitably cut slabs are ordered directly from the manufacturers. For more information see W. G. Cady, *Piezoelectricity*, McGraw-Hill, New York, 1946.

The stresses produced in a crystal by these piezoelectrically induced strains can be obtained from the relationship $T_k = \sum_h c_{hk}S_h$. This is equivalent to writing:

$$\text{(stress tensor)} = (c \text{ tensor}) \cdot (\text{strain tensor})$$

which is the general three-dimensional formulation of Hooke's law. Some of the 36 components of this tensor vanish in actual crystals. In quartz, only 12 components remain and symmetry further reduces the number of independent elastic constants to 6, namely: c_{11}, c_{12}, c_{13}, c_{14}, c_{33}, and c_{44}. This elastic anisotropy of quartz has some bearing on the vibration of crystal plates of particular shapes in ultrasonic applications. Of particular interest are the compressional stress components which, for quartz, are:

$$X_x = c_{11}x_x + c_{12}y_y + c_{13}z_z + c_{14}y_z$$
$$Y_y = c_{11}y_y - c_{14}y_z + c_{12}x_x + c_{13}z_z \tag{4.11}$$

The stresses produced in a quartz crystal by the piezoelectrically induced strains are obtained by combining eqs. 4.10 and 4.11:

$$X_x = (c_{11}d_{11} - c_{12}d_{11} + c_{14}d_{14})E_x$$
$$Y_y = -(c_{11}d_{11} - c_{12}d_{11} + c_{14}d_{14})E_x \tag{4.12a}$$

This relationship between stress and field can be described by introducing the piezoelectric stress constants[6]

$$e_{ik} = \sum_h c_{hk}d_{ih}$$

Again, for quartz, the number of independent constants is reduced from 18 to only 2 in the equations:

$$X_x = e_{11}E_x$$
$$Y_y = -e_{11}E_x$$
$$Y_z = e_{14}E_x \tag{4.12b}$$
$$Z_x = -e_{14}E_y$$
$$X_y = -e_{11}E_y$$

The physical meaning of these relationships can be stated as follows: An electric field primarily produces forces on the ions within the crystal lattice, and these forces lead to an elastic stress. The strain resulting from the forces and the amplitude of vibration depend on the loading of the crystal by the adjoining media as well as on the elastic constants of the crystal itself.

The above notation primarily applies to crystals when used for transmitter purposes. For receiver applications another set of equations is available which relates the polarization of dielectric displacement on the crystal to the strain or stress that causes it. We give here only a brief account of such alternative formulations of piezoelectric response.

The charge produced by compression of a crystal can be obtained from the relationships for the polarization vector (see eq. 4.3):

[6] Equation 4.12 involves the product of the d tensor and the c tensor. This leads to a new piezoelectric tensor with the components e_{ik}.

$$P_i = \sum_k e_{ik}S_k$$

and

$$P_i = \sum_h d_{ih}T_h$$

An X-cut quartz disc that is mechanically deformed will consequently show a charge on the faces normal to the x axis, which is given by:

$$Q_x = [e_{11}(x_x - y_y) + e_{14}y_z]S \qquad (4.13)$$

The voltage resulting from this charge depends on the crystal capacity and therefore on its dielectric constant. For some crystals, in particular Rochelle salt, both piezoelectric constant and dielectric constant show large variations with temperature. However, the sensitivity in terms of voltage$_{out}$/force$_{in}$ is practically independent of temperature because of the small variations of the quotient d/ϵ. This has led to the development of the so-called "displacement" theory,[7] which expresses the piezoelectric behavior by a system of new constants h_{ik} and g_{jh}. They are related to e_{ik} and d_{ik} as follows:

$$h_{ik} = \frac{e_{ik}}{\epsilon_i'}\,\text{newton/coulomb} \qquad \text{and} \qquad g_{jh} = \frac{d_{jh}}{\epsilon_j}\,\text{volt}\cdot\text{meter/newton} \qquad (4.14)[8]$$

where ϵ is the free and ϵ' the clamped dielectric constant. A rigorous treatment of piezoelectricity requires the distinction between stiffness at constant electric field and stiffness at constant electric displacement. These details have been discussed widely in the literature.[9]

4.3 Fundamentals of Piezoelectric Transduction

We now proceed to develop the essential properties of piezoelectric transducers in a simple formulation. The tensor complications may be omitted if we bear in mind that the following equations are only approximations; though they are usually accurate enough for engineering applications.

We shall use the basic relations given by eqs. 4.1 to 4.4 inclusive. However, if we employ the relations for

Current: $\qquad i = \dfrac{dQ}{dt^i} = S\dfrac{dP}{dt}\ \text{amp}$

Voltage: $\qquad V = lE\ \text{volts}$

Velocity: $\qquad u = \dfrac{d\xi}{dt} = l\dfrac{dx}{dt}\ \text{m/sec}$

Force: $\qquad F = SX\ \text{newtons}$

[7] W. P. Mason, *Piezoelectric Crystals and Their Application to Ultrasonics,* Van Nostrand, New York, 1950, pp. 37–46. See also W. G. Cady, *Piezoelectricity,* McGraw-Hill, New York, 1946, §193.

[8] 1 newton/coulomb = 1 volt/m = $\frac{1}{3} \times 10^{-4}$ dyne/esu; 1 volt · meter/newton = 1 m^2/coulomb = $\frac{1}{3} \times 10^{-5}$ cm^2/esu.

[9] W. P. Mason and W. G. Cady, *loc. cit.* (see footnote 7).

we can express eqs. 4.3 and 4.4 in the more practical form

$$i = \frac{S}{l} e_{ik} \cdot u = \alpha_{ik}u \quad \text{(short circuited)} \tag{4.15}$$

$$F = \frac{S}{l} e_{hj} \cdot V = \alpha_{hj}V \quad \text{(clamped)} \tag{4.16}$$

where $\alpha_{ik,hj}$ is a transformation factor relating mechanical to electrical quantities.[10] These are basic formulas for transducer design; many problems can be reduced to manipulations of eq. 4.15 for receivers and eq. 4.16 for transmitters.

Transducers in operation are not short circuited or clamped, so there are additional effects which we must now include in the analysis. Consider a slab of piezoelectric material with an arbitrary thickness l, and a surface area S of dimensions much greater than the wavelength of the acoustic waves in the material or in the medium into which the slab vibrates and radiates energy. The applied voltage is $V = V_0 e^{j\omega t}$ and the velocity of the radiating face is:

$$u = U_0 e^{j\omega t} = j\omega\xi = j\omega A_0 e^{j\omega t}$$

The piezoelectric force F_p is the internally generated pressure times the surface area:

$$F_p = X_h S = e_{hj}E_j S = \frac{e_{hj}S}{l} V \tag{4.17}$$

The surface at $x = l$ is always in dynamic equilibrium, with the driving force (F_p) balanced by internal (F_i) and external (F_e) reaction forces:

$$F_p = F_i + F_e \tag{4.18}$$

These reaction forces, indicated in Fig. 4.2, arise from inertial and stiffness effects in the transducer material and in the radiation medium. These forces can be expressed in terms of the internal and external acoustic impedances Z_i and Z_e at the radiating face, the cross-sectional area S, and the velocity of the face:

$$F_i = Z_i S u \qquad F_e = Z_e S u \tag{4.19}$$

The internal impedance can be expressed directly by the hyperbolic tangent transmission-line equation (2.39) discussed in Chapter 2:

$$Z_i = R_i + jX_i = \rho_m c_m \tanh\left[\alpha_0 + j\left(\beta + \frac{2\pi l}{\lambda}\right)\right]_m \tag{4.20}$$

[10] In many practical cases $\alpha_{ik} = \alpha_{hj}$ and S is the *total* radiating or receiving surface.

in which $\rho_m c_m$ is the characteristic impedance of the transducer material. With proper choice of constants, and the necessary iterations of this equation to satisfy eq. 4.18, one can derive expressions for essentially all kinds of piezoelectric transducers: stiffness-controlled, resistance-controlled, or resonant, radiating directly or through one or more matching lines; and with any kind of backing, though this may require some modification of the simple situation depicted in Fig. 4.2. We shall work out here only a few elementary cases.

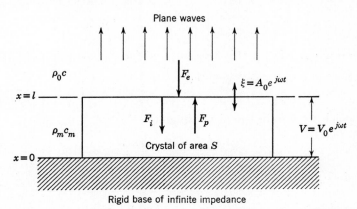

Fig. 4.2. Dynamic equilibrium of forces on the vibrating face of a rigidly backed crystal slab

Let us first assume that the transducer material and the medium are lossless, and that plane waves are radiated into a pure resistance, namely, the characteristic impedance of the loading medium. Then:

$$Z_e = \rho_0 c$$

If the face at $x = 0$ is rigidly clamped or located at a velocity null in a standing wave, such that no energy is radiated from that face, the wave constants are $\alpha_0 = 0$ and $\beta_{x=0} = \pi/2$, so the internal impedance is:

$$Z_i = \rho_m c_m \tanh j\left(\frac{\pi}{2} + \frac{2\pi l}{\lambda_m}\right) = -j\rho_m c_m \cot\left(\frac{2\pi l}{\lambda_m}\right) \qquad (4.21)$$

This simple case is shown in Fig. 4.2.

Long-wave approximation Next let the slab be very thin, $l \ll \lambda_m$, in which case:

$$-j \cot\left(\frac{2\pi l}{\lambda_m}\right) \simeq -j\frac{\lambda_m}{2\pi l}$$

In this limit the slab is stiffness controlled, and the internal force becomes:

$$F_i \simeq \rho_m c_m S \left(-j \frac{\lambda_m}{2\pi l} \right) j\omega \xi$$

If we use $2\pi/\lambda_m = \omega/c_m$, and replace the stiffness constant $\rho_m c_m{}^2$ for acoustic waves by the corresponding constant c_{hk} as defined in eq. 4.2, we obtain for the internal force:

$$F_i \simeq \frac{\rho_m c_m{}^2 S}{l} \xi = \frac{c_{hk} S}{l} \xi \qquad (l \ll \lambda_m) \qquad (4.22)$$

Evaluating eq. 4.18 for this case, we find for the condition of balance:

$$\frac{e_{hj} S}{l} V = \frac{c_{hk} S}{l} \xi + \rho_0 c S j\omega \xi \qquad (4.23)$$

from which we obtain the displacement:

$$\xi \simeq \frac{e_{hj} V (c_{hk} - j\omega \rho_0 c l)}{c_{hk}{}^2 + (\omega \rho_0 c l)^2} \qquad (4.24)$$

The velocity then is:

$$u = \frac{d\xi}{dt} \simeq \frac{\alpha V}{\rho_0 c S - j \dfrac{c_{hk} S}{\omega l}} \qquad (l \ll \lambda_m, \text{ rigid backing}) \qquad (4.25)$$

using $\alpha = \dfrac{e_{hj} S}{l}$ from eq. 4.16.[11]

Quarter-wave resonance   We see from eq. 4.25 that the velocity is equal to the driving force divided by a series combination of resistance and a large stiffness reactance.   This reactance diminishes as the slab gets thicker, and drops to zero at $f_0 = \omega_0/2\pi = c_m/4l$, because the factor $\cot(2\pi l/\lambda_m)$ vanishes ($Z_i = 0$).   This is the quarter-wave resonance at which the particle velocity at the radiating surface is $u \simeq \alpha V/\rho_0 c S = e_{hj} V/\rho_0 c l$, and hence the pressure amplitude in the sound wave is

$$p = u\rho_0 c \simeq e_{hj} E \qquad (4.26)$$

In the vicinity of this resonance the argument $2\pi l/\lambda_m$ in eq. 4.21 is

[11] In the following the subscripts will be dropped in the transformation factor α because only one value of e_{hj} or e_{ik} is important for each of the crystal cuts being used for the various piezoelectric materials.   The reader should be careful not to confuse this factor α with the reflectivity constant that appears in the form $e^{-\alpha_0}$ in the hyperbolic tangent transmission line eq. 2.39.

nearly $\pi/2$, so we can write

$$\tanh j(\beta + kl) = j \tan \left(\frac{\pi}{2} + kl \right)$$

$$= j \tan \left(\frac{2\pi l}{\lambda_m} - \frac{\pi}{2} \right) \simeq j \left(\frac{2\pi l}{\lambda_m} - \frac{\pi}{2} \right)$$

If we use this approximation and carry out the derivation corresponding to eqs. 4.22 to 4.25 we obtain for the velocity:

$$u \simeq \frac{\alpha V}{\rho_0 cS + j\omega \rho_m lS - j\pi \rho_m c_m S/2} \qquad (l \simeq \lambda_m/4, \text{ rigid backing})$$

$$= \frac{\alpha V}{Z_R + (j\omega M + K/j\omega)} \qquad\qquad (4.27)$$

The impedance is a resistance ($Z_R = \rho_0 cS$) in series with a reactance, composed of a stiffness[12] $K = \pi^2 c_{hk} S/4l$ and a mass $M = \rho_m lS$, which cancel at the resonance frequency $\omega = c\pi/2l$.

Half-wave resonance The rigid backing can be supplied by a $\lambda_m/4$ length of the same material added to the slab considered above and terminated in a zero impedance. Rigorously this requires a vacuum termination, but air is sufficiently low in impedance for this purpose if the slab is radiating into a liquid. The total length of this "piezoelectric" line is now $\lambda_m/2$, and the internal stiffness and inertia again cancel each other at resonance. The velocity generated by half of the crystal is again given by eq. 4.27 if V and l are taken as $\frac{1}{2}$ their total values for the $\lambda_m/2$ slab. However, the other half is also generating a wave with the same velocity, so the resulting velocity at the radiating face at resonance is

$$u = 2\alpha V/\rho_0 cS \qquad (l = \lambda_m/2, \text{ air backing}) \qquad (4.28)$$

Next consider a symmetrically loaded slab of $l = \lambda_m/2$, with both faces radiating into a medium of impedance $\rho_0 c$. The central plane is stationary in this case because the internal forces and external loads are completely symmetrical. The velocity of each radiating face at resonance is, therefore, the same as that for the $\lambda_m/4$ transducer; i.e.,

$$u = \alpha V/\rho_0 cS \qquad (l = \lambda_m/2, \text{ symmetrical load}) \qquad (4.29)$$

We see that the air-backed transducer develops twice as much velocity as the symmetrically loaded one, for the same voltage and dimensions.

[12] Note the difference between the static and the motional value of the stiffness: $K_{\text{mot}} = K_{\text{stat}} \pi^2/4$.

This arises physically from the internal wave which is totally reflected at the air surface and combines in phase to double the amplitude of the radiated wave. We shall thus define the *transformation factor* as $\alpha = e_{hj}S_R/l$, using the total radiating surface S_R. Note that this definition does not change eqs. 4.25 to 4.29 if we consistently replace S by S_R.

Power output and motional resistance   The acoustical power radiated is given by $W = U_{rms}^2 Z_R$, in which Z_R is the total mechanical radiation impedance, or the specific acoustic impedance Z_e multiplied by the total radiating area S_R. The total radiated power then is:

$$W = \alpha^2 V_{rms}^2/Z_R \text{ watts} \qquad \text{(symmetrical load, half-wave resonance)}$$
$$(4.30a)$$

$$\text{and} \quad W = 4\alpha^2 V_{rms}^2/Z_R \text{ watts} \qquad \text{(air-backed, half-wave resonance)}$$
$$(4.30b)$$

We can now define an electric resistance arising from the acoustical radiation, namely, the motional resistance R_e. This resistance determines the total power P dissipated acoustically into the load: $W = V_{rms}^2/R_e$. By comparison with eqs. 4.30 we obtain:

$$R_e = Z_R/\alpha^2 \quad \text{(for symmetrical load)} \qquad (4.31a)$$
$$\text{and} \qquad R_e = Z_R/4\alpha^2 \quad \text{(for air backing)} \qquad (4.31b)$$

In calculating α and Z_R for these equations we must use the total radiating area which in eq. 4.31a is $S_R = 2S$ and in eq. 4.31b is $S_R = S$. The velocity of the transducer gives rise to a motional current i which is obtained from the relationship: $i_{rms}^2 = W/R_e$. This is only the current due to the motional strain in the piezoelectric material. There is an additional current due to the dielectric displacement in the crystal acting as a condenser, as we will see below. The motional current can be calculated from eqs. 4.30 and 4.31 and is:

$$i_m = \alpha u \qquad \text{(for symmetrical load)}$$
$$i_m = 2\alpha u \qquad \text{(for air backing)} \qquad (4.32)$$

where u is the particle velocity at the surface. These equations are valid for either rms values (i and u) or peak values (I and U).

The theory developed above has permitted us to formulate expressions for particle velocity at the surface of the transducer, the motional current into the transducer, the power output, and the motional resistance at resonance. These expressions take a very simple form if the transformation factor α is used. In Table 4.2 the results of this section are summarized for the air-backed and the symmetrically loaded half-wave transducers. We will see in Section 4.4 that this presentation leads to a simple equivalent circuit of the piezoelectric transducer. The same general concept applies to all electromechanical transducers, and the modifications necessary for transducers using magnetic fields are discussed in Chapter 5.

Table 4.2   Basic Relationships for Half-wave Resonant Transducers

	Symbol	Unit	Air Backing	Symmetrical Load
Total radiating area	S_R	m^2	S	$2S$
Transformation factor	α	coulomb/m	$e_{hj}S/l$	$e_{hj}2S/l$
Total radiation impedance	Z_R	kg/sec	$\rho_0 c_0 S$	$\rho_0 c_0 2S$
Particle velocity at transducer face	u	m/sec	$2\alpha V/Z_R$	$\alpha V/Z_R$
Sound pressure at transducer face	p	newton/m^2	$2\alpha V/S$	$\alpha V/S$
Total acoustic power radiated*	W	watts	$4\alpha^2 V^2/Z_R$	$\alpha^2 V^2/Z_R$
Motional current	i_m	amp	$2\alpha u$	αu
Motional resistance	R_e	ohms	$Z_R/4\alpha^2$	Z_R/α^2

* From both faces in the case of symmetrical loading.

4.4   Simple Theory of Equivalent Circuits for Transmitters

An electroacoustic transducer is driven from some kind of electric generator. It is important to know what electric load the transducer

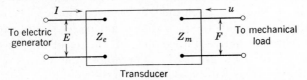

Fig. 4.3.   Electromechanical transducer as a four-terminal network.

offers to this power source. If radiation takes place from one side only, a transducer represents a four-terminal network with two electric input terminals and two mechanical output terminals (Fig. 4.3). At the output terminals a mechanical force F applied over the transducer face of area S produces particle motion of velocity u. For plane waves their ratio is the mechanical radiation resistance[13] Z_R:

[13] This mechanical impedance is a pure resistance for all practical purposes when plane compressional waves and media of low viscosity are considered. A case where the imaginary component is of importance is discussed in Chapter 8, Section 6.

$$Z_R = \frac{\text{force}}{\text{particle velocity}} = \frac{pS}{u} = \rho_0 c S$$

If the crystal is tuned to resonance the mechanical load resistance appears at the electric terminals of the transducer network as: $R_e = Z_R/4\alpha^2$. In order to find the total electric input impedance we must account for the fact that a voltage $V = V_0 e^{j\omega t}$ applied to the transducer also causes a displacement current

$$i_0 = dQ/dt = j\omega C_0 V \tag{4.33}$$

where C_0 is the static capacity defined by eq. 4.1. This is the current that will flow if all mechanical vibration of the transducer is prevented ($u = 0$). Hence the ratio V/i_0 is called the "clamped impedance." If the transducer vibrates, a motional current given by eq. 4.32 will flow in addition to i_0, and the total current then is (see Fig. 4.6)

$$i_{\text{total}} = i_0 + i_m \tag{4.34}$$

Thus at resonance the equivalent electric circuit of the transducer is simply a parallel RC combination.

The reactance $jX_0 = -1/j\omega C_0$ can be canceled by a shunt coil across the input terminals. In this case the electric input impedance is a pure resistance ($Z_{el} = R_e$). Figure 4.4 shows the value of R_e for air-backed quartz transducers at resonance. The product $R_e S$ (ohms·m^2) is plotted versus $f = c/2l$ for different loading media. We see that, for solids, R_e is generally very high, which limits the power that can be delivered to such media by conventional electronic equipment. Even for liquids the transducer impedance can be much higher than the electric source impedance of the electronic generator if frequencies below 1 mc are used. Therefore some means of matching must be provided, as will be discussed in Section 4.5.

It is shown in Chapter 2 how mechanical systems can be described by electric equivalent networks (Fig. 2.2 and eq. 2.14). In order to obtain electrical quantities, a conversion of units is required. The conversion factor depends on the dimensions of the transducer and its electromechanical coupling. At resonance this conversion from mechanical to electrical quantities simply amounts to multiplication by the transformation factor α (or 2α for air-backed crystals), as shown in Table 4.2. In the vicinity of resonance the transmission-line section that is represented by a vibrating disc or bar can be expressed by the lumped quantities M and $1/K$. Using the analogy between force and voltage, velocity and current (Fig. 2.2, arrow I) we obtain a series equivalent circuit. The equivalent electric elements of this circuit for the case of a symmetrically loaded transducer are:

$$R_e = Z_R/\alpha^2 \qquad L = M/\alpha^2 \qquad C = \alpha^2/K \qquad (4.35a)$$

and for the air-backed transducer:

$$R_e = Z_R/4\alpha^2 \qquad L = M/4\alpha^2 \qquad C = 4\alpha^2/K \qquad (4.35b)$$

This simple transformation permits us to represent the transducer by the equivalent circuit of Fig. 4.5. Here an ideal transformer of

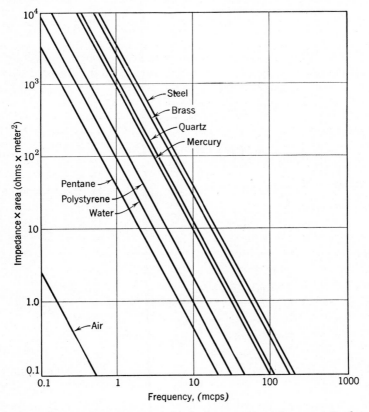

Fig. 4.4. Motional resistance of air-backed quartz transducers at fundamental resonance for several loading media.

the ratio $1:\alpha$ (for air-backing $1:2\alpha$) is inserted between the electrical and the mechanical sides of the transducer.

Limitations of equivalent circuits   Before discussing equivalent circuits further we should point out their limitations.   In the examples of Fig. 2.2, L, C, and R occur as true lumped constants while in our present mechanical system M and K are continuously distributed. As a consequence of this difference, a bar or disc can resonate in higher harmonics, namely at

$$f_n = n\frac{c}{2l} \qquad \text{with } l = \frac{n}{2}\lambda \qquad (n = 1, 2, 3, 4 \cdots) \qquad (4.36a)$$

if both faces of the bar or disc are loaded by low[14] impedances, e.g., the air-backed disc radiating into water; and at

$$f_n = n\frac{c}{4l} \qquad \text{with } l = n\frac{\lambda}{4} \qquad (n = 1, 3, 5 \cdots) \qquad (4.36b)$$

if one face is rigidly clamped or terminated by a high impedance and the other face loaded by a low impedance such as a gas or a liquid.

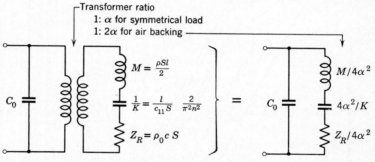

Fig. 4.5.   Equivalent circuit with ideal transformer between electric and mechanical sides of transducer.

In a *piezoelectric transducer, sound output is obtained only if n is an odd integer. Since the sign of the strains in a vibrating crystal changes along l each half wavelength for a given direction of the electric driving field, the strains cancel over each full wavelength.*

Near zero frequency the static values are valid for both M and K, namely,

$$M = \rho Sl \qquad \text{and} \qquad K = c_{hk}S/l \qquad (4.37a)$$

Near a resonance frequency f_n, however, the "motional" values (for a derivation see eq. 4.27) must be used, and these are smaller due to the sinusoidal distribution of the stress in a vibrating crystal.   They are:

$$M = \tfrac{1}{2}(\rho Sl) \qquad \text{and} \qquad K = n^2\pi^2 c_{hk}S/2l \qquad (4.37b)$$

[14] In all such discussions, "high" and "low" means that the impedance ratio $\rho_0 c/\rho_m c_m$ is much greater or much less than unity.

where n is the order of the harmonic; and we obtain from eq. 2.6,

$$\omega_n = 2\pi f_n = \sqrt{K/M} = \frac{n \cdot \pi}{l} \sqrt{c_{hk}/\rho} = 2\pi \cdot nc/2l \quad (4.37c)$$

Example For an example let us compute the network components near resonance for an air-backed quartz transducer with the following values:

$c_{hk} = c_{11} = 8.55 \times 10^{10}$ newtons/m^2

$\rho = 2.65 \times 10^3$ kg/m^3

$f_1 = 2.85$ mcps

$\rho_0 c = 1.5 \times 10^6$ kg/m^2/sec

$e_{ik} = e_{11} = 0.17$ coulomb/m^2

$l = 10^{-3}$ m

$S = 10^{-3}$ m^2

$\epsilon = 4.45$

$\epsilon_0 = \dfrac{1}{4\pi \times 9 \times 10^9}$ farad/m

Hence we obtain for the following:

transformation factor (air backing)	$2\alpha = 2\dfrac{e_{11}S}{l}$	$= 0.34$ coulomb/m
motional mass	$M = \frac{1}{2}\rho Sl$	$= 1.33 \times 10^{-3}$ kg
equivalent inductance	$L = \dfrac{M}{4\alpha^2}$	$= 11.4$ mh
motional stiffness	$K = \dfrac{\pi^2}{2}\dfrac{c_{11}S}{l}$	$= 42.5 \cdot 10^{10}$ newton/m
equivalent capacitance	$C = \dfrac{4\alpha^2}{K}$	$= 2.75 \cdot 10^{-13}$ farad
mechanical radiation resistance	$Z_R = \rho_0 cS$	$= 1.5 \times 10^3$ kg/sec
electric clamped capacitance	$C_0 = \epsilon\epsilon_0\dfrac{S}{l}$	$= 39.4 \cdot 10^{-12}$ farad

At the fundamental resonance frequency f_1 the mechanical reactances cancel, and at the electric terminals of the transducer appears an admittance $Y_e = G + jB$, where $G = 4\alpha^2/Z_R$ and $B = \omega C_0$. In the present example this is a resistance

$$R_e = 1/G = 13.15 \times 10^3 \text{ ohms} \quad (4.38a)$$

in parallel with C_0.

Sometimes it is desirable to convert a parallel mechanical (admittance) element in such a way that it appears in series (as an impedance) with the clamped impedance on the electrical side.   This can be accomplished by an ideal transformer of a turns ratio $\alpha' = \alpha/\omega C_0$, which yields $Y_{\text{mech}} \cdot \alpha'^2 = Z_e$.

In our example this leads to a resistance

$$R_e' \simeq 1/R_e \omega_1^2 C_0^2 = 150 \text{ ohms} \tag{4.38b}$$

in series with C_0.

4.5   Power Conversion and Matching

It is apparent from Fig. 4.6 that in our example the power factor at resonance (where $Z_e = R_e$) becomes:

$$\cos \phi = \frac{1}{\sqrt{1 + \omega_1^2 C_0^2 R_e^2}} \tag{4.39}$$

where ϕ is the phase angle between the total current into the transducer i and the current i_m through the resistor R_e.   For the above

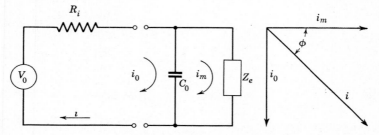

Fig. 4.6.   Power factor of unmatched transducer.

example, $\cos \phi \simeq 0.1$, which is a low power factor.   This situation is easily improved by tuning out $1/\omega C_0$ by a coil of reactance ωL_0 which can be inserted either in parallel or in series with the transducer, as is shown in Fig. 4.7.

The optimum operating condition for the crystal will be obtained if the source impedance R_i of the electric generator is equal to the input impedance R_e of the crystal at resonance after C_0 is tuned out. This calls for a tuned matching transformer[15] (Fig. 4.8) between the generator and the transducer, with a mutual inductance **M** given by:

$$\omega \mathbf{M} \simeq \sqrt{R_i \cdot R_e'} \qquad \text{with } R_e' \simeq \alpha^2/Z_R \omega^2 C_0^2 \tag{4.40}$$

If the transmission of maximum power from the transducer into a medium is desired irrespective of conversion efficiency, the matching

[15] For more detail on coupled circuits see F. E. Terman, *Radio Engineers Handbook*, McGraw-Hill, New York, 1943, p. 153.

requirements between electric generator and transducer may differ from the ones given above.   This depends largely on the nature of the electric generator to be used, on the limitations of the transducer material, and on the local impedance encountered.   For instance, if

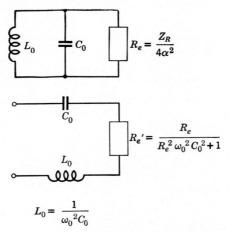

$$R_e = \frac{Z_R}{4\alpha^2}$$

$$R_e' = \frac{R_e}{R_e^2\,\omega_0^2\,C_0^2 + 1}$$

$$L_0 = \frac{1}{\omega_0^2 C_0}$$

Fig. 4.7.   Reactance cancellation by parallel or series coil.

intense ultrasonic signals are to be sent into a solid, as in flaw detection, the electric radiation resistance R_e may be of the order of 10^5 ohms (see Fig. 4.4).   The problem then is essentially to build an electronic generator capable of producing a very high driving voltage, irrespective of efficiency.   In addition, a quarter-wave plate of low impedance

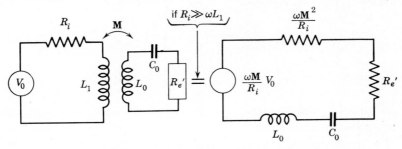

Fig. 4.8.   Matching of transducer to source impedance.

may be inserted between crystal and load material, which acts as an acoustical step-down transformer.[16]

With barium titanate (thickness-type) transducers in the megacycle range the practical realization of a desired matching transformer may

[16] See the discussion of crystal sandwiches in Section 4.12.

become forbiddingly difficult for another reason. Let us consider a waterloaded barium titanate transducer similar in dimensions to the 2.85-mcps quartz transducer of the above example. Because of the high dielectric constant ($\epsilon \approx 1500$) of barium titanate, its reactance is about $\frac{1}{300}$, and, because of its high piezoelectric constant, its parallel resistance is about $\frac{1}{1000}$ of that in the equivalent quartz transducer. For loads of such low impedance the matching to a transmitter tube becomes difficult. In some cases it may help to drive a thicker transducer in one of its harmonics. The remaining mismatch must be overcome by a generator capable of supplying a high enough driving current, irrespective of efficiency.

4.6   The Q of Transducers

The frequency characteristic of the radiated power is determined largely by the *mechanical Q* of the transducer. Let us assume that C_0 is tuned out by an inductance L_0, and that R_e is the only dissipative element in the circuit. Then the quality factor for the nth harmonic mode is:

$$Q_n = \left[\frac{\text{energy stored in } L}{\text{energy dissipated in } R_e} \right]_{\text{per cycle}} = n\omega_0 \frac{L}{R_e} \qquad (4.41)$$

or, converting to the mechanical circuit elements,[17]

$$Q_n = n \frac{\omega_0 M}{\rho_0 c S}$$

Using eq. 4.37b for M and $\omega_0 = 2\pi c/2l$ we finally obtain:

$$Q_n = n \frac{\pi}{2} \frac{\rho_m c_m}{\rho_0 c} \quad \text{with air backing} \qquad (4.42a)$$

and $\qquad Q_n = n \frac{\pi}{2} \frac{\rho_m c_m}{\rho_0 c + \rho_1 c_1} \quad \text{loaded at both sides} \qquad (4.42b)$

in which $\rho_m c_m$ refers to the crystal, $\rho_0 c$ to the load, and $\rho_1 c_1$ to the backing medium.

The mechanical Q is independent of the crystal dimensions, and proportional to the order of the harmonic. For an air-backed quartz transducer, as in the above example, we compute $Q_1 = 15$ if the load

---

[17] According to eq. 2.17, Q_n can also be expressed in terms of the damping constant κ as $Q_n = \omega_0/2\kappa = \pi/\delta$ where δ is the logarithmic damping decrement:

$$\delta = \frac{8}{\pi} \frac{\text{amplitude at resonance}}{\text{static displacement}}.$$

is water and $Q_1 = 50,000$ if the load is air. For air-backed barium titanate a theoretical value $Q_1 = 28$ is obtained with a water load. In air the Q of barium titanate transducers is only of the order of 200 because of the greater internal losses of this material.

The mechanical Q_n actually measured will be lower owing to mounting losses; sometimes it can be lower than the computed value by a factor 2.[18] Such additional damping reduces the intensity radiated from the transducer. If the effective Q of the mounted transducer has been determined experimentally the intensity of the sound radiation can be computed from:

$$\mathcal{I} = 3.9 \cdot 10^{-3} Q^2 V_{\text{rms}}^2 f^2 \ (\text{watt/cm}^2) \quad \begin{array}{l} (\text{air-backed quartz,} \\ \lambda/2 \ \text{resonance,} \\ \text{water load}) \end{array} \quad (4.43)$$

where V_{rms} is in kilovolts and f in megacycles.

It is often important to obtain quantitative values for the additional loading caused by the crystal holder. This loading can be expressed in terms of an effective holder impedance Z_H. With very light loads, as in measurements on gases by ultrasonic interferometry, the mechanical impedance Z_H may provide the major damping. We find for the total mechanical impedance of the transducer:

$$Z_m = Z_R + Z_H = 4\alpha^2 R_p$$

where R_p is the effective parallel damping resistance. If we neglect all losses other than mechanical we have:

$$Z_m = 4\alpha^2 Q'/\omega C_0$$

where Q' is the *electrical* quality factor of the mounted transducer at resonance; in other words, Q' is the power stored in C_0 divided by the power dissipated in R_p, per cycle. Hence, with a known load impedance Z_R and a measurement of $Q' \simeq \omega C_0 R_p$ of the mounted transducer we obtain:[19]

$$Z_H = 4\alpha^2 \frac{Q'}{\omega C_0} - Z_R \qquad (4.44)$$

If the crystal is loaded with a relatively high radiation impedance, as with liquids and solids, and if the mounting losses are relatively low $(Z_R \gg Z_H)$, the electrical quality factor becomes:

$$Q' = \frac{n\pi}{4k_c^2} \frac{\rho_0 c}{\rho_m c_m} \qquad (4.45)$$

---

[18] F. E. Fox and V. Griffing, *J. Acoust. Soc. Amer.*, **21** (1949), 359.
[19] W. J. Fry, *J. Acoust. Soc. Amer.*, **21** (1949), 79.

in which $k_c = e_{hj}/\sqrt{\epsilon\epsilon_0 c_{hk}}$ is the electromechanical coupling factor which is discussed in Section 4.8. We see in this equation that the electrical quantity Q' increases with increased loading ($\rho_0 c$), whereas the mechanical Q decreases with increased load, as shown in eqs. 4.42. This behavior is also evident from the circuit diagram in which the motional resistance is in parallel with the static capacitance of the crystal.

Practical questions regarding electrical matching can be studied with these equations. A calculation using eq. 4.45 will show, for example, that Q' for quartz is about sixteen times higher than Q' for barium titanate, if both materials are operated under the same conditions. One consequence is that a barium titanate transducer requires much tighter electric coupling to the generator.

Table 4.3   Mechanical Q of Quartz Transducers at the Fundamental Resonance with Various Backing Conditions*

Loading		Backing		
Medium	$\rho_0 c$	Air	Water or High-Loss Rubber†	Plastics $\rho_1 c_1 = 3 \cdot 10^6$
Air	420	10^4	15	8
Water	$1.5 \cdot 10^6$	15	7.5	5
Quartz‡	$15 \cdot 10^6$	1.5	1.4	<1.4
Mercury‡	$19.4 \cdot 10^6$	1.2	<1.2	<1.2

* Damping by the crystal holder is neglected here. It may be evaluated by use of eq. 4.44.

† Butyl rubber is useful in damping ultrasonic frequencies as described in U.S. Pat. 2,503,400 by W. P. Mason. The composition of this rubber is: 100 parts butyl rubber, 3 parts sulfur, 5] parts zinc oxide, 3 parts steric acid, and 1 part tetramethyl thiuramide disulfide.

‡ Perfect acoustic contact between transducer and load is assumed; bonding losses are neglected.

Bandwidth characteristics   The combined effect of the mechanical Q and the electric Q' determines the bandwidth characteristics of a transducer. Some ultrasonic applications, such as pulse delay lines and echo ranging, involve short transient signals which require a wide frequency band.[20] Consequently, one design criterion is a low mechanical Q for the transducer. We see from eqs. 4.42 that, if possible, the loading medium should have a high characteristic impedance. In any case the backing material should not be air, but

[20] H. N. Beveridge and W. W. Keith, *Proc. I.R.E.*, *40* (1952), 828, and J. E. May, Jr., *J. Acoust. Soc. Amer. 26* (1954) 347.

rather some material with high impedance and high loss.   Some values
are given in Table 4.3 to illustrate the magnitudes of Q with different
loading media and backing conditions.   Backing materials with a characteristic impedance $\rho_1 c_1 > \sqrt{2}\ \rho_m c_m$ such as steel, lead, or Cerroseal,
will yield even greater bandwidths.   In such cases, however, the Q
cannot be defined simply by eq. 2.18 because the frequency response
curve will have two peaks (see Section 4.7).

Another design requirement for good transient or pulse response
is a low value of the *electric* Q' as seen by the driving amplifier.   This
will insure the least possible change in relative amplitudes and phases
of the pulse throughout its frequency spectrum.   To satisfy this
requirement we must counteract the loading effect of C_0 on the electrical source.   The required band-pass filter action is obtained by

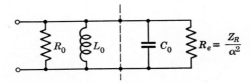

Fig. 4.9.   Circuit for wide band-pass characteristics.

tuning out C_0 by a parallel inductance at or near the center frequency
of the band and by damping down this parallel circuit $(C_0 L_0)$ by a
resistance (R_0).   In this case the electrical quality factor of the circuit
shown in Fig. 4.9 becomes:

$$Q'' = \frac{Q'}{1 + Q'/\omega C_0 R_0} \tag{4.46}$$

We see from eq. 4.45 that a high load impedance $\rho_0 c$, required to
keep the mechanical Q low, gives a high value of Q'.   Equation 4.46
shows, however, that Q' can be reduced to any desired value Q'' by
using a suitable low shunt resistance R_0.

4.7   Resonance and Antiresonance

Let us consider the case $R_e = 0$, which corresponds to a transducer
that is completely unloaded.   From Fig. 4.5 we find that the clamped
electric impedance $1/j\omega C_0$ and the mechanically derived impedance
$[Z_R + j(\omega M - K/\omega)]/4\alpha^2$ are connected in parallel.   Setting $Z_R = 0$,
we obtain for the total admittance:

$$Y = j\omega C_0 - \frac{j4\alpha^2}{\omega M - K/\omega} \tag{4.47a}$$

where the second term gives the *motional admittance*. Equation 4.47a can be rearranged to:

$$Y = j\omega \frac{\omega^2 \dfrac{M}{K} C_0 - \dfrac{4\alpha^2}{K} - C_0}{\omega^2 \dfrac{M}{K} - 1} \tag{4.47b}$$

There are two extreme values for the total admittance:

1. If the denominator of eq. 4.47b vanishes, the total impedance goes to zero at a frequency

$$\omega_r = \sqrt{K/M} \tag{4.48a}$$

which is the *resonance* frequency of the mechanical series branch of the transducer.

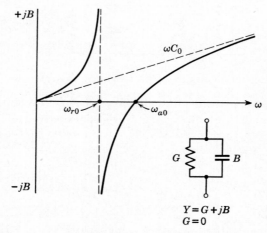

$$Y = G + jB$$
$$G = 0$$

Fig. 4.10. Admittance of unloaded lossless transducer.

2. If the numerator of eq. 4.47b vanishes we obtain $Y = 0$ (infinite impedance) at a frequency:

$$\omega_a = \sqrt{\frac{K}{M} + \frac{4\alpha^2}{C_0 M}} \tag{4.48b}$$

which represents the parallel *antiresonance* of the complete network.

Figure 4.10 shows the general appearance of the admittance curve for an unloaded transducer as given by eqs. 4.47. The susceptance is plotted along the ordinate and the frequency along the abscissa. The corresponding impedance curve is shown in Fig. 4.11. If the transducer is damped by loading or mounting ($R_e' \neq 0$), the poles of the curves for admittance and impedance will have finite values, and the resonance frequencies (ω_r; ω_a) will be somewhat higher. An interesting coupling phenomenon occurs when a piezoelectric transducer material of characteristic impedance $\rho_m c_m$ radiates into a medium of impedance $\rho_0 c > \sqrt{2}\,\rho_m c_m$. The response curve has the appearance of a band-pass filter curve at over-critical coupling. This is illustrated in Fig. 4.12, which shows the dependence of transducer

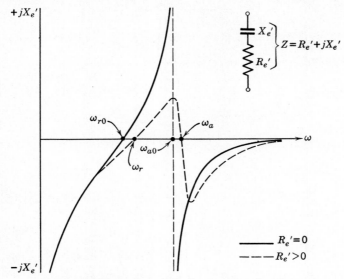

Fig. 4.11.   Transducer impedance versus frequency.

conductance G on the frequency ratio ω/ω_0, for air-backed crystals with various loads. The ordinate is the product Gq, in which the factor:

$$q = \frac{\pi^2}{2}\,k_c^2\,\frac{S}{l^2}\,\frac{1}{\rho_m c_m} \tag{4.49}$$

makes the curves universal for all types and shapes of piezoelectric transducers. The curve for nickel shows this special behavior. As $\rho_0 c$ approaches infinity, the peaks approach the frequencies $f_0/2$ and $3f_0/2$, which means that the crystal has become essentially a quarter-wave resonator.

Motional admittance and impedance   A rigorous treatment of admittance and impedance of loaded transducers[21] involves lengthy

[21] W. G. Cady, J. Acoust. Soc. Amer., 22 (1950), 579.   See also W. Roth, I.R.E., 37 (1949), 750 and Tech. Rept. 43, July 1947, Research Laboratory of Electronics, Massachusetts Institute of Technology.

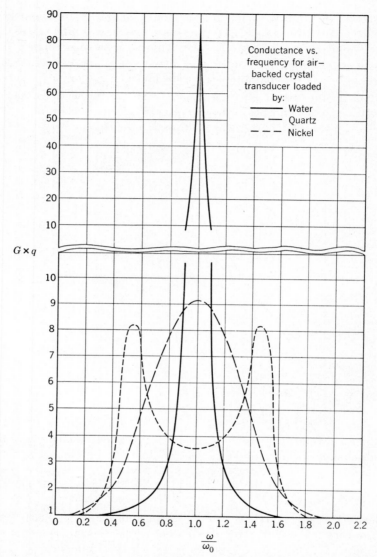

Fig. 4.12.   Frequency dependence of conductance, normalized for all transducer
materials (W. Roth).

manipulations of eqs. 4.17 to 4.20. We shall simply discuss the physical significance of the resulting expressions without deriving them. The admittance of the air-backed piezoelectric transducer is given in general by:

$$Y = \frac{\alpha^2}{Z_R} A + j\left(\omega C_0 - \frac{\alpha^2}{\rho_m c_m S} 4D\right) \tag{4.50}$$

where

$$A = \frac{m^2(1 - \cos \beta)^2}{\sin^2 \beta + m^2 \cos^2 \beta}$$

$$D = \frac{(1 - \cos \beta) \sin \beta (1 + m^2 \cos \beta)}{\sin^2 \beta + m^2 \cos^2 \beta}$$

$$Z_R = \rho_0 c S$$

$$\beta = \frac{\omega}{c_m} l \quad \text{and} \quad m = \frac{\rho_0 c}{\rho_m c_m} \tag{4.51}$$

($\rho_0 c$: load; $\rho_m c_m$: crystal)

For light loading ($m \ll 1$) and for small deviations from resonance ($\beta \simeq \pi$) we can make the following approximations in the above expression for D: $\cos \beta \simeq -1$, $\sin \beta = -\sin(\beta - \pi) \simeq -(\beta - \pi)$. Hence we obtain:

$$D \simeq \frac{2 \sin \beta (1 - m^2)}{\sin^2 \beta + m^2} \simeq -\frac{2}{\sin \beta} \simeq \frac{2}{\beta - \pi}$$

which can be transformed to

$$D \simeq \frac{\rho_m c_m S}{\omega M - K/\omega} \tag{4.51a}$$

where $M = (\rho_m S l)/2$ and $K = (c_{hk} S \pi^2)/2l$. With the use of this approximation for D the susceptance in eq. 4.50 takes the form of eq. 4.47a, which had been derived from a simple equivalent circuit. This shows clearly that such equivalent circuits are approximations only and that their use is limited to the conditions specified above, namely, relatively high mechanical Q ($m < 1$) and frequencies near resonance ($\omega/\omega_0 \simeq 1$).

The total impedance of a piezoelectric transducer can be derived from transformations of eq. 4.50. The result in its most general form is:

$$Z = \frac{\alpha^2}{Z_R} \frac{A}{\omega^2 C_0^2} + \frac{1}{j\omega}\left(\frac{1}{C_0} + \frac{\alpha^2}{\rho_m c_m S} \frac{4D}{\omega C_0^2}\right)$$

$$= R_e' - j(X_0 + X_e') \tag{4.52}$$

If the clamped reactance $X_0 = 1/\omega C_0$ is subtracted from the total impedance, one obtains the *motional impedance:* $Z' = R_e' - jX_e'$.

The vector Z' describes a circular loop in the complex plane. A loop of this type is formed whenever a reactance function of the form illustrated in Fig. 4.11 is combined in the complex plane with a resistance function of the form A/ω^2 (see eq. 4.52). The resistance function, which controls the frequency dependence of R_e', is plotted in

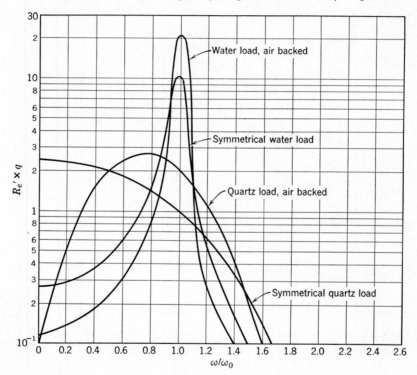

Fig. 4.13. Frequency dependence of resistance, normalized for all transducer materials (W. Roth).

Fig. 4.13. The curves of this figure are normalized by the use of $R_e'q$ for the ordinate scale and of ω/ω_0 for the abscissa scale, where q is given by eq. 4.49. In this form Fig. 4.13 defines the resistive response of all piezoelectric transducers, both air-backed and symmetrically loaded, for two particular loading media, water and quartz. In general, an increase of the load impedance broadens and lowers the response curve, and reduces the frequency at which R_e' has a maximum value. A detailed discussion of motional impedance loops has been given by W. G. Cady.[22] Their shape approximates a perfect circle very closely for $m^2 \ll 1$, which represents loading by most liquids and all gases.

As an example, Fig. 4.14 represents the impedance of a barium titanate transducer[23] in the region of its fundamental resonance at

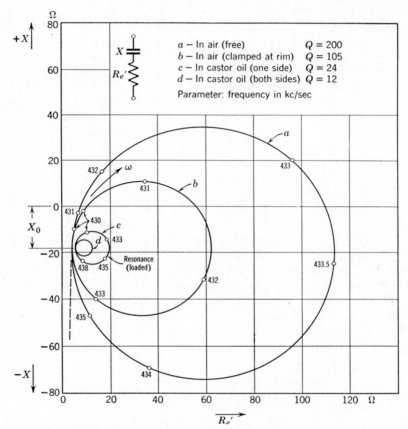

Fig. 4.14. Impedance loops of barium titanate transducer under various matching conditions, according to O. Mattiat.

400 kcps. Such curves are obtained with a suitable impedance bridge[24] or with a Q meter. The frequency increases in the clockwise

[22] W. G. Cady, *Piezoelectricity*, McGraw-Hill, New York, 1946, p. 333.

[23] According to data taken with a Brush ceramic bowl by O. Mattiat of the Brush Development Company, Cleveland, Ohio.

[24] For instance, for the frequency range from 50 kcps to 5 mcps by the General Radio bridge 916 AL. Automatically sweeping "vector impedance plotters,"

direction and changes most rapidly at the right side of a loop. The four different loops have been obtained under different loading conditions. Loop a represents a measurement on the free transducer in air, while loop b was obtained from the same bowl in air after it was mounted by clamping around its edges. We see that mounting has introduced considerable damping. Loop c represents the mounted bowl loaded by transformer oil on one face and backed by air on the other face. Loop d shows the additional damping obtained from loading both faces with transformer oil.

The diameter of a motional impedance loop is inversely proportional to the characteristic impedance of the loading medium. In the absence of loading and damping, the diameter of the loop becomes infinite in accordance with a purely imaginary value of admittance (see eq. 4.47a). Only in this case are the previous definitions of resonance and antiresonance strictly valid. Figure 4.14 also shows that the maximum total current (impedance minimum) is not drawn at mechanical resonance but at a slightly lower frequency. We define mechanical resonance as the frequency of maximum power output at constant voltage. This occurs practically at the impedance minimum for gaseous loading and practically at the impedance maximum for liquid loading. The frequency at which maximum power output is obtained depends on the driving condition. If the *voltage* is held constant the maximum output occurs at a lower frequency than if the *current* is held constant. This behavior is analogous to that of a simple mechanical oscillator as discussed in Section 2.4. The expressions for power and frequency of maximum output are given in the following set of equations in which $L = M/4\alpha^2$ and $C = 4\alpha^2/K$.

	Power Output	Frequency for W_{max}	
$V = $ constant	$W = V^2 R_e/|Z|^2$	$\omega = (1/LC)^{1/2}$	(4.53)
$I = $ constant	$W = I^2 R_e'$	$\omega = [(1 + C/C_0)/LC]^{1/2}$	(4.54)

The frequency of maximum power output at constant voltage is represented by point $\mathbf{R}$ in Fig. 4.15 which gives a schematic representation of the motional impedance circle. For liquid loads this point practically coincides with the point $\mathbf{R_1}$, where the power maximum at constant current results. Point $\mathbf{P}$ is the locus of the motional impedance values for all even harmonics. As pointed out in Section 4.4, no mechanical vibration can be excited by the driving field at an even harmonic, so the crystal acts as if it were clamped. As the frequency is increased above the second harmonic one obtains additional

---

which present the circle diagram directly on a CRO screen, are available for qualitative studies.

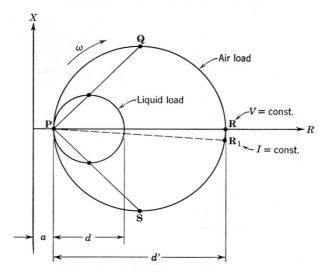

Fig. 4.15.   Schematic representation of motional impedance circle.

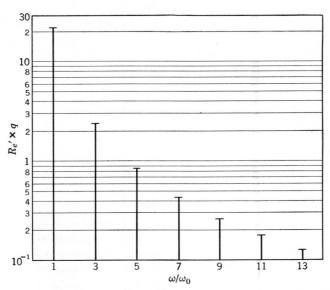

Fig. 4.16.   Series resistance at high harmonic modes, or power output at constant current.

circles for the higher odd harmonic resonances. Their radii decrease inversely as the square of the number of the harmonic, as can be seen from Fig. 4.16 in which the values of R_e' at the odd harmonics are plotted for air-backed waterloaded transducers. Figure 4.16 can be used for all transducer materials and shapes, since the product $R_e'q$ is plotted along the ordinate (for q see eq. 4.49) and the relative frequency ω/ω_0 is plotted along the abscissa.

4.8 The Electromechanical Coupling Factor

It can easily be shown that the frequency separation between resonance and antiresonance of an unloaded transducer, or between

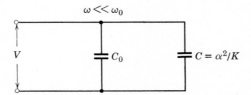

Fig. 4.17. Storage of electric and mechanical energy.

the impedance minimum and impedance maximum of a loaded transducer, is a measure of the degree of electromechanical energy conversion. From Eqs. 4.48b we obtain:

$$\frac{\omega_a^2}{\omega_r^2} - 1 = \frac{4\alpha^2}{C_0 \cdot K} = \frac{C}{C_0} \tag{4.55}$$

which can be rewritten as

$$\frac{(\omega_a - \omega_r)}{\omega_r^2} \cdot 2\omega_r \simeq 2\frac{(f_a - f_r)}{f_r} \approx \frac{C}{C_0} \tag{4.56}$$

if the approximation $\omega_a + \omega_r \simeq 2\omega_r$ is used.

The capacitance ratio C/C_0 is related to the piezoelectric activity of a crystal. Therefore the frequency separation $\Delta f = f_a - f_r$ between the extremes in impedance, admittance, or total current is large for materials of high piezoelectric coupling. Let us consider the low-frequency case where the transducer essentially consists of a parallel combination of C_0 and C (Fig. 4.17). If a voltage V is applied across the terminals, the ratio of energies stored is:

$$\frac{\text{energy stored mechanically}}{\text{energy stored electrically}} = \frac{CV^2/2}{C_0V^2/2} = \frac{C}{C_0}$$

Using eq. 4.55, 4.1, 4.16, and 4.37b we obtain:

$$\frac{e_{hj}^{2}}{\epsilon\epsilon_0 c_{hk}} \simeq \frac{\pi^2}{4}\frac{(f_a - f_r)}{f_r} \simeq k_c^{2} \tag{4.57a}$$

The quantity $k_c = [(\pi^2/8)(C/C_0)]^{\frac{1}{2}}$ has been defined as the *electromechanical coupling factor*. It is related to the transformation factor α by:

$$\frac{k_c^{2}}{\alpha^{2}} = \frac{\text{mechanical compliance}}{\text{clamped capacitance}} = \frac{1/K}{C_0} \tag{4.57b}$$

Eq. 4.57a indicates a convenient method of determining k_c^{2} from a measurement of the frequency separation between maximum and minimum current into a transducer operated at constant voltage. The additional measurement of ϵ and c_{hk} will then permit a determination of the effective piezoelectric constant. Table 4.4 gives the coupling factors and the piezoelectric and dielectric constants for the most important transducer materials.

Table 4.4   Electromechanical Properties of Transducer Materials

	Quartz X-cut	Rochelle salt 45° X-cut (at 20°C)	ADP 45° Z-cut	Lithium Sulfate Y-cut	Barium Titanate* (between 30°C and 100°C)			Tourma-line
Eff. piezoelectric constant e_{hj} (coulomb/m²)	0.17	3.5	0.47	1	10 to 17			0.065
Dielectric constant ϵ	4.5	200	15	10	1200 to 1500			7.5
Elastic constant $c^2\rho$ (newton/m²)	$8.7 \cdot 10^{10}$	$2.5 \cdot 10^{10}$	$2.1 \cdot 10^{10}$	$9.4 \cdot 10^{10}$	$15 \cdot 10^{10}$ (thickness)	$4.5 \cdot 10^{10}$ (shear)		$16 \cdot 10^{10}$
Coupling coefficient k_c (%)	10	54	29	35	bar 50	plate 40	radial 20	10

* Only approximate values of e_{hj}, ϵ, and k_c can be given since they depend on the pretreatment of the ceramic.

From Fig. 4.17 we see that a charge flowing into a transducer will be stored in part dielectrically and in part piezoelectrically. When determining the true dielectric constant of a transducer by a capacity measurement only the dielectric storage must be considered. Since it is difficult to suppress piezoelectric strains completely by clamping, the measured capacity C' must be corrected. The clamped capacity of the vibrating crystal then is:

$$C_0 = C'/(1 + 8k_c^{2}/\pi^2) \tag{4.58}$$

4.9 Determination of Transducer Efficiency from the Circle Diagram

Useful information on transducer losses can be obtained from a plot of the measured motional impedance circle. The equivalent network of a transducer with losses is shown in Fig. 4.18 where the resistance R_D shunting the clamped capacity C_0 represents the dielectric losses, and the resistance R_L, which is in series with the motional resistance R_e, represents the losses due to internal damping of the transducer. Referring to Fig. 4.15 we note that the intersection **P** of the circle with the real axis is displaced by amount a from the origin. Point **P**

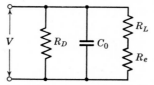

Fig. 4.18.   Resonant transducer with losses.

represents the second harmonic frequency where the mechanical series branch is open, $(R_e \sim \infty)$. Hence a is simply the series loss resistance of the clamped capacitance C_0 at the frequency $2\omega_0$:

$$a \simeq \frac{1}{R_D \cdot 4\omega_0{}^2 C_0{}^2} = \frac{\tan \delta}{4\omega_0 C_0} \tag{4.59}$$

where $\tan \delta$ is the dielective loss factor.[25]

From the equivalent network of Fig. 4.18 we can also compute the total series resistance at the fundamental frequency ω_0 which, in the circle diagram, corresponds to the distance

$$d = \frac{(R_D + R_e + R_L)}{R_D(R_e + R_L)} \cdot \frac{1}{\omega_0{}^2 C_0{}^2} \tag{4.60}$$

if the transducer is loaded with a mechanical impedance $\rho_0 c S = Z_R = 4\alpha^2 R_e$

In turn, if the transducer is operated without external load $(R_e = 0)$ we find the distance:

$$d' = \frac{R_D + R_L}{R_D \cdot R_L} \cdot \frac{1}{\omega_0{}^2 C_0{}^2} \tag{4.61}$$

The efficiency of a transducer is defined as

$$\eta = \frac{\text{power radiated into load}}{\text{total input power}} = \frac{W}{W + W_L + W_D} \tag{4.62}$$

[25] For quartz $\tan \delta \simeq 10^{-4}$, for barium titanate $\tan \delta \simeq 2 \cdot 10^{-2}$.

If a driving voltage V is applied to the input terminals of the circuit in Fig. 4.18, the power dissipated in the resistive branches is:

$$\text{radiation:} \quad W = \frac{V^2}{2} \frac{R_e}{(R_e + R_L)^2}$$

$$\text{mechanical loss:} \quad W_L = \frac{V^2}{2} \frac{R_L}{(R_e + R_L)^2}$$

$$\text{dielectric loss:} \quad W_D = \frac{V^2}{2R_D}$$

Equation 4.62 then becomes:

$$\eta = \frac{R_e \cdot R_D}{(R_e + R_L)(R_e + R_L + R_D)}$$

If the resistances are expressed in terms of d, d', and a, using eqs. 4.59, 4.60, and 4.61, the efficiency is:

$$\eta = \left(\frac{d' - d}{d' - 4a}\right)\left(\frac{d - 4a}{d}\right) \tag{4.63}$$

For crystals that have a sufficiently small $\tan \delta$, we can consider that d' and d are large compared with $4a$. In this case[26] a close approximation for the transducer efficiency is

$$\eta \simeq \frac{d' - d}{d'} \tag{4.64a}$$

At higher ultrasonic frequencies the diameter d of the impedance loop of a loaded transducer may be very small. Then a determination of d becomes difficult, while d_1, the diameter in air, can still be measured quite accurately. However, the measurement of d_1 in air is sufficient to find the efficiency if a transformation of eq. 4.64a is used. Assuming $\tan \delta \ll d_1 \omega_1 C_0$ and using eqs. 4.60, 4.61, 4.57b, and 4.58, we find in first approximation:

$$\eta \approx \frac{m/k_c{}^2}{m/k_c{}^2 + \dfrac{X_1}{d'}(1.27 + k_c{}^2)} \tag{4.64b}$$

where $m = \rho_0 c / \rho_m c_m$, k_c is the electromechanical coupling factor, and $X_1 = 1/\omega_0 C$ (C is the capacity actually measured by a bridge at low frequencies). For a properly mounted quartz transducer this gives

[26] L. Fein, J. Acoust. Soc. Amer., 21 (1949), 511.

about 99 per cent efficiency.   For barium titanate transducers in the thickness mode, as exemplified in Fig. 4.14, an efficiency of about 75 per cent is obtained.

In sonic engineering we are interested in the amount of the electric d-c input power that is converted into acoustically radiated power. This depends on the operating characteristics of the tube, the matching of the transducer to the tube, and the efficiency of the transducer itself.   If η_1 is the transfer efficiency of the tube, η_2 the efficiency of the matching network, and η_3 the efficiency of conversion within the transducer according to eq. 4.64, the total efficiency of the system is:

$$\eta_{total} = \eta_1 \cdot \eta_2 \cdot \eta_3$$

The following values are easily attainable with class C amplifier operation in the vicinity of 1 mcps:

$$\text{for quartz} \qquad \eta_{total} \simeq 0.7 \times 0.9 \times 0.99 \simeq 62\%$$

$$\text{for barium titanate} \qquad \eta_{total} \simeq 0.7 \times 0.6 \times 0.8 \simeq 34\%$$

Matching becomes more difficult with quartz operated at lower fundamental frequencies owing to the increase in motional resistance R_e (see Fig. 4.4), which may reduce η_2.   With barium titanate, however, thicker transducers are matched more easily and this increases η_2. As a rule the power rating of the transmitter tube should be one and a half to two times the desired acoustical power output for a quartz transducer, and three to four times the desired acoustical power for a barium titanate transducer.

4.10   Piezoelectric Response of Common Transducer Materials

Up to this point we have used mainly quartz, the classic piezoelectric material, to illustrate the analysis of piezoelectric transducer properties.   We now show that the relations derived can be applied to any other piezoelectric crystals.   Practical considerations in the choice of particular crystals for special applications are given in Chapter 7.   At this point, however, sufficient data will be given to compute the sound intensities of plane compressional waves obtainable from four of the most important transducer materials:

1. Quartz.
2. Ammonium dihydrogen phosphate (ADP).
3. Rochelle salt.
4. Barium titanate.

The piezoelectric strain constants of these materials are given in Table 4.1.   For crystals, the required cut can be determined by inserting their main d_{ih}-constant into the matrices of eqs. 4.9 and finding the corresponding strain.

For instance, in ADP the main constant is d_{36}, which leads to a strong shear strain in the x-y plane if a field is applied in the z direction. Thus a cut normal to the z axis, a Z cut is required. The Z cut has been used to generate face-shear modes and to obtain torsional vibrators. If a rectangular plate is cut in this plane in such a fashion that its length extends at $45°$ to the x and y crystallographic axes, a longitudinal motion will result from the shearing action. In

Expander bar cut at 45° from Z–cut plate

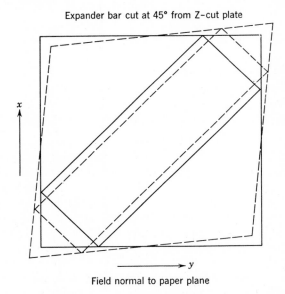

Field normal to paper plane

Fig. 4.19.   Deformation of a shear plate as in ADP transducers.

fact, every shear in a solid will involve compressions or dilations at the diagonals of the distorted rectangle, as illustrated in Fig. 4.19. It is evident that only a component of the piezoelectrically induced shearing strain contributes to this expansion. Hence for a $45°$ cut, the effective piezoelectric strain constant of ADP is found to be $d_{36}/2$.

Similarly, in Rochelle salt the main constant is d_{14}, which requires a cut in the y-z plane normal to the crystallographic x axis. Hence a $45°$ X cut can be used for longitudinal vibrations, and the effective constant d for longitudinal vibrations is $d_{14}/2$.

Table 4.5 gives data for the four transducer materials discussed in this section. Simple equations for the sound intensity apply if one face of a disc (quartz and barium titanate) or of a bar (ADP and

Rochelle salt) radiates into a load while the opposite face is terminated in air. In each case the intensity is obtained from modification of eqs. 4.30. Introducing an effective piezoelectric constant $2H = $ pressure$_{\text{out}}$/field strength$_{\text{in}}$ (factor 2 for pressure doubling), it can be written in the form

$$\mathcal{g} = \frac{W}{S} = \frac{p^2}{\rho_0 c} = 4\frac{H^2 E_{\text{rms}}{}^2}{\rho_0 c} \tag{4.65}$$

For the thickness mode $H = \alpha l/S = e_{ik}$, which with $l = c_m/2f$ and $i = k$ becomes

$$\mathcal{g} = \frac{1}{S}\frac{V_{\text{rms}}{}^2}{Z_R}4\alpha^2 = \frac{16e_{ii}{}^2 f^2 V_{\text{rms}}{}^2}{\rho_0 c c_m{}^2} \tag{4.65a}$$

where $\rho_0 c$ is the characteristic impedance of the loading medium, c_m is the sound velocity of the crystal material, and f is the fundamental resonance frequency. For the longitudinal mode of crystal slabs driven by a transverse field $H = \alpha t/S = d_{ik}/2s'$, and the intensity becomes

$$\mathcal{g} = 4\frac{H^2}{\rho_0 c}\left(\frac{V_{\text{rms}}}{t}\right)^2 = \left(\frac{d_{ik}}{s'}\right)^2\frac{E_{\text{rms}}{}^2}{\rho_0 c} \tag{4.65b}$$

where t is the crystal dimension in the direction of the applied field E, and w is the crystal width. We note from Fig. 4.19 that for the indirect coupling in ADP and Rochelle salt, the field produces primarily a shear strain specified by the constant d, which in turn produces a longitudinal stress specified by the compliance s'. In this case the stress is proportional to d/s'. The effective compliance[27] s' is equal to $1/\rho_m c_m{}^2$, taken in the direction of vibration.

It is important to bear in mind that the sound velocity c of some crystals is a function of temperature. Therefore, if the crystal heats up during operation its stiffness will change, and this can be a serious limitation as to stability of operation. In quartz the sound velocity is practically constant between $-20°C$ and $+60°C$. In barium titanate a 15 per cent drop occurs in the neighborhood of the lower transition point which lies between $+5°C$ and $-40°C$, depending on the amount of lead or calcium titanate additions. Rochelle salt is quite unstable at $24°C$ where it has a Curie point; and ADP shows a 2.5 per cent decrease in sound velocity if the temperature increases from $0°C$ to $60°C$. These variations are illustrated in Fig. 4.20.

In some cases this temperature dependence can be reduced by

---

[27] This is actually the reciprocal stiffness at constant field strength.

Table 4.5 Simplified Equations for Sound Intensity

Material	Mode of Vibration	Crystal Cut	Effective* Piezo Modulus H (coulombs/m²)	Sound Velocity c (m/sec)	Density ρ (kg/m³)	Sound Intensity in Water for Air-backed Transducer† $\mathfrak{g}$ (watts/m²)	Units rms values for V and E
Quartz	Thickness	X	$H = e_{11}$ $= 5.2 \cdot 10^4$ esu $= 0.17$ coulombs/m²	$5.72 \cdot 10^3$	$2.65 \cdot 10^3$	$f_0^2 V^2 \cdot 10^4$	V in kv f in mcps
Quartz	Longitudinal	X	$H = d_{11}/s'$ $= 5.4 \cdot 10^4$ esu $= 0.18$ coulombs/m²	$5.44 \cdot 10^3$	$2.65 \cdot 10^3$	$0.087 \cdot E^2 \cdot 10^4$	E in kv/cm
ADP	Longitudinal	45°Z	$H = d_{36}/2s'$ $= 1.57 \cdot 10^4$ esu $= 0.473$ coulombs/m²	$3.28 \cdot 10^3$	$1.8 \cdot 10^3$	$0.6E^2 \cdot 10^4$	E in kv/cm
Rochelle salt (0°C)	Longitudinal	45°X	$H = d_{14}/2s'$ $= 1.06 \cdot 10^6$ esu $= 3.5$ coulombs/m²	$3.4 \cdot 10^3$	$1.77 \cdot 10^3$	$33 \cdot E^2 \cdot 10^4$	E in kv/cm
Barium titanate (40°C)	Thickness	Polarized normal to thickness	$H = e_{33}$ $= 3$ to $5 \cdot 10^6$ esu $= 10$ to 17 coulombs/m²	$5 \cdot 10^3$	$5.5 \cdot 10^3$	$0.005f_0^2 V^2 \cdot 10^4$ to $0.014f_0^2 V^2 \cdot 10^4$	V in volts f in mcps

* The quantity s' in the relationship $H = d_{ih}/s'$ is the effective compliance in the direction of longitudinal vibration.
† Without the factor 10^4, this column gives the sound intensity in watts/cm².

rotating the plane of the cut at a specific angle. Of course this will involve a sacrifice in piezoelectric activity, but will improve the stability of the transducer. In Rochelle salt, the 45° Y cut (using d_{25}) has

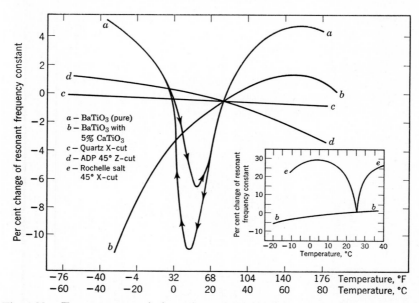

Fig. 4.20. Temperature variations of sound velocity in common transducer materials (frequency constant = resonance frequency × characteristic length l_c; in cases a, b, and c, l_c = disk thickness; in cases d and e, l_c = bar length).

proved satisfactory for underwater microphones with small temperature variation.

4.11 Simple Theory of Piezoelectric Receivers

We saw in Section 4.1 that a charge Q is produced by a strain in a piezoelectric crystal. In the static case we obtain from eq. 4.3 for X-cut quartz: $Q_i = e_{ik} \cdot x_k S$, and using eq. 4.2 we obtain:

$$Q_i = e_{ik} F / c_{hk}$$

This charge across the capacitance, $C_0 = (\epsilon \epsilon_0 S)/l$, produces a voltage

$$V = F e_{ik} l / c_{hk} \epsilon \epsilon_0 S$$

This can be written in terms of a transformation ratio $\alpha = e_{ik} S / l$

and a coupling coefficient $k_c = e_{ik}/\sqrt{c_{hk}\epsilon\epsilon_0}$, which yields a value for the static *sensitivity*, defined as voltage$_{out}$ per force$_{in}$:

$$V/F = k_c{}^2/\alpha \;(\text{volts/newton})^{28} \tag{4.66}$$

Dynamic behavior below resonance   Let us now consider the dynamic case in terms of an equivalent circuit. For simplicity we assume that the transducer is terminated into an infinite electric impedance and that losses can be neglected. For operation in the region of flat response below resonance we can then use the network of Fig. 4.21 where all circuit elements are converted to the *mechanical* side using the transformation factor α. The mechanical particle

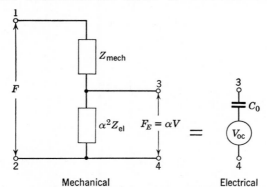

Mechanical   Electrical

Fig. 4.21.   Basic equivalent circuit for piezoelectric receivers.

velocity $u = d\xi/dt$ is analogous to a current that flows through the two impedances in series. Its value is given by:

$$u = \frac{\text{Force}}{\text{Total impedance}} = \frac{F}{Z_{\text{mech}} + \alpha^2 Z_{\text{el}}} \tag{4.67}$$

In the electrically derived branch of the network a force is generated:

$$F_E = \alpha V = u(\alpha^2 Z_{\text{el}})$$

Using eq. 4.67 this force becomes

$$F_E = \alpha V = F\,\frac{\alpha^2 Z_{\text{el}}}{Z_{\text{mech}} + \alpha^2 Z_{\text{el}}} \tag{4.68}$$

With the definition of the electromechanical coupling coefficient,

$$k_c{}^2 = \frac{\alpha^2/K}{C_0} = \frac{\alpha^2 Z_{\text{el}}}{Z_{\text{mech}}}$$

---

[28] Using eq. 4.14 this equation can be written in the form $V/F = h_{ik}/K$, where $K = c_{hk}S/l$.

we obtain for the dynamic sensitivity of an open-circuited receiver well below resonance:

$$\frac{V}{F} = \frac{1}{\alpha} \frac{k_c^2}{1 + k_c^2} \qquad (4.69)$$

Sensitivity of Rochelle salt hydrophone   For an example we calculate the sensitivity of a 45° X-cut Rochelle salt plate, of length l, width w and thickness t.[29] For longitudinal forces applied normal to the surface, $S = wt$, the piezoelectric stress constant is $H = d_{14}/2s_{22}'$. The transformation factor becomes $\alpha = HS/t = d_{14}w/2s_{22}'$, where s_{22}' is the compliance in the direction of the plate length l:

$$s_{22}' = \tfrac{1}{4}(s_{22} + 2s_{23} + s_{44}s_{33})$$

$$= 3.2 \cdot 10^{-11} \text{ m}^2/\text{newton}$$

With the electromechanical coupling factor $k_c^2 = d_{14}^2/(4s_{22}'\epsilon_x\epsilon_0)$, one obtains for the force sensitivity

$$\frac{V}{F} = \frac{1}{w} \frac{2s_{22}'d_{14}}{d_{14}^2 + 4s_{22}'\epsilon_x\epsilon_0} = \frac{\mathbf{K}_1}{w} \qquad (4.69a)$$

and for the pressure sensitivity

$$\frac{V}{P} = \frac{V}{F} S = \mathbf{K}_1 \cdot t \qquad (4.69b)$$

The quantity $\mathbf{K}_1$ in meters/coulomb is plotted versus temperature in Fig. 4.22.[30] We see that the maximum variation of sensitivity is only 17 per cent, in spite of the large variations of ϵ_x and d_{14} with temperature in Rochelle salt.   In practical applications several such crystal plates are stacked together, as we will see below.

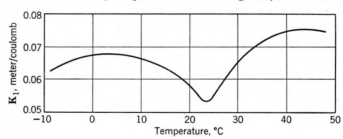

Fig. 4.22.   Sensitivity of Rochelle salt element.

From eq. 4.69b the pressure sensitivity of lengthwise piezoelectric elements is found to be proportional to the crystal thickness but inde-

---

[29] W. Guettner, "Underwater Crystal Microphone" (in German), *Z. angew. Phys.* *2* (1950), 206.

[30] For conversion to CGS units we use:

$$1 \text{ coulomb} = 1 \text{ watt/sec-volt} = 10^7 \text{ ergs/volt} = 3 \cdot 10^9 \text{ ergs/statvolt}$$

Hence $1 \text{ m/coulomb} = \tfrac{1}{3}10^{-7} \text{ (statvolt-cm/dyne-cm}^2) = 10^{-5} \text{ volt-cm/dyne}$

pendent of all other dimensions. By adjusting w we can therefore obtain the same sensitivity with elements made of different piezo-electric materials. The electric and mechanical impedance, however, are also of importance in a receiving device. The electric impedance determines the low-frequency cut-off. The mechanical impedance determines the upper limit of the flat response because of the resonance condition $\omega_0{}^2 = K/M$.

In practice the open-circuit condition for the electric terminals of a crystal receiver which had been assumed above cannot be maintained

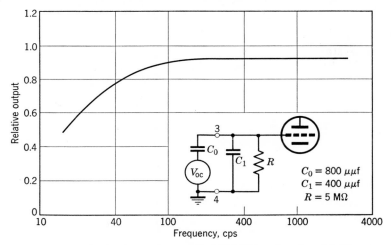

Fig. 4.23. Pressure sensitivity of barium titanate bender element (Courtesy of Gulton Mfg. Corp., Metuchen, N.J.).

because of cable or tube capacities. To account for this effect we must rearrange the equivalent circuit of Fig. 4.21. The equivalent electric current i that flows through the total impedance Z and across terminals 1 and 2 is: $i = \alpha u = \alpha F/Z_{\text{tot}}$, where, at low frequencies,

$$Z_{\text{tot}} = Z_{\text{mech}} + \alpha^2 Z_{\text{el}} = Z_R + j\left(\frac{K}{\omega} + \frac{\alpha^2}{\omega C_0}\right)$$

Across the terminals 3 and 4, then, a voltage $V_{\text{oc}} = i \cdot Z_{\text{el}}$ appears. The equivalent electric circuit that we have to consider in this case is then represented by a constant voltage source $V_{\text{oc}} = \alpha(F \cdot Z_{\text{el}}/Z_{\text{tot}})$ in series with the clamped electric impedance $Z_{\text{el}} = 1/\omega C_0$. The complete circuit of a crystal receiver loaded by cable and tube imped-ance is given in Fig. 4.23. Also shown is the effect of the shunt capacity C_1 on the low-frequency response of a barium titanate pick-up connected by a 400 $\mu\mu$f cable to a 5 megohm grid resistance. At the lower end of the response curve the sensitivity drops by about 3 db per octave.[30a]

If a crystal receiver for a given frequency band is to be made, the choice of the piezoelectric material depends largely on the desired microphone dimensions. Let us compare the relations for the important properties of a receiver element, namely, sensitivity, capacity, compliance and mass:

$$\text{force-sensitivity:} \quad \mathbf{K}_1/w$$

$$\text{capacity:} \quad \epsilon\epsilon_0 \frac{wl}{t}$$

$$\text{compliance:} \quad \frac{1}{Y_0} \frac{l}{tw}$$

$$\text{mass:} \quad \rho tlw$$

We see that it is possible to adjust for the three constants ϵ, Y_0, and ρ of different piezoelectric materials by varying the physical dimensions w, l, and t. We can thus attain the same frequency response with elements of Rochelle salt, ADP, barium titanate, or quartz; or we can get identical sensitivity and either the same low- or high-frequency cut-off with any of these materials if we have full freedom in the choice of the dimensions. Often, however, the element that has the smallest physical dimensions will be preferred.

Table 4.6 gives as an example the dimensions for three elements of approximately equal though arbitrarily chosen capacity, mass, and stiffness for operation as longitudinal expander bars.[31]

Table 4.6   Equal Impedance Piezoelectric Slabs

($C_0 = 0.0033$ μf; compliance = 1.57×10^{-7} m/newton)

	Rochelle Salt	ADP	Barium Titanate
l (cm)	1.5	1.2	1.4
w (cm)	1.0	8.7	0.4
t (cm)	0.03	0.004	0.03
V_{out} for 1 newton	9.2	2.1	1.1

Operation at resonance For certain applications, particularly in ultrasonics, the use of tuned receivers is desirable. The highest output is obtained if the operation takes place both at mechanical and at electric resonance. The former requires that the length or thickness of the transducer is a half wave at the receiving frequency.

[30a] See discussion accompanying Fig. 4.39.

[31] B. B. Bauer, *Radio-Electronic Eng.*, August 1948.

The latter requires a shunt inductance which cancels the capacitive reactance of both the crystal and the cable. Figure 4.24a shows the equivalent network for this case with $Z_{\text{mech}} = Z_R = \rho_0 cS$, and $Z_{\text{el}} = R_l r/(R_l + r)$, in which R_l is the amplifier input resistance and r is the electrical equivalent of all transducer losses. In order to determine the effect of the load Z_{el} on the voltage V generated by sound

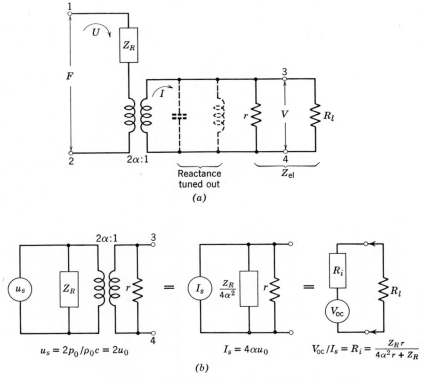

Fig. 4.24.   Equivalent circuits for tuned crystal receivers with losses.

waves of a pressure p_0 and incident on a receiver of area S, we have to specify an equivalent driving source.

Let us examine the effect of an open circuit ($G_{\text{el}} = 1/Z_{\text{el}} = 0$) on the mechanical side of the network of Fig. 4.24a: Both the current I in the electrical branch and the particle velocity U in the mechanical branch vanish. The transducer then behaves like a rigid reflector, which causes pressure doubling if its face is struck by a plane sound wave. The force in the mechanical source then has the value $F = 2p_0 S$, and instead of a constant-force generator in series with Z_R as in Fig. 4.24a, we can use a generator of constant velocity $u_s = F/Z_R = 2p_0/\rho_0 c$ in parallel with Z_R, as shown in Fig. 4.24b. If now a shunt is produced across the electric terminals ($Z_{el} = 0$), the crystal behaves like a soft reflector which doubles the particle velocity of the wave; hence we find for the strength of the constant velocity source $u_s = 2u_0$.

If we take the equivalent velocity source through the ideal transformer $2\alpha{:}1$ to the electrical side, it becomes a constant-current source $I_s = 4\alpha u_0$ (see eq. 4.32), as shown in Fig. 4.24b. This source, in turn, can be transformed into an equivalent voltage source of internal impedance $R_i = Z_R r/(4\alpha^2 r + Z_R)$ and open-circuit voltage

$$V_{oc} = (p_0 S/\alpha)/(1 + Z_R/4\alpha^2 r) \tag{4.70}$$

The voltage V developed across the terminals in the presence of the load resistance R_l then becomes

$$V = V_{oc} R_l/(R_i + R_l) \tag{4.70a}$$

and the pressure sensitivity of a resonant crystal receiver is found by combining eqs. 4.70 and 4.70a:

$$\frac{V}{p_0} = \frac{4\alpha/\rho_0 c}{1/R_l + 1/r + 4\alpha^2/Z_R} = \frac{4\alpha}{\rho_0 c G} \tag{4.70b}$$

in which $G = I_s/V$ is the total conductance connected to the current source I_s in Fig. 4.24b.

We shall now consider the condition for maximum power transfer from the transducer to the amplifier, as well as the attainable efficiency $\eta = W_l/W_0$ of conversion of power W_0 carried by the sound wave to power W_l delivered to R_l. From the discussion in Section 4.4 it follows that an ideal resonant transducer without losses ($r = \infty$), which is perfectly matched by providing a load resistance $R_l = \rho_0 c S/4\alpha^2$, becomes a perfect absorber, no energy being reflected from the crystal face.[32]

If losses are taken into account the matching condition for maximum power transfer to R_l is

$$\frac{1}{R_l} = \frac{1}{r} + \frac{4\alpha^2}{Z_R} \tag{4.71}$$

[32] Under these conditions the voltage generated in the transducer by the received energy leads to the emission of waves of equal amplitude and opposite phase as the reflected wave.   See W. G. Cady *A Generalized Theory of the Crystal Receiver for Plane Waves.*   ONR Contract N6 ONR-262 Task Order 1, November 20, 1950.

The power delivered to R_l is $W_l = V_{rms}^2/R_l$, which with eqs. 4.70 and 4.70a becomes $W_l = (I_s^2)_{rms}/R_lG^2$. Since $W_0 = (u_0^2)_{rms}Z_R$, we obtain for the efficiency

$$\eta = \frac{W_l}{W_0} = 4\frac{4\alpha^2/Z_R}{R_lG^2} \tag{4.72a}$$

If the matching condition of eq. 4.71 is fulfilled, we find an optimum efficiency which is controlled by r:

$$\eta_m = (1 + Z_R/4\alpha^2 r)^{-1} \tag{4.72b}$$

The voltage V_p developed across a transducer which is matched for optimum power transfer may then be obtained from $V = I_s/G$ and eq. 4.71. It is

$$V_p = \frac{1}{2}\frac{I_sZ_R/4\alpha^2}{(1 + Z_R/4\alpha^2 r)} = \frac{1}{2}\frac{p_0S/\alpha}{(1 + Z_R/4\alpha^2 r)} \tag{4.73}$$

A comparison between eqs. 4.73 and 4.70 shows that $V_p = \frac{1}{2}V_{oc}$. The relationships expressed in eqs. 4.70 to 4.73 are exemplified in Fig. 4.25 for a tuned assembly of ADP crystals. The curves plotted in this figure demonstrate the great importance of the loss resistance r for the transducer performance.

Matching of ADP receiver mosaic As an example, we give some data computed for a large underwater sound receiver consisting of 64 Z-cut ADP plates which form a mosaic with receiving area $S = 64$ cm^2. For an operating frequency of 40 kcps at the longitudinal mode the plate dimensions are $l_z = 4.1$ cm, $l_y = 2$ cm, $l_x = 0.5$ cm. The resulting values for the optimal efficiency η, the required load conductance $G_l = 1/R_l$ for maximum power transfer ($G_l = G_{Fmax}$), and the associated transducer voltage V_p for a given parallel loss resistance r are plotted in Fig. 4.25. The numbers on the ordinate are to be multiplied by the following factors, in which ξ is the input sound amplitude in meters:

Quantity	Symbol	Unit	Multiply by
Loss resistance	r	ohms	10^3
Load conductance for max. voltage	$G_{v_{max}}$	mhos	10^{-5}
Load conductance for max. power	$G_{p_{max}}$	mhos	10^{-5}
Open circuit voltage	V_{oc}	volts	$10^7 \times \xi$
Max. voltage	V_{max}	volts	$10^7 \times \xi$
Voltage for max. power	V_p	volts	$10^7 \times \xi$
Power for max. voltage	$P_{v_{max}}$	watts	$2 \cdot 10^{12} \times \xi^2$
Max. power	P_{max}	watts	$2 \cdot 10^{12} \times \xi^2$

Note that the power outputs are defined by the relationships $P_{v_{max}} = V_{max}^2 G_{v_{max}}/2$ and $P_{max} = V_p^2 G_{p_{max}}/2$.

From Fig. 4.25 we can also find the open circuit voltage V_{oc} as a function of the loss resistance for values of $r \leq Z_R/4\alpha^2$; and the required load conductance $G_{v\max}$ for a maximum attainable sensitivity $V/\rho_0 S = 1/2\alpha$, corresponding to the constant voltage $V_{\max}$ on the graph. This sensitivity can be attained if $r \geq Z_R/4\alpha^2$ and

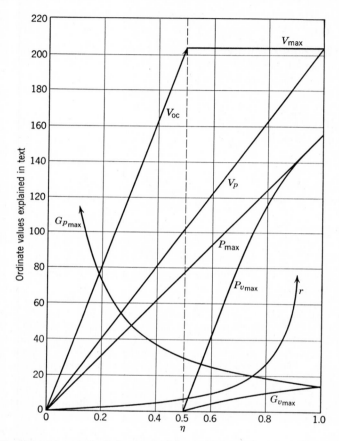

Fig. 4.25. Matching and efficiency of 40-kcps ADP receiver mosaic, according to W. G. Cady (see ref. in footnote 32).

is associated with a power output $P_{v\max}$. We note that in the absence of losses $(r = \infty)$ $G_{p\max}$ becomes equal to $G_{v\max}$, so that $P_{v\max} = P_{\max}$ and $V_p = V_{\max}$, which corresponds to an efficiency $\eta = 100\%$.

The matching of thickness-type receivers of quartz or barium titanate can be treated in an analogous manner, which will result in a similar plot.

There are two common methods for assembling piezoelectric stack mosaics which are widely used for underwater sending and receiving in the range between 20 and 60 kcps.[33]   Such assemblies may consist of stacks of half wave length slabs (Fig. 4.26a) which are cemented with their back faces on a pressure-release material such as Corprene or foam rubber.   Alternatively, stacks of quarter wavelength (Fig. 4.26b) can be cemented with their back faces to quarter-wave steel blocks.   The whole system will then resonate in a half-wave mode with a pressure maximum at the steel-crystal interface.   If the unit is used as a transmitter, the output of the quarter-wave system is limited by the strength of the cement layer.

The construction of an individual element is illustrated in Fig. 4.27. To prevent shorting of the crystal electrodes through the steel, an

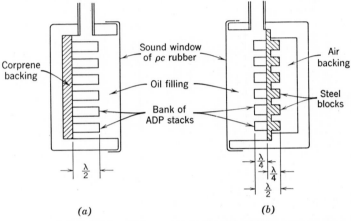

(a)   (b)

Fig. 4.26.   Multielement transducer.   (a) Half-wave stacks with pressure release backing.   (b) Quarter-wave stacks, steel backed.

insulating wafer of ceramic may be interposed between the crystal and the steel sections.   Electrodes are plated onto the faces of the individual slabs in the stack, and thin metal foils (usually gold plated) are glued to the electrodes for leads.   The slabs are glued to each other by Duco or Vulcalock cement.   In a complete assembly the number and thickness of crystals in each stack may vary in order to meet special directivity requirements.   Some of the principles involved in controlling the beam characteristics of such transducers are discussed in Section 5.9.

Because of their solubility in water, ADP and Rochelle salt crystals must be operated under oil, such as electrical-grade castor oil from

[33] Another promising technique uses arrays of large barium titanate tubes which are liquid filled.   The sound pressures are generated by a squirting action.   See Leon Camp, *J. Acoust. Soc. Am.*, *25* (1953), 297.

which air and water vapor have been removed.   The presence of the
oil also suppresses the onset of cavitation at the transducer faces.
The transducer case is sealed off from the surrounding water by a
sound-transparent window made of special rubber whose characteristic

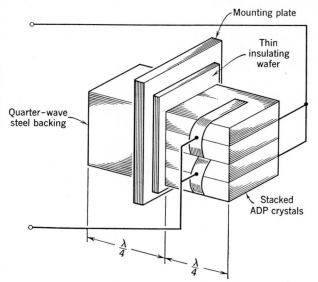

Fig. 4.27.   Design of quarter-wave ADP stack.

impedance ρc is matched to that of water in the normal temperature
range.

4.12   Multiple-Layer Transducers

Transducers operating in the frequency range 10^4–10^5 cps and having
large radiating surface area are generally composed of many elements
in a mosaic.   The dimensions of the surface are often ten to one
hundred times the wavelength, that is, up to several feet.   If quartz
is used, sufficiently large single slabs of the crystal are difficult to
produce uniformly and economically.   It is more practical to use
small mosaic elements of reasonable dimensions.   A large-area transducer using crystals with transverse field drive, such as 45° X-cut
Rochelle salt and 45° Z-cut ADP crystals, must be assembled as a
mosaic in order to provide properly spaced electrodes for the driving
voltage.   Magnetostriction transducers also are more economically
constructed as a mosaic of small stacks which lend themselves to mass
production and quality control.

The elements of a mosaic must be consolidated on a structural member that holds them firmly and maintains their alignment.   This function is served by a back plate or front plate or both.   These plates become an integral part of the vibrating system.   Their dimensions and materials are selected in such a way that the transducer as a whole will have the required values of resonance frequency, damping, and impedance as seen by the electric circuit.

At higher ultrasonic frequencies (above 10^5 cps) the use of a single piezoelectric slab becomes practicable.   For example, a quartz disc about 5 cm in diameter and 3 mm thick can be used to radiate at 1 mcps into water, where the wavelength will be about $\frac{1}{30}$ the diameter of the transducer.   Even in such cases, however, it is often useful, if not necessary, to use plates on one or both sides of the piezoelectric element to adjust the transducer characteristics.

In Section 4.11 we discuss the simplest cases of multiple-layer transducers[34] in which a single block is combined with a piezoelectric element to form a half-wave resonant system.   In the following paragraphs we discuss more general cases involving several plates and arbitrary impedance transformation.

Design of crystal sandwiches   The combination of a half-wave crystal and a half-wave plate is a simple form of a sandwich transducer. Such a system constitutes an elementary application of line theory as discussed in Chapter 2.   The load impedance of the crystal is transformed by the half-wave metal plate at a 1:1 ratio.   This mechanical load impedance in turn is transformed by the crystal into an electric input impedance.   In general, the electric input impedance will be determined by the transformer action of both the crystal and the plate.   The plate will also influence the shape of the frequency-response curve of the system.   If the plate is in resonance, the Q of the system is increased in proportion to the number of half wavelengths in the plate.   If the plate is not in resonance, the Q of the system will be reduced and will have its lowest value when the plate is a quarter-wave thick.   It is therefore possible to change the bandwidth of a transducer by proper choice of plate thickness.[35]

Both the half-wave and quarter-wave plates are simple cases in which a resistive load is transformed through the line as a pure resistance.   In all other cases a reactive component is introduced.   For a plate thinner than a quarter wave, the impedance becomes mass-like

---

[34] Similar considerations apply to magnetostriction transducers; see Section 5.7.

[35] W. G. Cady, *J. Acoust. Soc. Amer.*, *21* (1949), 65, has computed the Q of a 45° Z-cut ADP transducer with air backing that radiates through a Lucite diaphragm into sea water.   Without the diaphragm $Q = 5.9$; for a quarter-wave diaphragm $Q = 1.98$; for half-wave diaphragm $Q = 6.7$.

(inductive) and lowers the resonance frequency of the system. If the plate thickness is between quarter wave and half wave, the impedance becomes stiffness-like (capacitive) and raises the resonance frequency of the system.

Through a quarter-wave plate the resistive load impedance is transformed according to the ratio $(\rho_p c_p)^2/\rho_0 c_0$, in which the subscripts p and 0 refer to the plate and load, respectively. The crystal itself looks into a changed load impedance which depends on the characteristic impedance $\rho_p c_p$ of the quarter-wave plate. The electric input impedance, finally, is determined by the load (acoustic) impedance, taken through the electromechanical transformer of $1:\alpha$ equivalent turns ratio.

The question arises whether it is possible to obtain a suitable electric input impedance for any given acoustic load impedance and frequency by an adjustment of the transmission-line sections represented by a crystal and a plate. Such a procedure involves the use of the hyperbolic functions discussed in Chapter 2. Langevin gave the first description of a device[36] designed in this manner. He recognized that a quartz crystal transducer at frequencies below 100 kcps would have to be more than 2.8 cm thick for resonance and this thickness would necessitate excessively high driving voltages in order to obtain sufficient field strength for the desired sound intensity. From Fig. 4.4 we see that the impedance of such a transducer would be several megohms. Langevin showed that the impedance can be considerably reduced by a vibrating system consisting of a sandwich[37] composed of a thin quartz wafer cemented between two steel plates. He also showed that the power factor of this device is optimal if the front plate has quarter-wave thickness and if the quartz layer and the back plate follow the relationship

$$\tan \frac{2\pi d_m}{\lambda_m} \cdot \tan \frac{2\pi d_b}{\lambda_b} = \frac{\rho_m c_m}{\rho_b c_b} \tag{4.74}$$

where the indices m and b refer to quartz and back plate, respectively, and where d is the thickness of the layer. Equation 4.74 is easily obtained if one specifies the following requirements: We have seen above that the value of the electric input impedance depends on the transformation factor α. We recall that

$$R_e = Z_R/4\alpha^2$$

[36] P. Langevin, Brit. Pat. 145,691, (1921).
[37] See U.S. Pat. 2,427,348, September 16, 1947, by W. C. Bond and W. P. Mason.

where α is equal to $e_{hj}S/l$.   In order to obtain a small input impedance, α must be made as large as possible by choosing the crystal thickness l as small as possible.   The crystal layer itself then becomes stiffness controlled, and its motional impedance has a large capacitive reactance. In order to keep the power factor large, this reactive component must be canceled.

If the steel front plate is given quarter-wave thickness the low impedance of the load is transformed into a very high impedance at the interface between the crystal and the front plate.   In a first approximation we can assume the crystal to be clamped (infinite impedance) at this interface.   In this case there appears at its opposite face a reactance: $-\rho_m c_m \tan [k_m d_m + \pi/2]$.   This reactance is to be canceled by the reactance of the backing plate.   Owing to the air load on the other side of this place the impedance at the interface between the backing plate and crystal is simply $\rho_b c_b \tan (k_b d_b)$.   For cancellation of reactances these two expressions must be added and set equal to zero.   The result is eq. 4.74.

A sample design of a Langevin sandwich is as follows: A quartz-steel transducer resonant at 40 kcps would have an outer plate of 3-cm thickness, a quartz wafer of 1.5-cm thickness, and a back plate of 0.6-cm thickness.

Electric input impedance of sandwich transducers   Figure 4.28 gives different examples of quartz transducer sandwiches providing different degrees of impedance transformation.   The calculated electric input impedances at 800, 400, and 200 kcps, and the relative pressure distribution within the vibrating system are given for water load and air backing.   In the case of quartz transducers of radiating area smaller than 10^2 cm and at frequencies below 3 mcps, it is often desirable to be able to reduce the electric input impedance in order to improve matching.   This, however, applies only for narrow band operation and if the power transfer must be optimized.   Sandwich transducers of low input impedance have a high Q and are not suitable for transmission of short pulses.

In Fig. 4.28 the first example (a) represents a half-wave plate, which has already been discussed above.   Example b shows the Langevin-type sandwich.   We see that the pressure amplitude P within the system reaches much higher values than in example a and, in fact, is about twenty-six times higher in one interface and thirty-one times higher in the other interface than in the radiating surface of the transducer.[38]   This high interface pressure imposes

[38] K. von Sanden, Doctor's thesis, Technische Hochschule, Hanover, Germany (1950).

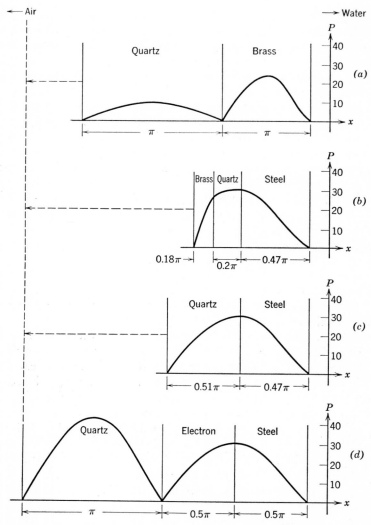

Fig. 4.28. Pressure distribution within 4 types of quartz sandwich transducers (ordinate: internal pressure relative to pressure at radiating face; abscissa: $2\pi d/\lambda$).

Electric input impedance of sandwich in kilohms ($S = 11$ cm^2)

Frequency, kcps	a	b	c	d
800	170	8	17	0.6
400	680	33	68	2.2
200	2720	132	272	8.8

severe requirements on the cement used to bind the faces together
when sound intensities above 1 watt/cm^2 are generated.   Many available cements do not withstand such high pressure for long periods
of time.

Let us consider only the case of a thin quartz wafer for which $k_m d_m$
is about equal to $\pi/5$.   We then obtain for the electric impedance of
this Langevin-type sandwich (b)

$$R_e \approx \frac{1.2}{4\alpha^2} Z_R \qquad\qquad (4.75)$$

and the following approximate dimensions can be used:

$$d_m \approx \lambda/10 \qquad \text{quartz wafer}$$

$$d_d \approx \lambda/4.3 \qquad \text{front plate}$$

$$d_b \approx \lambda/11 \qquad \text{back plate}$$

The third example (c) shows a combination of quartz and steel, both
of which are almost quarter-wave thick.   Computations show that
in this case the optimum power factor is obtained if the quartz layer
is just slightly thicker than the steel layer.   In this transducer, the
pressure at the interface also is very high, which may be a limitation
when high pressures have to be generated at the radiating surface.

In example c the approximate value for the electric input impedance
at resonance is:

$$R_e \simeq \frac{1}{4\alpha^2} Z_R \left[4\frac{m_1^2 - 1}{m_1^4} \right] \qquad (4.76a)$$

where $m_1 = \rho_d c_d / \rho_m c_m$, which must be larger than $\sqrt{2}$.[39]   Here the
impedance is reduced both by the increase of the transformation
factor α (by a factor of about 2); and by the bracketed term in the
equation, which represents a transformation of the mechanical load
impedance.   If a quarter-wave steel plate is used, the bracketed term
has a value of about 0.39; the combined result is an over-all reduction
of R_e by a factor of 10.

Example d shows a sandwich consisting of an air-backed $\lambda/2$ quartz
crystal with two transforming line sections in front, each a quarter-
wave thick.   In this case the load impedance is taken through a
quarter-wave steel plate, transforming it into a very high impedance,
which in turn is taken through a quarter-wave plate of a lightweight
aluminum alloy, transforming it to an impedance considerably lower

[39] The significance of the $\sqrt{2}$ condition is discussed in Section 4.7.

than the original load impedance at the face of the half-wave quartz crystal.

The electric input impedance of such a transducer has a value:

$$R_e \simeq \frac{1}{4\alpha^2} Z_R (\rho_2 c_2 / \rho_1 c_1)^2 \qquad (4.76b)$$

where the subscripts 1 and 2 refer to the face plate and middle plate, respectively.

If a steel-Polystyrene-quartz combination of the above-mentioned dimensions is used the bracket factor will have the approximate value 3.4×10^{-3}. Since α is not changed, the input impedance is reduced only by this factor.

For a sandwich combination of quartz and steel resonating at 800 kcps and radiating from one face of 11-cm^2 area, the resulting electric input impedances are in a, 170 kilohms; in b, 8.2 kilohms; in c, 17 kilohms; and in d, 600 ohms. These calculations assume a perfect cement of high strength and no losses. In all the examples the reactances of the transforming layers cancel out so that the motional impedance becomes resistive at resonance.

The four cases discussed here are special applications of the line theory discussed in Chapter 2. It is apparent that the equations for the electric input impedance contain two terms: one for the electromechanical transformation and the other for the mechanical impedance transformation. Useful approximations can often be obtained from simple physical considerations involving quarter- or half-wave transformation-line sections.[40]

We shall now discuss design criteria for a close-coupled transmission system that can be tuned over a wide frequency range. If the loading medium has a much lower acoustic impedance than the transducer element the condition for resonance can be stated on the basis of the same considerations which led to Eq. 4.74 above as:

$$\tan \gamma_m + \tan \alpha_b = 0$$

or

$$\gamma_m + \alpha_b = n\pi$$

$$(4.77a)$$

where $\gamma_m = \omega_n d_m / c_m$ can be obtained from the significant crystal dimension d_m,[41] c_m is the sound velocity in the crystal, and ω_n is the

---

[40] Computation charts for the general case of three-layer sandwiches can be found in W. J. Fry, J. M. Taylor, and B. W. Henvis, *Design of Crystal Vibrating Systems*, Dover Publications, New York, 1948. A more detailed analysis has been given by K. von Sanden, Doctor's thesis, Technische Hochschule, Hanover, 1950.

[41] The dimension d_m is always taken normal to the radiating crystal face. For quartz and barium titanate, d_m is the plate thickness; for ADP and Rochelle salt d_m is the plate length.

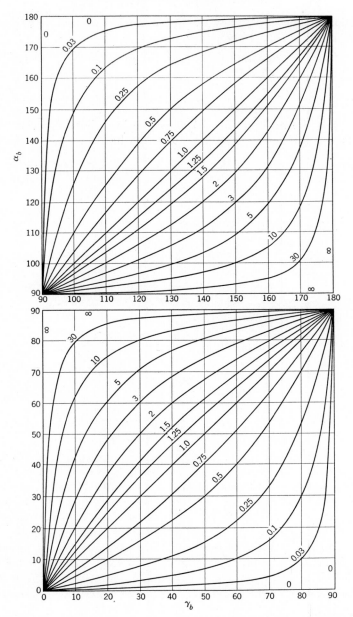

Fig. 4.29. Relationship $\alpha_b = f(\gamma_b)$ for the backing of sandwich transducers (W. J. Fry et al.).

desired resonance frequency of the system.   For the second term in eq. 4.77a line theory gives:

$$\tan \alpha_b = \frac{\rho_b c_b}{\rho_m c_m} \tan \left(\frac{\omega_n d_b}{c_b} \right) \qquad (4.77b)$$

$$= m \tan \gamma_b$$

where m is the ratio of the characteristic impedances of the backing and the crystal, and γ_b is the quantity that has to be determined.   To

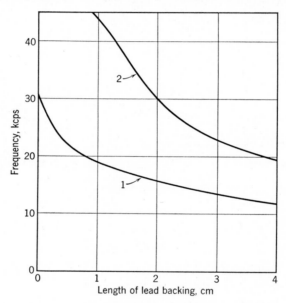

Fig. 4.30.   Resonance frequencies of lead-backed ADP.

find the length (or thickness) $d_b = \gamma_b c_b / \omega_n$ of the backing material to give resonance at ω_n, we first determine α_b from eq. 4.77a and then γ_b from eq. 4.77b.   The relationship between α_b and γ_b expressed in eq. 4.77b is plotted in Fig. 4.29 with the impedance ratio m as parameter.   The rapid rise of the curves for small γ_b and large impedance ratios indicates a rapid lowering of resonance frequency for small thicknesses of backing material of high characteristic impedance. Near the center of the graph is a region in which the resonance frequency is relatively insensitive to changes in length of the backing material.

This procedure can be used to resonate a given crystal at frequencies other than the harmonics of the crystal itself, by providing a backing of suitable material and dimensions. For example, Fig. 4.30 gives the resonance frequencies obtainable with a system consisting of a 5-cm ADP bar backed with a lead block ($\rho_b c_b = 14.2 \times 10^6$ kg/m^2/sec) of arbitrary length.[42] The upper curve shows the second resonance of the composite system, which cannot be excited if the length of the backing block goes to zero.

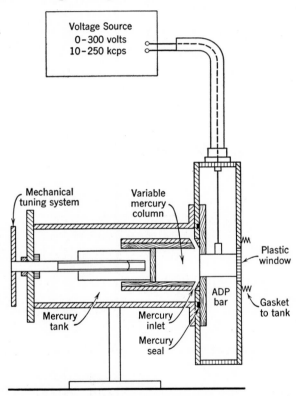

Fig. 4.31.   Variable-frequency transducer, according to W. J. Fry.

Figure 4.31 shows another system[43] using mercury ($\rho c = 19.8 \times 10^6$ kg/m^2/sec) as backing medium for a 90-kcps stacked ADP transducer. The length of the liquid column can be adjusted by moving a piston of pressure-release material in the mercury.   To provide good mechanical contact between the crystal and the mercury, a coupling layer of silver-palladium alloy is glued to the ADP and is wetted by the mer-

[42] W. J. Fry, J. M. Taylor, and B. W. Henvis, *op. cit.* p. 16 (see footnote 40).
[43] W. J. Fry, R. B. Fry, and W. Hall, *J. Acoust. Soc. Amer.*, *23* (1951), 94.   See also U.S. Pat. 2,507,770, May 16, 1950, by H. H. Claassen.

cury.   The frequency variability of such a system is shown in Fig. 4.32.
Over a frequency range of 1 octave the output power varies about
20 db if the system is driven at constant voltage.

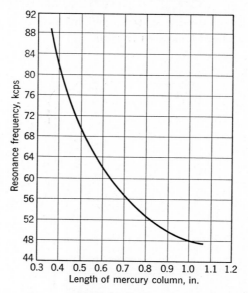

Fig. 4.32.   Range covered by variable-frequency transducer.

4.13   Non-Directional Cylindrical Receivers

In this section we consider some special properties of non-directional
receivers.   Complete non-directionality can be obtained by using a
spherical transducer smaller than the wave length.   However, a
cylindrical uniformity of response is often sufficient.   Small cylinders
of barium titanate ceramic[44] have proved useful for many types of
sonic measurements.

The dimensions of these cylinders are determined by the frequency
range in which a flat response is desired.   The upper limit of the flat
range is given by the lowest vibrational mode.   There are three possible fundamental modes of vibration in a cylinder, as shown in
Fig. 4.33.

1. *Length mode.*   Its fundamental resonance frequency is determined essentially by the length of the cylinder.   The vibrating tube
becomes longer and shorter.

2. *Radial mode.*   Its fundamental resonance frequency is deter-

[44] Brush Development Company, *Tech. Bull.* E-104.

mined essentially by the tube diameter.   The vibrating tube becomes larger and smaller in diameter.

3. *Wall-thickness mode.*   Its fundamental resonance is determined essentially by the wall thickness.   The vibrating wall becomes thicker and thinner.

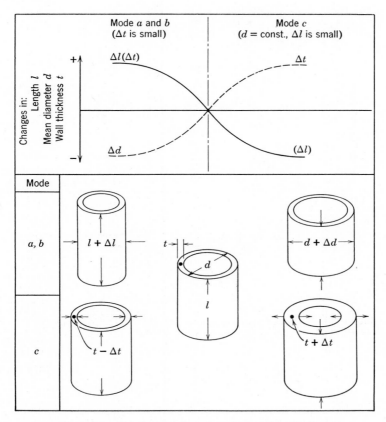

Fig. 4.33.   Fundamental modes of ceramic cylinders.

There is considerable coupling between the length mode and the radial mode, while the thickness mode is relatively independent of the other two modes.   Above the critical region ($l/d \simeq 1.5$) where largest coupling occurs, the radial resonance frequency of a long tube is approximately

$$f_r \simeq \frac{1}{\pi d_m} \sqrt{\frac{Y_0}{(1 - \sigma^2)\rho}} \qquad (4.78)$$

in which d_m is the mean diameter of the tube, Y_0 is Young's modulus, σ is Poisson's ratio, and ρ is density.[45] For barium titanate the product $f_r d_m \simeq 1.43$ kcps × meters (56.5 kcps × inches). In Fig. 4.34 this product is plotted against the ratio l/d_m for both the radial mode and the length mode of barium titanate tubes surrounded with

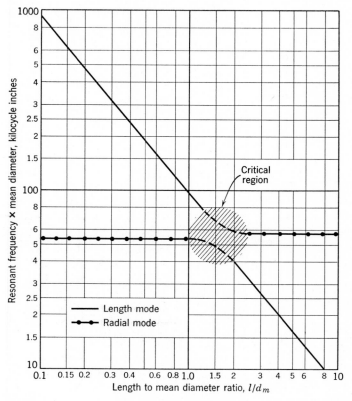

Fig. 4.34. Resonant frequencies of the fundamental length and radial modes for ceramic cylinders (multiply ordinate by 2.54×10^{-2} to obtain kilocycle meters).

water and filled with air. Liquid-filled cylinders that are of interest in liquid flow processing are discussed in Chapter 7.

[45] For a pulsating thin hollow sphere the fundamental resonance frequency is:

$$f_s = \frac{2}{\pi d_m} \sqrt{\frac{Y_0}{2(1 - \sigma)\rho}} = \sqrt{\frac{\mu}{\rho} \frac{1 + \sigma}{1 - \sigma}}$$

See also A. E. H. Love, *The Mathematical Theory of Elasticity*, Dover Publications, New York, 1944, p. 286.

Since a uniform outside pressure causes both radial and tangential stresses in a cylinder, both piezoelectric constants d_{33} and d_{31} are involved. Because these constants have opposite signs, the charges generated by the two kinds of stresses in the polarized ceramic partly cancel each other. The degree of cancellation depends on the thickness-to-diameter ratio. Figure 4.35 shows the dependence of the

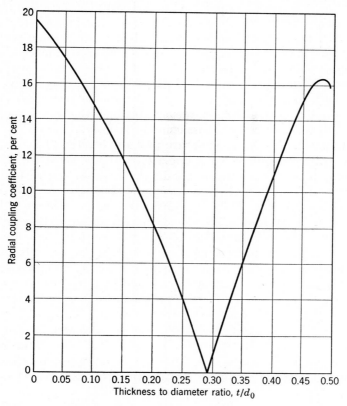

Fig. 4.35.   Radial coupling coefficient of barium titanate cylinders.

coupling coefficient k (for the radial mode) on the ratio t/d_0, in which d_0 is the outer tube diameter. Between $t/d_0 = 0.22$ and 0.35 the response is very poor, owing to the cancellation effect.[45a]

A sample design for a cylindrical receiver is as follows: outer diameter 2.8 cm, length 5.5 cm, and wall thickness 0.4 cm. The resulting coupling coefficient is about 12 per cent; the sensitivity is about -115 db ref 10 volt/newton/m^2 (ref 1 volt/dyne/cm^2); and the response is

[45a] R. A. Langevin, *J. Acoust. Soc. Amer.*, 26 (1954), 421.

substantially flat up to 35 kcps.   In the final assembly the cylindrical element may be covered with a pressure-molded neoprene sheath which is bonded to the cylinder surface and to the neoprene jacket of the cable.   Units designed along these lines have found useful applications in geophysical and underwater sound studies.

Extremely small probes of millimeter dimensions may be required for detailed studies of complicated sound fields or for measurements at ultrasonic frequencies to several megacycles.   In such probes the sensitive element may be much smaller than its supporting structure. Special care must then be exercised to keep the sound intercepted by the support sufficiently insulated from the sensitive element.   The required amount of reduction depends on the uniformity of the sound field.   As a rule, the insulation should be about 20 db greater than the maximum range of pressure levels to which the element and any parts of the structure are exposed simultaneously.

A sample design[46] of a miniature probe is illustrated in Fig. 4.36. The sensitive element is a barium titanate tube of outer diameter $\frac{1}{16}$ in., wall thickness 0.012 in., and length $\frac{1}{16}$ in.   Silver electrodes are fired on its inner and outer cylindrical surfaces.   The tube is supported on a No. 24 Formex-insulated copper wire which also serves as a central lead.   The element is positioned on this wire with two minute latex rubber washers.   The washers provide a compliant support against which the element can contract, and they also provide some degree of acoustic insulation against vibrations which may exist in the central wire.   Electric connection to the inner electrode is made by four 0.0005-in.-diameter platinum wires.   The different components are held together by Duco cement.   A space of approximately $\frac{1}{36}$ in. is maintained between the element and the end of the supporting tube.   This space is partially filled with latex rubber. The non-conducting surfaces are painted with a graphite suspension, and the whole tip is electroplated with copper to a thickness of approximately 0.0005 in.   The supporting structure itself is insulated to minimize acoustic pick-up.   As seen in Fig. 4.36, there is an outer metal tube that is separated from the inner tube by a layer of Fiberglas.

Calibration Procedures.   The absolute calibration of microphones (or hydrophones) over a wide frequency range can be accomplished on the basis of the general electro-acoustic mesh equations discussed in Section 5.1 (eqs. 5.4a and 5.4b).   The required procedures are quite elaborate: they may involve considerable test facilities to provide for free field conditions (anechoic rooms, or tanks), or special

[46] Pennsylvania State College, *Final Report on Atmospheric Physics* (1950), by H. Schilling et al.

equipment such as small closed pressure chambers.   Some techniques call for the use of two test transducers (a reversible transducer and a source), in addition to the microphone to be calibrated.[46a]   It is therefore recommended for those, who are primarily interested in the industrial applications of sonics, to calibrate their receiving elements by comparison with a secondary standard.   In this case, the receiver to be tested is compared by a substitution method in a well-defined sound field and for each particular frequency with one of the commercially available standard microphones.[46b]   The choice of such a

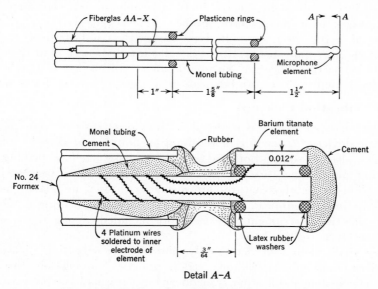

Fig. 4.36.   Design of small barium titanate probe.

standard depends on the desired frequency range and on the medium in which the calibration is to be performed.

At ultrasonic frequencies above 200 kcps the calibration techniques described above become increasingly difficult since no commercial standards are available.   In this range, then, an indirect calibration against a radiation pressure-type indicator (see Section 2.12) or a

[46a] L. L. Foldy and H. Primakoff, *J. Acoust. Soc. Amer.* *17* (1945), 109, and *19* (1947) 50.   A general discussion of the reciprocity technique of calibration is given by L. L. Beranek "Acoustic Measurements," John Wiley & Sons, New York, 1949, Chapter 4.

[46b] Suitable standard microphones for use in gases are, for example, the Western Electric type 640-AA and the Brush Model BL-4111; for use in liquids the Brush Hydrophone BM-101 and the Massa M-101.

pulse reflection technique[46c] must be used.   Calibration by the above
mentioned substitution method of small cylindrical receivers of the
type shown in Fig. 4.36 have shown that the response from 10 to 100
kcps is flat within 1 db at a sensitivity of −143 db ref 1 volt/dyne/
cm². The useful range extends up to 900 kcps, where the first radial
resonance occurs.   Above 100 kcps, however, corrections must be
applied for diffraction effects and for circumferential variations in
sensitivity of the element.

Electrokinetic Hydrophones   Wherever very low-frequency response is a requirement, electrokinetic hydrophones have considerable
advantages over piezoelectric probes.   Their sensitivity is of the
order of −100 db ref 1 volt/dyne/cm² with a cut-off near 1 cps.
Their thermal noise below 10 cps is substantially lower than that for
piezoelectric transducers.   No preamplifiers are needed so that electrokinetic hydrophones can be operated at great depths under water.[47]

4.14   Vibration Pick-ups

The instruments we considered in previous sections were piezoelectric devices for sending or receiving in liquids and gases.   Sonics
applies also to solids, both in processing tasks such as drilling or
cutting, and in analytical endeavors such as geophysical prospecting.
Vibrations in solid structures are also encountered in related fields
such as instrumentation and vibration-control engineering.   Vibra-
tion-detecting instruments are therefore included among the special
tools analyzed in this book.

We shall discuss in detail only piezoelectric vibration pick-ups.
Devices employing resistance strain gauges, moving-coil electrodynamic systems, and other transducer mechanisms have been extensively used in the past, and there is considerable literature on their
properties.[47a]   Developments since 1949 in artificial piezoelectric
materials have widened the possibilities for their application to many
specialized and difficult measurements.

[46c] In this so-called "self-reciprocity" technique, the transducer is caused to
emit short pulses which are reflected from a perfect reflecting surface and, in turn,
received by the same element.   See E. L. Carstensen, *J. Acoust. Soc. Amer.* **19**
(1947) 961.

[47] For details see E. V. Hardway, *Instruments*, **26** (1953), 1186, and U.S. Pats.
2,615,940, 2,644,901, and 2,661,930 issued to the Beta Corporation, Richmond,
Virginia.   The underlying physical mechanisms of these transducers are discussed
in Chapter 6, Section 6.

[47a] For a general reference see: H. C. Roberts, *Mechanical Measurements by
Electrical Methods*, 2nd edition, Instruments Publication Company, 1951.   Useful
data on strain gauges are given in *Bull.* 279, 279a, and 279b of the Baldwin-Lima-
Hamilton Corporation, Philadelphia, Pennsylvania.

Let us start with a simple pick-up consisting of a reactangular block of piezoelectric material, suitably fastened on one face to a base plate which can be placed against the vibrating solid. The block can be a single slab or a stack of several slabs of material, with electrodes and connections for taking off the electric signals. Let the block (see Fig. 4.37) have a length l, cross-sectional area S, density ρ_m, and sound velocity c_m. The upper half of the block then has a mass $M = \rho_m l S/2$. The lower half can be considered to be a "spring" of mechanical stiffness $K = 2\rho_m c_m^2 S/l$. These values for M and K were found to be low-frequency approximations for a transmission line (See Equ. 4.37a).

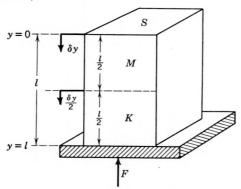

Fig. 4.37.   Inertia-driven vibration pick-up.

A force F (which in general will be a vibrating force $F_0 e^{j\omega t}$) is applied vertically to the base and thereby accelerates the pick-up. During acceleration the piezoelectric block contracts or expands along its length. Let the total change in length be δy at any instant. In general, $\delta y = y_0 e^{j\omega t}$; the corresponding change in length of the lower half is therefore $\delta y/2$. At the midplane there is a dynamic balance of forces (inertia against stiffness) given by: $Ma = -K\delta y/2$, in which $a = A_0 e^{j\omega t}$ is the acceleration of the mass of the upper half. In this approximate derivation we neglect the change in length of the upper half when considering it as a lumped mass, and we ignore the (small) difference between its acceleration and that of the base at the point of application of the force.

Next we relate the strain $\delta y/l$ to the open-circuit voltage $V = V_0 e^{j\omega t}$ produced across the piezoelectric element. The necessary transformations are given in eq. 4.1 and 4.14, and in the discussion under Section 4.11 leading to eq. 4.66. The result is:

$$V = k_c^2 F/\alpha = k_c^2 \rho_m c_m^2 S\delta y/\alpha l = h_{ik}\delta y \qquad (4.79)$$

in which k_c is the coupling coefficient, α is the transformation ratio, and h_{ik} is the piezoelectric constant defined in eq. 4.14.

One way to express the vibration sensitivity of this device is to give the ratio of the generated voltage V to the applied acceleration a. This ratio is obtained directly from the above equations for M, K, dynamic balance, and V_0, and is:

$$\frac{V}{a} = \frac{V_0}{A_0} = -\frac{k_c^2 \rho_m l S}{2\alpha} = -\frac{h_{ik} l^2}{2 c_m^2} \text{ volts·sec}^2/\text{m} \qquad (4.80)$$

The minus sign in eq. 4.80 makes the voltage 180° out of phase with the acceleration if the constants are positive. Actually, h_{ik} can be either positive or negative depending on the kind of material.

The above derivation is a much simplified demonstration of the essential physics involved. The sensitive element is "free" everywhere except along the one face that is driven by the vibration. Therefore the only possible reaction is one of inertia, and we call this device an *inertia accelerometer*. The latter word indicates that the response to acceleration is independent of frequency, as we see from eq. 4.80. In fact, this result also says that there is a response at zero frequency; a continuous acceleration of the element in one direction produces a continuous deformation and hence a voltage.

Transmission-line analysis Strictly speaking, both the mass and the stiffness are uniformly distributed throughout the pick-up element (if it is a block of uniform area), and we must apply a wave analysis to obtain a rigorous expression for the response at all frequencies. We can use the transmission-line theory in Chapter 2. Let the line be terminated at $y = 0$ (see Fig. 4.37) by the surface S which looks into free space. We assume the termination impedance is $Z_0 = 0$, corresponding to zero radiation from the free surface. We also assume the line is lossless, and that its cross-sectional dimensions are much less than $\lambda/2$ at the driving frequencies.

The impedance at any position y along the line then is $Z_y = j\rho_m c_m \tan (ky)$, and the particle displacement in the compressional waves becomes $Y_y = y_0 \cos (ky)$. The difference between the displacements at $y = 0$ and at $y = l$ then is:

$$\delta y = Y_0 - Y_l = Y_l \left[\frac{1}{\cos (kl)} - 1 \right]$$

The acceleration at the input, $y = l$, is $a_l = -\omega^2 Y_l$, for sinusoidal motion. Substituting this for Y_l in the above equation we obtain:

$$\delta y = \frac{a_l}{\omega^2} \left[1 - \frac{1}{\cos (kl)} \right] \qquad (4.81)$$

We now put this value of δy into eq. 4.79 and obtain:

$$\frac{V}{a_l} = \frac{h_{ik}}{\omega^2}\left[1 - \frac{1}{\cos\,(kl)}\right]\;(\text{volts/m/sec}^2 \qquad (4.82)$$

This gives correctly the response of the inertia accelerometer at all frequencies for which the cross-sectional dimensions are much less than a wavelength, except in the vicinity of the longitudinal resonances. At these resonances eq. 4.82, gives an infinite value of voltage response, whereas the output is actually finite and is limited by the internal damping of the transducer material. The lowest longitudinal resonance occurs at $f_1 = c/4l$, where the line is a quarter wavelength long. When the lateral dimensions exceed a quarter wave there is

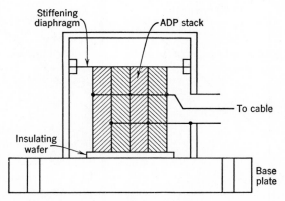

Fig. 4.38.   ADP accelerometer (Massa Laboratories, Hingham, Mass.).

considerable coupling between lateral and longitudinal vibrations, and the device is no longer useful as a simple accelerometer.

At very low frequencies eq. 4.82 reduces to eq. 4.80, which gives the "static response." At $\frac{1}{5}$ the fundamental resonance frequency the response is up about 4 per cent and at $\frac{3}{5}$ it is up about 60 per cent or 4 db. In practice the response drops off at low frequencies, owing to the fact that the electric reactance of the pick-up is very high relative to its low resistance and the input impedance of the amplifier. The low-frequency cut-off may also be influenced by temperature effects.

Commercial accelerometers A commercial example[48] of the inertia accelerometer is shown in Fig. 4.38. It contains a stack of

[48] Massa Laboratories, Hingham, Mass. For a discussion on accelerometer calibration see also M. Harrison, A. L. Sykes, and P. G. Marcotte, *J. Acoust. Soc. Amer.*, *24* (1952), 384.

45° Z-cut ADP slabs as the sensitive element.   At its free end the
stack is cemented to a thin membrane which suppresses flexural
vibrations.   The element will then respond only to that component
of an acceleration which is parallel to its axis.   In industrial vibration

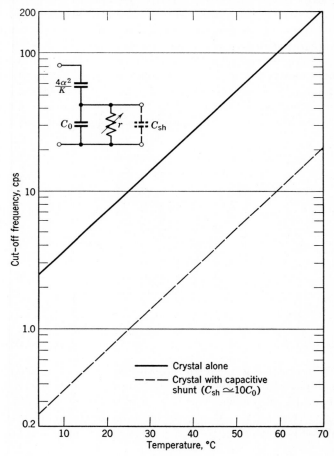

Fig. 4.39.   Low-frequency cut-off of ADP element.   (Courtesy of Massa Laboratories).

studies often three such elements at right angles to each other are
combined to determine the space vector of the acceleration.   The
acceleration response is essentially flat from 20 cps to 20 kcps, and
the fundamental (quarter-wave) resonance is at 23 kcps.   Internal
damping in the crystal limits the resonance peak so the response is
flatter than would be given by eq. 4.82 in which damping is ignored.

The low frequency cut-off of ADP elements depends on temperature since the electric loss resistance r of this material decreases with temperature and the cut-off is determined by $X = r$, as shown in Fig. 4.39. If a loss in sensitivity can be tolerated, the cut-off frequency can be lowered by adding a shunt capacity C_{sh}. This is indicated in Fig. 4.39 by the dashed line where $C_{sh} \simeq 10C_0$.

Similar considerations apply to barium titanate accelerometers of the type shown in Fig. 4.40. The sensitivity of the element increases with l/S, the ratio of thickness to cross-sectional area of the ceramic disc. This ratio cannot be made indefinitely large, however, because

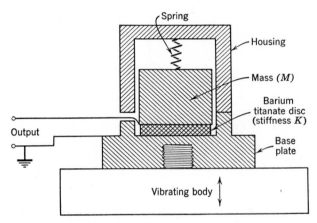

Fig. 4.40.   Barium titanate accelerometer (Gulton A-403).

a wide band of operation calls for high stiffness $K = Y_0 S/l$ to keep the resonance frequency $\omega = \sqrt{K/M}$ high, and for high capacity $C_0 = \epsilon\epsilon_0 S/l$ to move the cut-off to low frequencies. With barium titanate, the loss resistance r is much higher than the input resistance R_e of the amplifier. In this case no shunt capacitance, with its inherent sensitivity loss, is required to lower the cut-off frequency. Instead, one can increase the effective value of R_e by the use of a cathode follower circuit. One such circuit,[49] shown in Fig. 4.41, provides an input resistance $R_e = 100$ megohms. For a capacity of the ceramic disc of 0.0015 μf, a 3-db cut-off point of 1.2 cps is obtained. The sensitivity of a typical barium titanate accelerometer is 10 mv/g, over a useful linear range from 0.03 to 600 g.

[49] A. K. Guttwein and A. K. Dranetz, *Electronics*, October 1951, p. 123.   See also Acoustics Lab., Pa. State College, *Final Report on Atmospheric Physics and Sound Propagation*, September 1950.

Bimorph crystal pick-ups Vibrations in the audible frequency range can be detected by bender elements called *Bimorphs*.[50] These elements consist of two thin plates of Rochelle salt or ADP, cemented together; or of two thin (0.01-in.) strips of barium titanate soldered flat onto each side of a thin metal sheet. If the piezoelectric axes of the two crystal plates or ceramic strips are in opposite direction to each other, the voltages set up across each section by bending will add. We see from Fig. 4.42*a* that the upper section becomes thinner and the lower section thicker if a force is applied to the free end of the

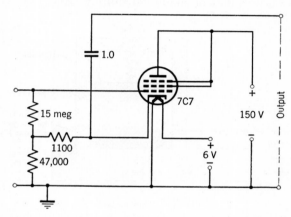

Fig. 4.41.   Cathode follower circuit for reducing low-frequency cut-off.

cantilever bar. Figure 4.42*b* shows another method, clamping at three points, which is used for Bimorph twister elements. Such elements are used widely in Rochelle salt microphones for the audio range. Figure 4.42*c* demonstrates still another type of mounting, where both ends of the double strip are supported while the force is applied in the center.[51]

In Table 4.7 are summarized the design data for three types of Bimorph elements. The first element consists of a plate formed by two thin square crystal slabs of Rochelle salt supported at three corners and driven at the free corner to give a twisting strain. The element is mounted on three thin rubber pads cemented to the crystal. These

[50] The name *Bimorph* is a registered trade mark of the Brush Development Company. A detailed analysis of Bimorph characteristics is given by S. Honda in *Sci. Repts.* Tohoku Univ. (Japan), Series B, *3* (1952), p. 96.

[51] A new type of ceramic pick-up using a thin-walled oval-section barium titanate tube is described in U.S. Pat. 2,596,494, June 12, 1948, by T. E. Lynch. For a brief description see *J. Acoust. Soc. Amer.*, *24* (1952), 806.

Table 4.7 Design Data for Bimorph Pick-up Elements

Crystal Element type	Rochelle Salt Square twister plate	ADP Square torque plate	Barium Titanate Bender strip
Electrode connection	Series	Series	Series
Support	At 3 corners	At 3 corners	At both ends
Drive	At free corner	At free corner	At center
Coupling factor k_c	54%	29%	12%
Transformer ratio* α	$1.87\,t$ coulomb/m	$0.136\,t$ coulomb/m	$8.6\,\dfrac{tw}{l}$ coulomb/m
Compliance* $1/K$	$4.5 \times 10^{-10} l^2/t^3 m$/newton	$4.4 \times 10^{-10} l^2/t^3$ m/newton	$2.5 \times 10^{-12} l^3/t^3 w$ m/newton
Effective mass M	$2.5 \times 10^2 l^2 t$ kg	$2.4 \times 10^2 l^2 t$ kg	$2 \times 10^3 lwt$ kg
Static capacity C_0	$1.76 \times 10^{-9} l^2/t$ farad (at 27°C)	$1.27 \times 10^{-10} l^2/t$ farad	$1.3 \times 10^{-8} tw/t$ farad

* In the technical bulletins of the Brush Development Company a different equivalent circuit is used in which N is the transformer ratio and C_m the compliance. Conversion to the quantities used in this book is obtained from the relations $N = k_c^2/\alpha$ and $C_m = (1 - k_c^2)/K$.

pads have a relatively low shear stiffness, resulting in a mounting loss of about 3 db.

Another common type of pick-up element consists of two thin ADP crystal slabs and operates in the same manner as that illustrated in Fig. 4.42b. In both cases the electrodes are connected in series as

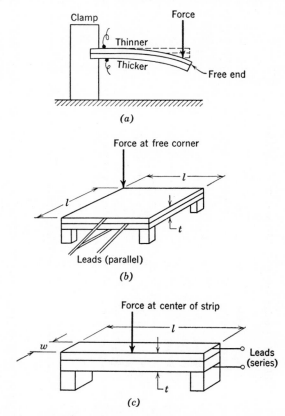

Fig. 4.42.   Basic forms of Bimorph pick-up elements.

shown in Fig. 4.42c. The third element is a thin narrow strip of barium titanate assembled as shown in Fig. 4.42c. It would also be possible to use Rochelle salt bender elements, but they are less sensitive than twisters.

The sensitivity of a Rochelle salt *twister* is about 16 db higher than that of a barium titanate bender, while a Rochelle salt *bender* is only 13 db more sensitive than a ceramic unit.[52] This difference is attribut-

[52] H. B. Miller, *Brush Strokes*, June 1952, p. 5 (published by Brush Development Company, Cleveland, Ohio).

able to the different values of coupling coefficient for the two designs. We note from Table 4.7 that the compliance and static capacity of such elements can be adjusted by varying the length l, thickness t, and width w of the transducer to meet impedance and bandwidth requirements. The flat response of such pick-ups is limited by their

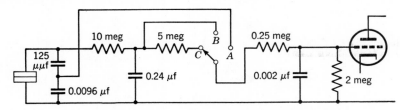

Fig. 4.43.   Integrating network for accelerometers.

resonant frequency.   In the case of a narrow thin strip as used in ceramic benders the first resonance occurs at:

$$f = \frac{0.56 R_g}{l_2} \sqrt{\frac{Y_0}{\rho}} \qquad \text{(clamped at one end)} \qquad (4.83a)$$

and

$$f = \frac{3.55 R_g}{l_2} \sqrt{\frac{Y_0}{\rho}} \qquad \text{(clamped at both ends)} \qquad (4.83b)$$

The quantity R_g is the radius of gyration of the bar, which for a rectangular cross section is given by:

$$R_g{}^2 = w^2/12$$

where w is the width of the strip.

For example, a double-clamped barium titanate Bimorph of 1.65-cm length and 0.7-mm thickness has its first resonance at approximately 4500 cps.

If an element of the type shown in Fig. 4.42c is mounted on a vibrating base, there will be forces set up on the center of the element, owing to the inertia of the transducer strip. At frequencies well below resonance, the voltage output of the unit is directly proportional to the acceleration a:

$$a = d^2\xi/dt^2 = F/M$$

If the output of the unit is integrated once or twice by an electric network of the type shown in Fig. 4.43, one obtains velocity or displacement.

For illustrative purposes let us assume a machine vibrating at a fundamental of 30 cps with a 0.001-in. displacement, and at a third harmonic of 90 cps with a 0.00033-in. displacement.   Figure 4.44 shows the patterns obtained with a cathode-ray oscilloscope for this complex vibration when the switch in the network of Fig. 4.43 is set

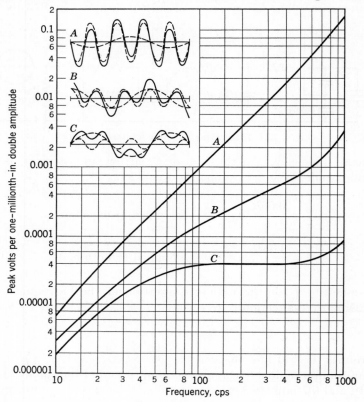

Fig. 4.44.   Insert in upper left shows waveforms of a complex vibration for acceleration (A), velocity (B), and displacements (C).   Main graph shows integrated outputs from commercial accelerometer versus frequency (Courtesy Shure Brothers).

to give an acceleration (A), velocity (B), or displacement (C) characteristic.   The three corresponding characteristics of a commercial device[53] are also shown in Fig. 4.44.

4.15   General Electroacoustic Relationships

The theoretical concepts and, to some extent, the practical considerations discussed in the preceding sections of this chapter can be

[53] Shure Brothers Inc., Chicago, Ill.

applied, with slight modifications, to other electromechanical coupling mechanisms. It is possible to express the stiffness, mass, and load impedance of any type of transducer in terms of mechanical equivalent circuit elements that are coupled through a transforming network to the electric impedance elements. In this chapter we used a simple approach that leads to the concept of an ideal coupling transformer of a turns ratio $1:\alpha$. A more general derivation is given in Chapter 5 for magnetic coupling using the concept of a mutual impedance in a four-terminal electromechanical network. It will be shown for magnetic transducers how both concepts are interrelated if the equivalent circuits are transformed according to the duality principle.

These general relationships are summarized in Table 4.8 for the four basic electromechanical transducer principles. This table illustrates the common features and facilitates the conversion from one coupling network to another. Part of the information contained in the table will be discussed in Chapter 5.

However, the reader will already recognize certain basic physical relationships. The charge Q in electrostatic transducers corresponds to the quantity $2\pi l B_0$ in electrodynamic transducers. The polarizing field strength E_0 in the electrostatic case corresponds to the piezo-electric modulus h_{ik} (defined in Section 4.2) and to the magneto-strictive constant λ (defined in Section 5.3). Physically, all three of these quantities express a special tensor property, namely, polarization, that is characteristic of most transducer mechanisms.

Table 4.8

	Electrostatic	Piezoelectric (Ferroelectric)	Electrodynamic	Magnetostriction
Schematic Diagram of Physical Configuration				
Mechanical parameter	Combined stiffness K_0 of membrane and air cushion	Stiffness of solid slab $K_0 = Y_0 S/l$	Stiffness of diaphragm K_0	Stiffness of solid rod $K_0 = Y_0 S/l$
Polarization	Applied field $E_0 = V_0/l$ or charge $Q_0 = E_0\epsilon_0 S$	Natural orientation of ions: $e_{ik}/\epsilon_{ik} = h_{ik}$ (induced orientation of internal domains)	Applied magnetic field H_0	Applied magnetic field H_0 orients internal domains
Clamped impedance Z_0	$1/j\omega C_0 = l/j\omega\epsilon_0 S$	$1/j\omega C_0 = l/j\omega\epsilon\epsilon_0 S$	$j\omega L_0 = j\omega N^2 S\mu\mu_0/l$	$j\omega L_0 = j\omega N^2 S\mu\mu_0/l$
Type T coupling: α'	$V_0/j\omega l = E_0/j\omega$	$e_{ik}/j\omega\epsilon\epsilon_0 = h_{ik}/j\omega$	$|2\pi r N B_0|$	$|\lambda N S\mu\mu_0/l|$
Ideal transformer coupling α	$E_0\epsilon_0 S/l = D_0 S/l$	$e_{ik}S/l = h_{ik}C_0$	$2B_0 l/\omega N\mu\mu_0 r$	$\lambda/N\omega$; for resonant rod: $n\lambda/\pi c N$
Stiffness reactance X_0	$K_0/j\omega$	$Y_0 S/j\omega l$	$K_0/j\omega$	$Y_0 S/j\omega l$
Electromechanical coupling coefficient $k_c^2 = \alpha^2 Z_0/X_0 = \alpha'^2/X_0 Z_0$	$\alpha^2/C_0 K_0 = \epsilon_0 S E_0^2/l K_0 = Q^2/\epsilon_0 S/l K_0$	$\alpha^2/C_0 K_0 = e_{ik}^2/\epsilon\epsilon_0 Y_0 = h_{ik}^2\cdot\epsilon\epsilon_0/Y_0 = g_{ik}\cdot d_{ik}\cdot Y_0$	$\alpha^2 L_0/K_0 = 4\pi B_0^2 l/\mu\mu_0 K_0 r^2 = (2\pi B_0 l)^2/\mu\mu_0 S/l K_0$	$\alpha^2 L_0/K_0 = \mu\mu_0\lambda^2/Y_0$

CHAPTER 5

Magnetostrictive Transducers

5.1 General Concept of Magnetic Coupling

Some of the relationships and concepts introduced in Chapter 4 have general validity for all types of electromechanical transducers, whether they are actuated by electric fields or by magnetic fields (see Table 4.8). In this chapter, we shall discuss the special features of magnetostriction transducers, using the relationships derived in Chapter 4 whenever they are applicable.

There is a physical difference between electric and magnetic coupling which leads to different forms of the equivalent circuits. In electric coupling the driving *voltage* is basically related to a mechanical force (see eq. 4.16). In magnetic coupling the force F (newtons) on a linear conductor of length l (meters) carrying a current i (amperes) in a magnetic field H_0 (ampere-turns/meter)[1] is:

$$F = \mu_0 H_0 l\, i \tag{5.1}$$

In this case the *current* is basically related to mechanical force.

As in Chapter 4, we like to use the expedient of an ideal transformer between the electrical and the mechanical sides of the electromechanical transducer. Hence, we rewrite eq. 5.1 in the form:

$$F = \alpha' i \tag{5.1a}$$

For example, in an electrodynamic loudspeaker we can define a transformer of a turns ratio[2] $\alpha' : 1$, with $\alpha' = 2\pi r N B_0$ volt·sec/m (r = coil radius in meters, N = number of turns of the coil moving in a radial magnetic field of flux density[3] B_0 volt·sec/m^2). On the other hand the *duality* principle (see Fig. 2.2) allows us to define another ideal

---

[1] The MKS unit of magnetic field strength H is ampere-turns/meter; 1 amp-turn/m = $4\pi/10^3$ oersted; 1 oersted = 79.5 amp-turns/m. The permeability of free space is $\mu_0 = 4\pi \times 10^{-7}$ volt · sec/amp · m.

[2] α' corresponds to D in *Vibration and Sound*, by P. M. Morse, McGraw-Hill, 1948, 2nd edition, p. 34.

[3] The mks unit of flux is the "weber"; 1 weber/m^2 = 1 volt·sec/m^2 = 10^4 gauss.

transformer of turns ratio $1 : \alpha$ which relates force to voltage and velocity to current. For example, in a magnetostrictive rod of uniform cross section this turns ratio is $\alpha = \Lambda/N\omega$, (Λ = magnetostrictive constant, N is the number of turns, and $\omega = 2\pi \cdot$ frequency). Usually one of the two possible forms of transformation leads to simpler expressions. The conventions used in the equivalent circuits which employ either $\alpha' : 1$ transformation or $1 : \alpha$ transformation are summarized in the following scheme:

$$
\begin{array}{ccc}
F & = & \alpha' \cdot & i \\
\| & & & \| \\
\alpha & & Z_0 & \alpha \\
\cdot & \nearrow & & \cdot \\
V & = & \alpha' \cdot & u
\end{array}
$$

We note that α and α' are interrelated through the clamped electric impedance Z_0: $\alpha' = \alpha Z_0$.

Let us return to the example of the electrodynamic loudspeaker to elucidate further the characteristic physical feature of magnetically driven transducers. A voltage $V = V_0 e^{j\omega t}$ across the electric terminals of a clamped loudspeaker coil will cause a current $i = I_0 e^{j\omega t}$ to flow. If we allow the coil to move freely under the force set up by the interaction of the current in the coil and the magnetic field, a voltage of opposite direction (*back emf*) to the driving voltage is induced (*Lenz's law*). The current is thus reduced, corresponding to an increase in input impedance. At resonance and without losses the back emf would be equal and opposite to the driving voltage, and no current could flow (infinite input impedance). The device would act as an open-circuited ideal transformer. We see that this behavior is not compatible with an equivalent circuit of the type shown in Fig. 4.6 where shunting of the mechanical side of the transducer (no load) produces a low electric impedance.

Mutual impedance   The four-terminal network of Fig. 4.3, however, has general validity. For the magnetic case, this network takes the form of Fig. 5.1. Looking into the electric terminals of the transducer network we encounter the clamped impedance $Z_0 = R_0 + j\omega L_0$ in series with a mutual impedance

$$
Z_{\mathrm{EM}} = \frac{\text{back emf appearing in electric mesh}}{\text{velocity } u \text{ in mechanical mesh}}
$$

Looking into the mechanical terminals we encounter the mechanical impedance $Z_m = j(\omega M - K/\omega) + R_m$ in series with a mutual impedance

$$Z_{\mathrm{ME}} = \frac{\text{force } F \text{ acting in mechanical mesh}}{\text{current } i \text{ in electric mesh}}$$

The two mutual impedances Z_{EM} and Z_{ME} are related by a reciprocity theorem which states[4] that $Z_{\mathrm{EM}} = \pm Z_{\mathrm{ME}}$. The positive sign, indicating symmetry, holds for electrostatic and piezoelectric coupling:

$$Z_{\mathrm{EM}} = +Z_{\mathrm{ME}} \text{ (electric field drive)} \tag{5.2}$$

In this case the electrical and mechanical sides of the transducer can simply be connected through an ideal transformer $1:\alpha$ as in Fig. 4.7.

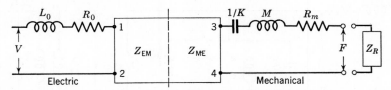

Fig. 5.1.   Coupling between electric and mechanical circuit elements through mutual impedances.

The negative sign, indicating antisymmetry, holds for electromagnetic and magnetostrictive coupling:

$$Z_{\mathrm{EM}} = -Z_{\mathrm{ME}} \text{ (magnetic field drive)} \tag{5.3}$$

For this case the following mesh equations among voltage, current, velocity, and force are valid for the network:

$$V = Z_0 i + Z_{\mathrm{EM}} u \tag{5.4a}$$

$$F = -Z_{\mathrm{EM}} i + Z_m u \tag{5.4b}$$

Equation 5.4b represents the condition of balance of internal and external forces for the electromagnetic case, just as eq. 4.23 does for the piezoelectric case.   Following the reasoning that led to the representation of Fig. 4.2 we find that the force F generated by the transducer is equal in magnitude and opposite in phase to the inertia force $Z_R u$ of the medium

$$F = -Z_R u \tag{5.5}$$

From eqs. 5.4 and 5.5 we obtain for the electric input impedance of the magnetic transducer:

$$\frac{V}{i} = Z_0 + \frac{Z_{\mathrm{EM}}{}^2}{Z_m + Z_R} \tag{5.6}$$

$$= Z_0 + Z_{\mathrm{mot}}$$

[4] H. M. Trent, *J. Appl. Mech.*, *15* (1948), 49.

The second term on the right side of eq. 5.6 is the motional impedance which at resonance and without losses other than radiation reduces to:

$$R_e = Z_{EM}^2/Z_R = Z_{ME}^2/Z_R = -\alpha'^2/Z_R \qquad (5.7)$$

Comparing eq. 5.4b with eq. 5.1 for the clamped case ($u = 0$) we find that Z_{ME} has the same value as α'. Equation 5.7 also shows that the motional impedance of a transducer operated by a magnetic field is proportional to its mechanical admittance Y_{mech} (*mechanical mobility*). Therefore, the complete electric equivalent circuit corresponding

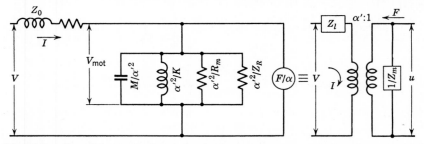

Fig. 5.2. Complete equivalent circuit for magnetic coupling. The complex clamped input impedance is represented in the right-hand diagram by Z_l and the motional impedance by Z_m.

to Fig. 5.1 consists of the clamped impedance Z_0 in series with the motional impedance:

$$Z_{mot} = R_e + jX_e = -\alpha'^2 Y_{mech}$$
$$= \frac{-\alpha'^2}{j\omega M + K/j\omega + R_m + Z_R} = \frac{1}{Y_{mot}} \qquad (5.8)$$

This amounts to connecting the reciprocal values of the individual mechanical impedance elements in parallel, as shown in Fig. 5.2.[5]

5.2   Phase Relationships in Magnetic Transduction

Some important features of this circuit are apparent. The *mechanical series elements* stiffness, mass, and damping appear with their reciprocal values as *electric parallel elements*. Mass converts to capacitance and compliance to inductance. Further, we note that clamping produces a shunt across the mechanical terminals, that the effective driving voltage V_{mot} is smaller than V by the drop iZ_0, and that the losses in R_m are proportional to the square of the total current into the transducer.

[5] The operations involved in eq. 5.8 and Fig. 5.2 are a direct consequence of the duality principle explained in Chapter 2 (see Fig. 2.2, arrow V).

The equivalent circuit of Fig. 5.2 is quite different from the one of Fig. 4.6 which was obtained for the piezoelectrical case. The turns ratio of the ideal transformer is $\alpha':1$ instead of $1:\alpha$, and mechanical admittances have been used in the magnetic transducer where mechanical impedances were used in the electrical case. This "antisymmetry"[6] results from the negative sign in eq. 5.3 which indicates a $180°$ phase shift between Z_{EM} and Z_{ME}.

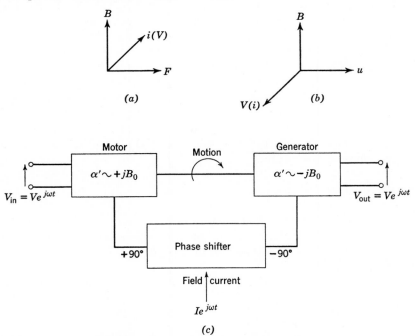

Fig. 5.3. Motor-generator analogy of antireciprocal coupling.

Let us now interpret the physical meaning of the phase relationships in the mesh equations 5.4. For the open-circuit case $(i = 0)$, eq. 5.4a simply describes the generation of voltage by an applied motion (dynamo principle) and we can apply the *right-hand rule* (Fig. 5.3a) for the relative orientation of the impressed motion, the magnetic field, and the induced voltage in space. In turn, for the clamped case $(u = 0)$, eq. 5.4b characterizes the performance of a motor and the *left-hand rule* applies, as shown in Fig. 5.3b. We see that the relation-

[6] F. V. Hunt, *Bull. 39th Meeting, Acoust. Soc. Amer.*, June 1950, p. 6 (B1). Electromechanical systems of the electric-field type are symmetrical and obey the reciprocity principle. Systems of the magnetic-field type show antisymmetry and are said, therefore, to be *antireciprocal*.

ship between mechanical and electrical quantities differs in the two cases (*a* and *b*) inasmuch as the electrical vectors have the opposite direction although the magnitude of the electromechanical coupling is the same. This reversal of the electrical vector in space can be expressed by a 180° phase shift in time by means of the ideal experiment represented in Fig. 5.3*c*. Here the transducer is visualized as a motor mechanically coupled to a generator. The transducer can be operated both ways, as a sender or as a receiver. In order to be able to use one equivalent circuit for both cases we must use a fixed relationship between voltage and motion.

For a given motion, the voltages V_{in} and V_{out}, as in the example of Fig. 5.3*c*, can be equal in magnitude and phase only if the phase of the magnetic field in the motor is of opposite phase to the one in the generator. This requirement is a consequence of Maxwell's law of induction, which is represented by the vector diagrams in Fig. 5.3*a* and 5.3*b*. They have no counterpart in the piezoelectric case where pressure P, field E, and electric displacement D always have the same mutual phase relationship.

In the actual transducer the field vector B_0 is, of course, fixed, but the phase-inversion characteristic of magnetic coupling occurs in the ideal transformer between the mechanical and electrical sides. In Fig. 5.3*c* this is obtained by setting α' proportional to $+jB_0$ at the left and to $-jB_0$ at the right. From this consideration, together with eqs. 5.1 and 5.7, we find that the magnitudes of α' and the mutual impedances are equal:

$$|\alpha'| = |Z_{\text{ME}}| = |Z_{\text{EM}}|$$

and that the phases are related by:

$$-j\alpha' = Z_{\text{EM}}$$
$$+j\alpha' = Z_{\text{ME}}$$

These yield: $Z_{\text{EM}} = -Z_{\text{EM}}$ in accordance with eq. 5.3, and also

$$Z_{\text{EM}}{}^2 = Z_{\text{ME}}{}^2 = -\alpha'^2 \tag{5.9}$$

which is a more fundamental relationship than eq. 5.3.

Let us now define an ideal transformer which connects the electric impedance directly to the mechanical impedance and which is consistent with the conventions adopted in Chapter 4. The transformer can be made phase-free if we apply the necessary phase shift to the mechanical quantities force and velocity by formally introducing:

$$-jF = F^* \qquad -ju = u^* \tag{5.10}$$

We can then rewrite eqs. 5.4a and 5.4b:

$$V = Z_0 i + \alpha' u^* \tag{5.11a}$$

$$F^* = \alpha' i + Z_m u^* \tag{5.11b}$$

Equations 5.11a and b can be presented on the basis of Kirchhoff's laws by the network of Fig. 5.4a, in which the terminals 1, 2 and 3, 4 of Fig. 5.1 have been connected by a T network with $+\alpha'$ in the leg of the T and $-\alpha'$ in both arms of the T. By means of conventional network transformation it can be shown that the circuit of Fig. 5.4a is equivalent to the circuit of Fig. 5.4b, where $\alpha = \alpha'/Z_0$ and $Z_m' = -\alpha^2 \cdot Z_0$.

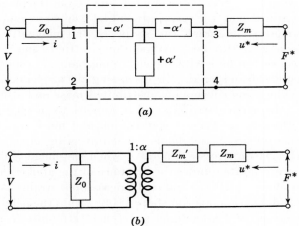

Fig. 5.4.   Equivalence between T network and ideal transformer.

In all later discussions the equivalent circuit of Fig. 5.4b will be used according to the procedures discussed in Chapter 4. In this equivalent circuit, the total mechanical impedance of a magnetostrictive transducer is:

$$Z_m^* = Z_m + Z_m' \tag{5.12}$$

With this notation the network equations 5.11a and b can be written in the form:

$$V = Z_0[i + \alpha u^*] \tag{5.13a}$$

$$F^* = \alpha Z_0 i + [Z_m^* + \alpha^2 Z_0]u^* \tag{5.13}$$

5.3   Magnetostrictive Properties

Basic equations   The magnetostrictive effect occurs in ferromagnetic materials such as iron, nickel, cobalt, and certain special alloys. If a magnetic field is applied parallel to the axis of a rod of such material a change in its length will result. Such a field can be generated in a suitable coil of N turns over a length of l meters by a current of i amperes. Without a magnetic core the field strength within the coil is:

$$H = iN/l \text{ amp-turns/m} \qquad (5.14)$$

With a magnetic core the field H set up by the current in the coil will produce a flux density B within the material:

$$B = \mu\mu_0 H \text{ weber/m}^2 \qquad (5.15)$$

where μ is the permeability relative to vacuum and μ_0 is the permeability of free space.[7] The value of μ is a function of the magnetic field, the temperature, and the pretreatment of the core material. All these parameters determine the shape of the magnetic hysteresis loop, as discussed in standard textbooks on electricity and magnetism.[8]

We are concerned here with the electromechanical properties of the ferromagnetic core material. In discussing its mechanical behavior we can use the same concepts of distributed mass and stiffness as in Chapter 4. In particular, Hooke's law applies, as defined in eq. 4.2.

The interlocking between magnetization and mechanical deformation is a consequence of the domain structure of ferromagnetic materials and the elastic stresses generated when the magnetic vectors of the domains are rotated under the influence of the applied field. The summation effect of all the induced microscopic strains is a change in the length dimension of a rod-shaped core within the field-producing coil. The strain $\Delta l/l$ as a function of field strength H in rods of annealed nickel or permalloy is plotted in Fig. 5.5. One finds that the sign of the deformation is independent of the direction of the applied field, which indicates a square-law type of relationship such as:

$$\Delta l/l = x_0 = \mathbf{c} \cdot B_0{}^2 \qquad (5.16)$$

where x_0 is the static strain produced by a dc-polarizing flux density B_0, and $\mathbf{c}$ $(\text{m}^4/\text{weber}^2)$ is a material constant. A linear effect is obtained if, in analogy to the procedure in electromagnetic telephone receivers, a large constant polarizing field B_0 is used in conjunction with a small a.c. driving field B. Differentiating eq. 5.16 with respect to B_0 and using the incremental quantities $x = dx_0$ and $B = dB_0$, we obtain the basic magnetostrictive strain equation:

$$x = 2\mathbf{c}B_0 B = \beta B \quad \text{(constant stress)} \qquad (5.17)$$

[7] $\mu_0 = 4\pi 10^{-7}$ henry/m; 1 henry = 1 volt·sec/amp

[8] George V. Mueller, *Introduction to Electrical Engineering*, McGraw-Hill, New York, Toronto, and London, 1948.

where β is a magnetostrictive strain constant with the dimension m^2/weber. Conversely, we define a basic relationship between the incremental stress X and the incremental flux density B for a clamped rod,[9]

$$F/S = X = \Lambda B \qquad (5.18)^{10}$$

From eqs. 5.17 and 5.18 and Hooke's law ($X = xY_0$) we obtain:

$$\Lambda = \beta Y_0 = 2cB_0Y_0$$

the magnetostriction stress constant in newtons/weber.[11] Nickel contracts with increasing B, so its Λ is negative. Permalloy, on the

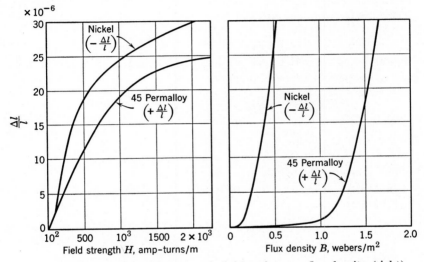

Fig. 5.5. Strain versus field strength (left) and versus flux density (right).

other hand, expands when magnetized and therefore Λ is positive. The interrelation of the constants involved in the magnetostrictive equations can be represented schematically as follows:

$$x \cdot Y_0 = X \qquad \text{mechanical}$$
$$\beta \qquad \Lambda \qquad \beta \qquad \text{magnetomechanical}$$
$$B = \mu\mu_0 \cdot H \qquad \text{magnetic}$$

[9] Note the analogy to eqs. 4.4 and 4.7.

[10] In the literature one also finds an equivalent relation with the magnetic polarization $M = \mathbf{K}\mu_0 H$ as independent variable, where $\mathbf{K} = \mu - 1$ is the magnetic susceptibility. Equation 5.18 then takes the form $X = \Lambda(1 + 1/\mathbf{K})M = \Gamma M$.

[11] 1 newton/weber $= 10^{-3}$ dynes/gauss·cm^2.

The two main diagonals express the reversibility of the magneto-strictive effect.

Dynamic behavior   The dynamic properties of a magnetostrictive rod are obtained from the condition that the magnetostriction force F_m, the internal elastic force F_i, and the external inertial force of the medium F must be balanced[12]

$$F = F_i - F_m$$

We shall first apply this condition to the frequency range below mechanical resonance.   In complete analogy with the derivation given in Chapter 4, eqs. 4.18 to 4.23, and using eqs. 5.5 and 5.18, the condition for dynamic equilibrium is:

$$F = -S[Y_0 x - \Lambda B_i] \tag{5.19}$$

Since the magnetostrictive effect is reversible a similar condition holds for the balance of internal magnetic fields in the presence of a strain:

$$H = \frac{B_i}{\mu_i \mu_0} - \Lambda x \tag{5.20}$$

We see that the behavior of a magnetostrictive core is analogous to that of a piezoelectric condenser where a mechanical strain x creates ionic displacements which oppose the internal field.

Polarizing flux and coupling factor   Inserting eq. 5.20 into eq. 5.19 we obtain:

$$F = S\Lambda \mu_i \mu_0 H - S[Y_0 - \mu_i \mu_0 \Lambda^2] x \tag{5.21}$$

$$= S\Lambda B - SY' x$$

in which $$Y' = Y_0 \left[1 - \frac{\mu_i \mu_0 \Lambda^2}{Y_0} \right] = Y_0 [1 - k_c^2] \tag{5.22}$$

and μ_i is the slope of the B-H curve at the operating point B_0.   Equation 5.22 expresses the important physical fact that the induction of a polarizing flux $B_0 S$ in a magnetostrictive material lowers the value of Young's modulus.[13]   The reduced stiffness Y' at strong polarization also lowers the Q of magnetostrictive transducers by an amount which depends on the pretreatment of the core material.   The quantity k_c

---

[12] Compare with Fig. 4.2, which illustrates the dynamic equilibrium of forces in the piezoelectric case.

[13] In general, all types of electromechanical coupling involve some changes in the mechanical stiffness.   Usually the change is less than 10 per cent, for quartz transducers less than 1 per cent.   Hence, a sufficient degree of approximation was obtained in the discussion of Chapter 4 by substituting $Y' \simeq Y_0$.

in Eq. 5.22 is a measure of the degree of magnetostriction coupling; see eqs. 4.57 for piezoelectric materials) and is called the *electromechanical coupling factor*:

$$k_c = \sqrt{\mu_i \mu_0 \Lambda^2 / Y_0} = 2cB_0 \sqrt{\mu_i \mu_0 Y_0} \qquad (5.23)$$

We note that the degree of coupling depends on the dynamic permeability μ_i *and* on B_0, and thus on the operating point on the magnetization curve of the core material. Table 5.1 gives values for the three important transducer materials in both MKS and CGS units: annealed nickel, 45 *Permalloy* (45 per cent nickel, 55 per cent iron) and *Alfer*, an alloy of 13 per cent aluminum and 87 per cent iron. For nickel

Table 5.1　Magnetomechanical coefficients of Three Important Magnetostrictive Materials at Internal Polarizing Field H_0*

Coefficient	Annealed Nickel MKS	Annealed Nickel CGS	45 Permalloy MKS	45 Permalloy CGS	Alfer (13 % Al, 87 % Fe) MKS	Alfer (13 % Al, 87 % Fe) CGS
H_0 amp/m oersted	160 (1200)	2 (15)	600	7.5	800	10
B_0 Volt·sec/m² gauss	0.25 (0.51)	2500 (5100)	1.43	14,300	1.15	11,500
μ	1250 (340)		1900		1150	
μ_i	137 (41)		230		190	
$\Delta l/l$ at H_0	-8×10^{-6} (-26×10^{-6})		14×10^{-6}		26×10^{-6}	
c m⁴/weber² gauss⁻²	-1×10^{-4}	-1×10^{-12}	6.9×10^{-6}	6.9×10^{-14}	19.5×10^{-6}	19.5×10^{-14}
Λ newton/weber dynes/gauss·cm³	-4.8×10^6 (-20×10^6)	-4.8×10^3 (-20×10^3)	2.7×10^6	2.7×10^3	6.7×10^6	6.7×10^3
Y_0 newtons/m² dynes/m²	20×10^{10}	20×10^{11}	13.8×10^{10}	13.8×10^{11}	15×10^{10}	15×10^{11}
ρ kg/m³ g/cm³	8.7×10^3	8.7	8.25×10^3	8.25	6.7×10^3	6.7
k_c %	14 (31)		12.4		27	
ρ_c ohm·m ohm·cm	7×10^{-8}	7×10^{-6}	7×10^{-7}	7×10^{-5}	9×10^{-7}	9×10^{-5}

* The number of external ampere-turns per meter required to produce H_0 depends on the shape of the core. For closed magnetic loops H_{ext} is equal to H_0. For rod-shaped cores external fields larger than H_0 are necessary to compensate for the demagnetizing effect of the poles at the free ends.

the values for two different polarizing conditions (160 amp-turns/m and 1200 amp-turns/m) are presented; the latter appear in parentheses.

We are now ready to give a direct physical interpretation of the equivalent circuit given in Fig. 5.4b. Comparing the equivalent force equations (5.21 and 5.13) we obtain:

$$-jS\Lambda B = \alpha Z_0 i \tag{5.24a}$$

and
$$jSY'x = [Z_m{}^* + \alpha^2 Z_0]u^* \tag{5.24b}$$

Combining eqs. 5.24a and 5.14 and considering that the impedance of a coil wound on a ferromagnetic core is[14]

$$Z_0 = j\omega L_c = j\omega N^2 S\mu_i\mu_0/l$$

we find for the transformation ratio:

$$\alpha = -j\frac{SN}{l} \cdot \frac{\mu_i\mu_0\Lambda}{Z_0} \tag{5.25}$$

$$= -\Lambda/\omega N$$

Let us now analyze eq. 5.24b after rewriting it with the use of eq. 5.10 and $u^* = \omega xl$:

$$-\frac{jS}{\omega l}[Y_0 - \Delta Y_0] = Z_m{}^* + \alpha^2 Z_0 \tag{5.26}$$

where $\Delta Y_0 = \mu_i\mu_0\Lambda^2$.

The first term on either side of this equation represents the pure mechanical stiffness reactance $Z_m{}^* = -jK/\omega$ of the rod without magnetostrictive interaction. The second term in eq. 5.26 represents the decrease of the effective stiffness of the rod due to the internal magnetic flux:

$$\alpha^2 Z_0 = jS\Delta Y_0/\omega l = -Z_m{}'$$

The additional impedance $Z_m{}'$ which resulted from the network transformation carried out in Fig. 5.4 has thus found a physical explanation.

---

[14] This equation pertains only to closed magnetic loops. If an air gap is present the inductance is

$$L = \frac{\mu_0 N^2}{(l_c/\mu S_c + l_a/S_a)}$$

where the subscripts c and a indicate the core and air gap, respectively. See F. E. Terman, *Radio Engineers Handbook*, McGraw-Hill, New York, 1948, pp. 90–109.

5.4 Eddy Currents and Hysteresis

Magnetostrictive transducers have been used primarily in the range between 10 and 100 kcps. At these frequencies eddy currents of considerable magnitude are induced in the core materials. In order to keep the resulting losses as low as possible, one generally constructs magnetostrictive transducer stacks of laminated sheet

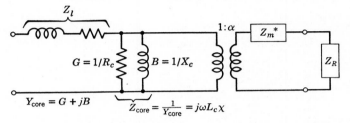

Fig. 5.6.   Equivalent circuit of magnetostrictive transducer including losses.

material. But even then the loss effect is not negligible and leads to a complex core impedance:

$$Z_c = R_c' + jX_c' = j\omega L_c \chi \tag{5.27}$$

in which

$$\chi = \chi_{RE} - j\chi_{IM} = |\chi|e^{j\zeta}$$

is the complex eddy current factor,[15] whose magnitude decreases with frequency. Its phase angle is determined by

$$\tan \zeta = \chi_{IM}/\chi_{RE} = R_c'/X'$$

and increases with frequency.

If all losses in a magnetostrictive transducer are considered, the total clamped impedance Z_0 must be represented as the core impedance Z_c in series with a leakage impedance Z_l. Leakage was neglected in the previous sections since it plays no part in the magnetostrictive mechanism. With this new definition, $Z_0 = Z_c + Z_l$, the circuit of Fig. 5.4b takes the form shown in Fig. 5.6. The simple representation of the core impedance Z_c as a parallel combination of $j\omega L_c$ and associated loss resistance R_c is possible if the frequency is lower than a critical value.[16] For laminated-core materials this critical frequency is

$$f_c = \frac{\rho_c}{2\pi^2 \mu_i \mu_0 t^2} \tag{5.28}$$

[15] S. Butterworth and F. D. Smith, *Proc. Phys. Soc. (London)*, B, *43* (1931), **2,** 166.

[16] Because of the skin effect.

where ρ_c = resistivity in ohms $\times$ meters and t = lamination thickness in meters. For $f < f_c$ the real part χ_{RE} of the eddy current factor in eq. 5.27 is approximately equal to unity and the imaginary part $\chi_{IM} \approx f/3f_c$. In Fig. 5.7, f_c (in kcps) is plotted versus lamination thickness (in meters) for two core materials: nickel and Alfer (see Table 5.1). For frequencies between 10 and 100 kcps, lamination

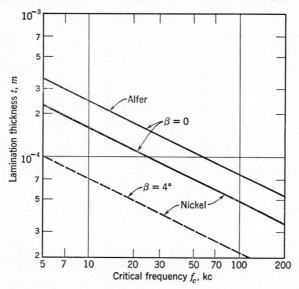

Fig. 5.7. Lamination thickness versus frequency (β = phase angle due to hysteresis, see eq. 5.29).

thicknesses between 0.2 mm and 0.05 mm are required to keep the phase angle ζ of the eddy current factor small.

Let us now convert eq. 5.27 to admittance:

$$Y_{core} = G_c + jB_c$$

We then find for the parallel loss resistance of the core shown in Fig. 5.6: $R_c = 6\pi L_c f_c$, and, for the core reactance, $X_c = \omega L_c$.

The fact that the presence of eddy currents leads to a complex core impedance (see eq. 5.27) must be expressed in the transducer equations which were derived above. Generally, the complex impedance Z_c must be substituted for the clamped inductance Z_0. However, if the core has thin laminations and the frequency is low ($f/f_c \ll 1$) the above equations which simply use Z_0 give a good approximation for the magnitudes. But there is one important consequence regarding the phase relationships which cannot be neglected.

Phase relationships Let us examine more closely the physics underlying eqs. 5.14 and 5.15. We remember that the permeability μ is not a constant but depends on the applied field H. This leads to the familiar hysteresis loop of the B-H curve, part of which is schematically represented in Fig. 5.8. The operating point is determined by the polarizing current I_0 which determines the operating point H_0, B_0. If a driving current $i = Ie^{j\omega t}$ is superimposed, a small hysteresis loop is circumscribed because μ is generally a complex function of H. This loop can be approximated by an ellipse whose

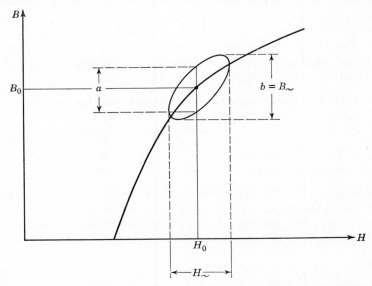

Fig. 5.8.   Determination of phase angle $\beta = \arcsin (a/b)$ from dynamic B-H loop.

angle of inclination determines the magnitude of the dynamic permeability μ_i. We see from Fig. 5.8 that the phase angle β of μ_i is given by $\sin \beta = a/b$, and we thus obtain for the dynamic permeability

$$\mu' = |\mu_i| e^{-j\beta}$$

It follows that current i and magnetic flux density B are not in phase, i.e., that the core impedance is complex:

$$Z_c = \frac{V}{i} = \frac{NS}{i}\frac{dB}{dt} \simeq j\omega L_c e^{-j\beta} \tag{5.29}$$

where

$$L_c = \frac{N^2 S}{l} |\mu_i| \mu_0$$

Comparing eqs. 5.29 and 5.27 we find that both eddy currents and hysteresis give rise to a complex core impedance. The combined effects lead to a modification of eq. 5.15,

$$B = \mu'\chi\mu_0 H$$

$$\approx |\mu_i|\mu_0 H e^{-j\varphi} \qquad \text{(for } f/f_c < 1 \quad : \quad |\chi| \approx 1) \qquad (5.30)$$

where $\varphi = \beta + \zeta$ is the phase shift between H or i and B. We have seen that the phase angle ζ is reduced by providing laminations of suitable thickness. The presence of hysteresis losses in the core materials requires that the lamination thickness be further reduced. This is indicated for nickel in Fig. 5.7 where the dashed line refers to a loss angle $\beta = 4°$ while the solid lines refer to $\beta = 0$. Typical values of the phase angle φ are given in Table 5.2 for frequencies equal to f_c, $0.5f_c$, and $0.1f_c$ (see eq. 5.28).

Table 5.2   Phase Angle between Current and Flux for Nickel

	Rectangular Laminations	Ring Laminations
$f/f_c = 1$	18°	30°
$f/f_c = 0.5$	10°	25°
$f/f_c = 0.1$	2°	12°

As a consequence of eq. 5.30 the phase factor $e^{-j\varphi}$ must be introduced in all the previous magnetostrictive coupling equations. This is accomplished by assigning a phase angle to the transformation ratio α. Equation 5.25 then has to be rewritten as

$$\alpha = -\frac{\Lambda}{\omega N} e^{-j\varphi} = |\alpha| e^{-j\varphi} \qquad (5.31)$$

Since mechanical impedances are converted to the electrical side of the equivalent circuit by dividing by α^2, the phase factor $e^{-j2\varphi}$ enters into the relationships for motional impedance.

5.5   The Motional Impedance Loop

With knowledge of the angle φ, we can construct an impedance diagram as shown in Fig. 5.9. Let us first determine the motional impedance vector D at mechanical resonance. In this special case the impedance $Z_m{}^*$ in Fig. 5.6 reduces to the mechanical loss resistance R_m. The total load then is the internal loss resistance R_m in series with the radiation resistance Z_R. This load $R_m + Z_R$ transforms to the electric terminals of the electromechanical transformer as an admittance:

$$Y_p = \frac{|\alpha|^2 e^{-j2\varphi}}{R_m + Z_R}$$

This in turn can be converted to an impedance in series with the core reactance, namely, to the motional impedance:

$$D = \omega^2 L_c{}^2 Y_p = \frac{\omega^2 L_c{}^2 |\alpha|^2 e^{-j2\varphi}}{R_m + Z_R} \tag{5.32}$$

As was explained in Section 4.9, D is the diameter of the motional

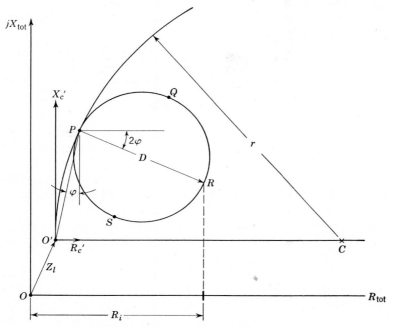

Fig. 5.9.   Construction of motional impedance loop.

impedance loop at mechanical resonance.   According to eq. 5.32 the impedance vector $D = R_{\text{mot}} + jX_{\text{mot}}$ is inclined by an angle 2φ:

$$\tan 2\varphi = (X_{\text{mot}}/R_{\text{mot}})_{\omega_0}$$

The *dip angle* 2φ is about 20° for a rod-shaped nickel core consisting of flat laminations 0.2 mm thick and operated at a frequency of 20 kcps $(f \sim 0.5f_c)$.

A different expression can be used for D if the mechanical Q of the system has been determined by measurement.   We recall that:

$$Q = \frac{\omega_0 M}{R_m + Z_R} = \frac{\sqrt{MK}}{R_m + Z_R} \qquad (5.33)$$

where the effective mass M and stiffness K are defined as in eq. 4.37b.[17] Combining eqs. 5.31, 5.32, and 5.33 we obtain:

$$D \simeq \frac{4}{\pi^2} k_c^2 L_0 \omega_0 Q \qquad (5.34)$$

where k_c is the electromechanical coupling coefficient of the laminated core material and ω_0 the resonance frequency. After the vector $D = P - R$ has been determined we can draw the motional circle $PQRS$, as shown in Fig. 5.9.

As a second step in the construction of the motional impedance diagram we will determine the position of the point P in the complex impedance plane. From eq. 5.27 and 5.30 we find the clamped core impedance vector:

$$Z_c \simeq j\omega_0 L_0 e^{-j\varphi}$$

as represented by O'-P in Fig. 5.9. In the frequency range $f_c > f_0 > 0.5 f_c$ the clamped impedance vector describes approximately a circle around the point C on the real axis, with the radius $r \approx Z_c^2/2R_c'$, where R_c' is the series resistance defined by eq. 5.27. It can be shown that $2r \approx R_c$ if the shunt resistance R_c defined in Fig. 5.6 is much larger than X_c.

So far we have neglected the leakage impedance Z_l. Its presence will further shift the position of the point P with respect to the origin of the X-R coordinate system by a vector $Z_l = R_l + jX_l$. This is achieved in Fig. 5.9 by going to the final coordinates X_{tot} and R_{tot}.

It has been shown above how the motional impedance of a magnetostrictive transducer can be predicted from such properties as Q, core impedance Z_c, phase angle φ, and electromechanical coupling factor k_c. In practice one will often use the converse procedure in order to check the actual performance from a measurement of the impedance circle. As was pointed out in Chapter 4, the transducer efficiency can be determined from a comparison between the circles measured in air and in water.

In order to obtain valid measurements in water, one must observe certain precautions. Full loading of the transducer by the water will be obtained only if the transducer face is free of air bubbles. The water in the test tank should be degassed (by boiling), and a

---

[17] For core shapes other than rods, M and K will have different values, as discussed in Section 5.8.

wetting agent should be employed to secure good contact between the transducer and the load.

It is also important to minimize the reflection of sound from the walls of the container back to the transducer face. This can be achieved, at least in part, by lining the tank walls with absorptive material.[18]   Some control can be obtained by shaping the tank walls in such a way as to break up the standing waves and scatter the sound in the tank diffusely.   For optimum conditions both expedients may be combined to provide multiple reflections at highly absorbing surfaces.   Without these precautions, the measured impedance circle will be distorted: if the transducer face is small compared with wavelength, the value of the circle diameter will be incorrect; large transducers of high directivity may exhibit distorted circles with indentations, or even additional re-entrant circles.

5.6   Efficiency and Matching

If good circles diagrams have thus been obtained, the efficiency

$$\eta = \frac{\text{power into load}}{\text{power into transducer}}$$

of the transducer can be determined from the circle diameters.   At resonance this leads to[19]

$$\eta = \frac{Z_R}{R_i} \frac{D_W}{R_m + Z_R} \tag{5.35}$$

where R_i is the real part of the total electric input impedance, Z_R is the load impedance, R_m represents the internal transducer losses, and D_W is the circle diameter of the loaded transducer.   From eq. 5.32

---

[18] W. P. Mason and F. H. Hibbard, *J. Acoust. Soc. Amer.*, *20* (1948), 476. E. Meyer and K. Tamm, *Acustica, Akust. Beih.*, *2* (1952), AB 91.   E. Meyer and H Oberst, *Acustica, Akust. Beih.*, *3* (1952), AB 149.   M. S. Weinstein, *J. Acoust. Soc. Amer.*, *25* (1953), 101.

[19] Generally, the efficiency of a four-terminal network is

$$\eta = \left[\frac{I_2}{I_1} \right]^2 \frac{R_L}{R_i}$$

where I_1 and I_2 are the currents into either side of the network, R_L is the resistive load, and R_i its reflected value which appears at the input terminals.   From eqs. 5.4 and 5.6 we find for the square-bracket factor:

$$\left[\frac{I_2}{I_1} \right]^2 = \left[\frac{u}{i} \right]^2 = \left[\frac{Z_{\text{em}}}{Z_m + Z_R} \right]^2 = \frac{Z_{\text{mot}}}{Z_m + Z_R}$$

At resonance $Z_m = R_m$ and $Z_{\text{mot}} = D_W$.

we find that for no load ($Z_R = 0$) the circle diameter becomes $D_A = \alpha^2 Z_0{}^2 / R_m$ and that:

$$\frac{D_W - D_A}{D_A} = \frac{R_m}{R_m + Z_R} - 1 = -\frac{Z_R}{R_m + Z_R}$$

Combining this result with eqs. 5.33 and 5.35 we have

$$\eta = \frac{D_W}{R_i} \frac{D_A - D_W}{D_A} = \frac{D_W}{R_i}\left[1 - \frac{Q_W}{Q_A}\right] \qquad (5.36)$$

$$\eta = \eta_{\mathrm{em}} \cdot \eta_{\mathrm{ma}}$$

The bracket-factor in eq. 5.36 can be interpreted as a mechano-acoustical efficiency η_{ma}, and in turn the factor D_W/R_i as an electro-mechanical efficiency η_{em}. Some typical values[20] are given in Table 5.3 for four different laminated ($t \sim 0.1$ mm) nickel transducers all of which are designed for a power output of about 40 watts[21] at fundamental resonance.

Table 5.3   **Magnetostrictive Transducer Efficiency**

	Resonance Frequency in kcps				
	15	30	80	175	500
Dimension of radiating face in wavelengths	$0.5\lambda \times 0.5\lambda$	$3\lambda \times 2\lambda$	$4.5\lambda \times 4.5\lambda$	$5\lambda \times 5\lambda$	$10\lambda \times 10\lambda$
Q_{air}	190	185	136	142	42
Q_{water}	35	50	22	32	22
$\eta_{\mathrm{em}} = \dfrac{D_W}{R_i}$	0.90	0.64	0.40	0.21	0.16
$\eta_{\mathrm{ma}} = \left(1 - \dfrac{Q_W}{Q_A}\right)$	0.82	0.73	0.84	0.77	0.48
η_{tot}	0.74	0.53	0.34	0.16	0.08

Even though the mechanoacoustical efficiency η_{ma} has a large and essentially constant value over the range from 15 to 175 kcps, the electromechanical efficiency η_{em} and hence the total efficiency decreases considerably with frequency. The cause for this drop of η_{em} is two-fold: there are hysteresis losses which increase linearly with frequency; and eddy losses which increase with the square of frequency.

In the foregoing discussion of efficiency we have considered only the transducer element. Let us now turn our attention to the problem of matching. It was pointed out in Chapter 4 that we have to provide

[20] H. Thiede, *Funk und Ton, 4*, No. 1 (1951), 32.

[21] In the 175-kcps transducer of Table 5.3, this power is obtained by an a-c current of 6.5 amp at a voltage of 50 volts across a 1.5-turn driving coil. This gives a radiated sound intensity of 2.5 watts/cm^2.

the electric driver with a load which is resistive and comparable to the internal driver impedance. The coil reactance of magnetostrictive transducers is usually tuned out by a series capacitor which at the same time blocks the d-c-polarizing bias from the RF driver. Let the transducer be operated at resonance and all losses be neglected, so that the motional impedance D represents the total load. In this case eq. 5.32 takes the form

$$R = \frac{N^2 S^2}{l^2} \frac{\Lambda^2 \mu_i^2 \mu_0^2}{\rho_0 c S} \tag{5.37}$$

It is apparent that R can be matched directly to the internal impedance of the electric generator by a proper choice of the number of turns N. In many cases, however, one prefers to use in the transducer itself a smaller number of turns of heavier wire. In this way the copper losses are reduced and one avoids high voltages which would cause insulation problems. Most of the matching then is done in the output transformer of the driver.

As an example, let us compute the electrical data for a rod-shaped stack of nickel laminations of 13-cm length and square cross section of area $S = 1.7$ cm², whose resonance occurs at about 20 kcps. With a length-to-width ratio of 10 the formation of magnetic poles at the ends of this stack leads to a demagnetization factor $n^* \approx 0.02$. According to Table 5.1 a high coupling coefficient (31 per cent) is obtained at an internal polarizing flux density $B_0 = 0.51$ volt·sec/m² (5100 gauss). The number of ampere-turns per meter required to generate this flux density depends on the demagnetization factor n^* and the permeability μ as follows:

$$\frac{NI}{l} = \frac{B_0}{\mu\mu_0} [1 + n^*(\mu - 1)]$$

$$\approx \frac{B_0}{\mu\mu_0} (1 + n^*\mu)$$

In our case $B_0/\mu\mu_0 = 1200$ amp/m and $n^*\mu = 6.8$, so that $NI/l \approx 9300$ amp/m. This can be realized, for example, by a coil of 6-cm length which has 80 turns and carries a d-c current of 7 amp. Neglecting losses, we can use eq. 5.37 to find the electric load impedance at resonance. Taking the values for Λ and μ_i from Table 5.1 and with $NS/l = 0.225$ m, $Z_R = 2.55 \times 10^2$ kg/m²/sec¹, we get $R_e = 210$ ohms. The associated coil reactance $Z_0 = j\omega N^2 S \mu_i \mu_0/l$ then becomes $Z_0 = j116$ ohms. On the other hand, if a coil of 12-cm length and 160 turns ($N/l = $ constant) is chosen, the coil reactance is twice as large. The relationship between turns ratio and impedance is plotted in Fig. 5.10 for the 20-kcps transducer of our example. We also note from Fig. 5.10 that for a particular driving field (9300 amp-turns/m in this case) the required biasing current depends on the number of turns.

The presence of losses in the transducer usually has little effect on the magnitude of the electric load impedance R_e. Computations based on eq. 5.37 give a good approximation to the actual loading conditions. The mechanical transducer losses R_m appear in the denominator of eq. 5.32 and tend to lower R_e. From Table 5.3 (water loading) we find $\eta_{\text{ma}} = Z_R/(R_m + Z_R) \approx 0.8$ and hence $R_m \approx 0.25Z_R$, which leads to a 20 per cent reduction of the motional impedance:

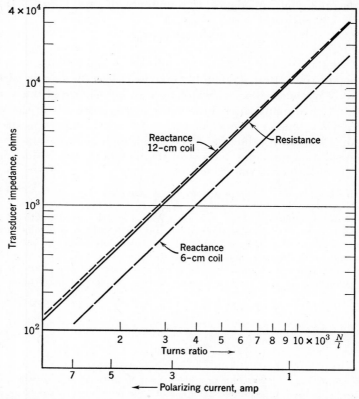

Fig. 5.10. Impedance versus turns ratio for a laminated rod-shaped nickel core resonant at 20 kcps. Also shown is the polarizing current required to produce a flux density of 5100 gauss.

$D \approx 0.8R_e$. On the other hand, Table 5.3 also indicates a value of about 0.8 for η_{me} and hence $R_i \approx 1.25D$. The actual load impedance in the presence of losses therefore turns out to be $R_i \approx 1.25 \times 0.8R_e$, i.e., in this frequency range we have $R_i \approx R_e$.

5.7   Design Considerations for Laminated Stacks

There are several possible configurations for a laminated core. The simplest, indicated in Fig. 5.11a, consists of a stack of thin rectangular sheets of nickel, or any other suitable magnetostrictive material, which are bolted together. The individual laminations should be insulated electrically to minimize eddy currents. Insulation may be achieved by a suitable spacing material or simply by annealing the nickel sheets before assembly. Annealing produces a non-conducting oxide layer at the surface and also reduces the area of the hysteresis loop.

Stacks of the type shown in Fig. 5.11a yield a relatively low electromechanical coupling because of leakage flux and demagnetization. Therefore one usually provides a closed path for the magnetic flux, as shown in Fig. 5.11b. The driving coil is wound on the two legs l_1 and l_2 of the transducer. A V-shaped protruding ridge in the center facilitates clamping the assembly at the velocity node. Another

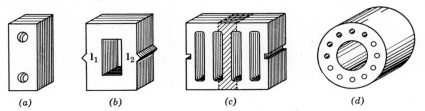

(a)   (b)   (c)   (d)

Fig. 5.11.   Common types of laminated stacks.

arrangement (Fig. 5.11c), having a multiplicity of legs, has found wide application for large-area transducers. A couple of grooves may be cut into the laminations for the purpose of clamping. Finally, there is the ring-type assembly, Fig. 5.11d, which serves as a cylindrical sound generator or receiver with uniform azimuthal sensitivity. Transducer cores of the type shown in Fig. 5.11b and 5.11c can be analyzed approximately as a system of two masses M_1 and M_2 connected by a spring $K = Y_0 S_l / l$, where S_l is the cross section through the legs and l the length of the legs. The resonance frequency then is:

$$f = \frac{1}{2\pi}\sqrt{\frac{K}{M}} \simeq \frac{1}{2\pi}\sqrt{\frac{Y_0 S_l (M_1 + M_2)}{l M_1 M_2}} \qquad (5.38)^{22}$$

At any particular value of resonance frequency, the overall length of such a system is slightly smaller than that of the corresponding solid-rod transducer.

The longitudinal vibrations of constricted cores can be analyzed by transmission-line theory (see Chapter 2). Let us consider the shaded section in Fig. 5.11c which has been redrawn schematically in Fig.

---

[22] The fundamental radial frequency of a ring stack is $f = c/2\pi r$ where $2r$ is the mean ring diameter and c is the sound velocity in the ring material.

5.12. Such a section is equivalent to a rod whose cross-sectional area is q times smaller in the middle than at the end: $S_l = qS$. Then the mechanical impedance for the section B-A is: $Z_{BA} = \rho_m c_m S$, and for

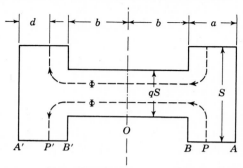

Fig. 5.12. Transmission-line sections of constricted core.

the section OB is: $Z_{OB} = \rho_m c_m qS$. Using eqs. 5.1, 5.4b, and 5.5, we obtain for the velocity at the radiating end A:

$$u_A = F_{A\,(oc)}/(Z_m + Z_R) \qquad (5.39)$$

where $Z_m = \xi Z_{BA}$ is the impedance at A looking back into the transducer, ξ is the transformation coefficient of the acoustic transmission line, and $F_{A\,(oc)}$ is the open-circuit force appearing at A (clamped case). Equation 5.39 leads to the equivalent circuit of Fig. 5.13 where $F_{A\,(oc)}$

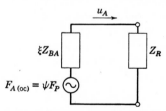

Fig. 5.13. Equivalent circuit for magnetostrictive driving force in constricted cores, and for air backing.

is expressed in terms of the internal magnetostrictive force F_P appearing at the driving point P within the transducer. The transformer action of the line can then be expressed by the force factor ψ in the equation:

$$F_{A\,(oc)} = F_P \psi$$

The equivalent circuit in Fig. 5.13 corresponds to the following physical situation.[23] The internal magnetostrictive stress that is dis-

[23] Y. Kikuchi and K. Fukushima, *Science Repts. Tôhoku Univ.*, B *1*, *2*, 141 (1951). The coefficients ξ and ψ are analog to the function ϕ in eq. 2.36.

tributed along B'-B (see Fig. 5.12) is equivalent to a driving force concentrated at the face A. This force is ψ times larger than the internal force, and it looks into an internal impedance ξZ_{BA}.

It is convenient to express the frequency response of a magneto-strictive transducer in terms of the coefficients ψ and ξ. These coefficients are plotted versus ω/ω_0 in Fig. 5.14 for symmetrical transducer sections that have the geometrical proportions $a/b = 1$ and $d = a/2$. The parameter in Fig. 5.14 is the cross-sectional area coefficient q. The curves $q = 1$ apply to a laminated stack of uniform cross section (see Fig. 5.11a). We note that ψ goes to zero at even harmonics, which means that they cannot be excited, just as in piezo-electric elements. As q decreases, the fundamental resonance ($\xi = 0$) drops to lower frequencies, which means that for any given frequency the transducer will have to be shorter than at $q = 1$. At ω_0 the force factor becomes $\psi = 2 \cos{(\gamma d)} \approx 2$, which corresponds to an amplitude doubling because of the air backing.

The resonance condition $\xi = 0$ leads to the expression:

$$\tanh{(\gamma a)} \times \tanh{(\gamma b)} + q = 0 \qquad (5.40a)$$

where $\gamma = j\omega \sqrt{\rho/Y} = j\omega/c$ is the propagation constant and Y the *complex* elastic modulus.[24] An equation of the same form (see eq. 4.77b) has been derived, on the basis of line theory, for crystal sandwiches.

Let us investigate further the fundamental resonance condition if a and b are not equal, i.e., if the legs of the transducer sections have arbitrary lengths. If we introduce $a = \alpha\lambda_0/4$ and $b = \beta\lambda_0/4$, with $\lambda_0 = c/f_0$ (c equals the longitudinal sound velocity in the transducer material) and if mechanical losses are neglected, eq. 5.40a becomes:

$$\tan{(\alpha\pi/2)} \times \tan{(\beta\pi/2)} + q = 0 \qquad (5.40b)$$

This equation is satisfied for the family of curves in Fig. 5.15, from which we can find the necessary value for b for any desired length a, to give resonance at f_0. In this figure the cross-sectional coefficient q is the parameter. We also find $(\alpha + \beta)$, the total resonance length in terms of half wavelengths $\lambda_0/2$, as a function of β. For instance, for $q = 0.4$ at a length of the leg $2b = \lambda_0/5.25$ (corresponding to

---

[24] Internal mechanical damping leads to a complex modulus $Y = Y_0\left(1 + j\dfrac{\eta\omega}{Y_0}\right)$ (see Section 8.1). If we neglect these losses ($\eta = 0$), eq. 5.40 becomes

$$\tan{\left(\frac{2\pi}{\lambda} a\right)} \times \tan{\left(\frac{2\pi}{\lambda} b\right)} + q = 0.$$

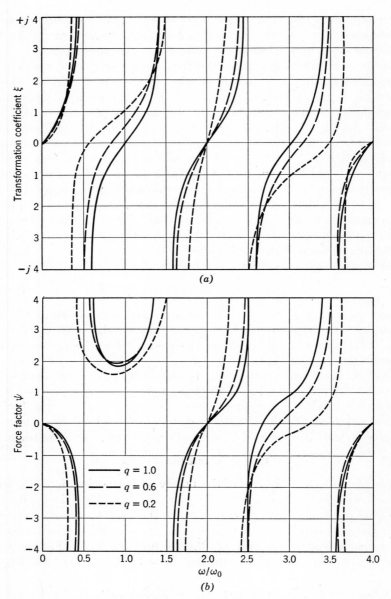

Fig. 5.14.   Transformation coefficients ψ and ξ versus ω/ω_0.

$\beta = 0.38$), we find $\alpha + \beta = 0.72$ and the total length of the transducer section is $0.36\lambda_0$.

Figure 5.15 further allows us to determine the corresponding pairs of α and β for the ratios of slot length to total length $b/(a + b) = \frac{1}{2}$,

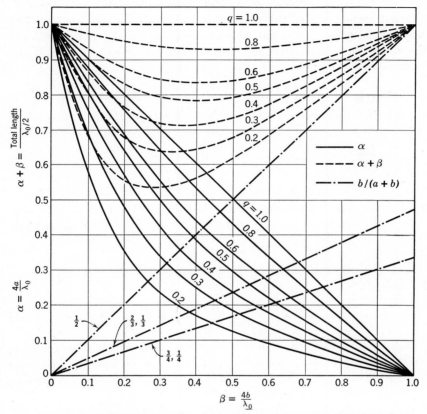

Fig. 5.15.   Relative lengths α and β of transducer sections as a function of cross-sectional coefficient q.   The straight lines through the origin represent certain ratios of slot length to total length $b/(a + b)$.   Their intersections with the solid lines determine corresponding values for α and β.   For ratios $b/(a + b) < 0.5$ the ordinate gives the value for β and the abscissa that for α at the particular intersection.

$\frac{2}{3}$, and $\frac{3}{4}$, as well as for the ratios $\frac{1}{3}$ and $\frac{1}{4}$ by use of the straight lines through the origin.   The dimensions of magnetostrictive transducers are thus fully determined by the relations expressed in Fig. 5.15.   It can be shown that the error due to the simplifying assumptions used in this theory is less than 1.3 per cent if $q \geq 0.5$ and $\alpha/(\alpha + \beta) \geq 0.6$.   These ranges cover most practical cases.

There exists a further design principle for laminated stacks of this kind, which becomes quite important if the end masses of the laminations are not equal.[25]   In this case the driving coil is located nearer to the end with the smaller mass.   High efficiency is retained, however, only if the center of mass of the transducer still lies within the constricted region, where the magnetic flux density is maximal.[26]   The node of velocity and the antinode of stress are located at the center of mass.   It is evident that optimal driving conditions prevail if the maxima of flux density and stress coincide.

5.8   Determination of Equivalent Lumped Constants

As we have demonstrated extensively in Chapter 4, it is convenient to describe a mechanical vibration system in the vicinity of resonance by the lumped constants M, K, and R.   For laminated stacks of the type described in Section 5.7 we have:

$$Z_m = \xi Z_{AB} = R_m + j(\omega M - K/\omega)$$

From the slope of the function ξ in Fig. 5.14 taken at resonance ($\xi = 0$, $\omega M = K/\omega$) one can determine[27] the equivalent mass to be

$$M_{\text{eq}} = \sigma_m M/2$$

where M is the total mass of the stack and σ_m is the equivalent mass coefficient:[28]

$$\sigma_m = 1 + \frac{\beta}{\alpha + \alpha\beta}\left(\frac{1 - q}{q}\right)^2 \sin^2\left(\alpha\pi/2\right) \tag{5.41}$$

which is plotted in Fig. 5.16 as a function of the constriction factor q. Four curves are drawn for different ratios $b/(a + b)$ of slot length to total length: curve 1 for the ratio $\frac{1}{2}$, curve 2 for the ratio $\frac{1}{4}$, curve 3 for the ratio $\frac{2}{3}$, and curve 4 for the ratio $\frac{3}{4}$.

The dynamic stiffness of a uniform rod is $K = \dfrac{\pi^2}{2}\dfrac{Y_0 S}{l}$ (see eq. 4.37b).

[25] Such unsymmetrical laminations can be calculated according to the method discussed above if eq. 5.40a is set up independently for the transducer sections on either side of the center of mass.

[26] According to L. W. Camp, (U.S. Pat. 2,530,224, November 14, 1950, and also *J. Acoust. Soc. Amer.*, *21* (1949), 382), it is of advantage to have the center of mass coincide with the plane of the change of cross-sectional area.

[27] Y. Kikuchi and K. Fukushima, *loc. cit.* (see footnote 23), p. 161.   This paper also gives a detailed calculation of laminated ring stacks.

[28] See also L. Camp, *J. Acoust. Soc. Amer.*, *20* (1948), 616.   In this paper it is shown how the area constriction factor q determines the Q of the transducer. A change of q from 1 to $\frac{1}{6}$ will reduce Q by a factor of 3.

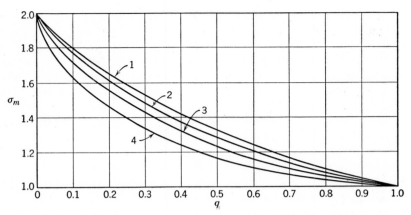

Fig. 5.16.   Equivalent mass coefficient σ_m as a function of cross-sectional coefficient q

For laminated stacks with constricted legs this reduces to

$$K_{\text{lam}} = \tau K$$

where τ is the equivalent stiffness coefficient

$$\tau = (\alpha + q\beta)\sigma_m \qquad (5.42)$$

The coefficient τ is plotted in Fig. 5.17 as a function of q, with the ratio α/β as parameter.

The equivalent loss resistance R_m is due to internal friction (imaginary part of complex modulus) and also to friction losses at the windings,

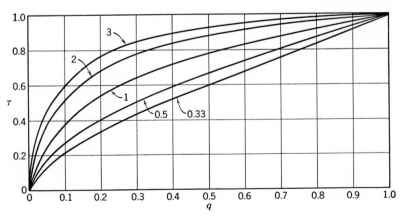

Fig. 5.17.   Equivalent stiffness coefficient τ as a function of cross-sectional coefficient q.

between laminations, and in the mounting structures. It must be evaluated empirically from motional impedance diagrams with the help of eq. 5.33. The presence of binding material (such as Bakelite cement or Cycleweld C-3) in the spaces between laminations reduces the transformation ratio α somewhat and may also lead to a slight decrease in resonance frequency.

5.9 Some Practical Aspects of Magnetostrictive Transducers

Magnetostrictive transducers are rather inefficient above a frequency of 80–100 kcps, as we can see from Table 5.3. Their main range of application is between 10 and 60 kcps. Here thickness-type piezoelectric drivers are generally impracticable because of their high impedance. Transversely driven stacks of ADP or Rochelle salt are widely used in this range, but they are less rugged than magnetostrictive stacks. The ruggedness and ease of assembly has led to the widespread use of magnetostriction in commercial depth-sounding devices for ships. Other applications are discussed in Section 7.3

Simple circuits At the low pulse repetition rates that are used for sounding to large depths, the transducers can be actuated simply by condenser discharge. Figure 5.18 schematically represents the simple circuit required for such shock excitation. In Fig. 5.18a the switching of the condenser terminal **P** may be done by mechanical relays or by a thyratron. The arrangement in Fig. 5.18a requires a high dc charging voltage, whereas the one in Fig. 5.18b uses high current at low voltage. If the circuit is interrupted at P_1, the magnetic energy $L_1 I^2$ in the choke L_1 converts into electric energy $C U^2$ in the condenser. If the ratio L/C is large a very high voltage U is developed across C at time $T = \pi/2 \sqrt{L_1 C}$. At this instant the glow tube **G** will fire so that condenser C discharges through coil L, which offers a much smaller impedance than the choke. In this way, a damped wave train is generated whose length depends on the Q of the transducer.

In many applications where the generation of sonic power is desired, modulation (60 or 50 cps) can be tolerated. In this case, self-rectifying self-generating circuits can be used which have the advantage of simplicity and low component cost.

If a magnetostrictive transducer is used for receiving only, it is sufficient to flash-polarize the core once by a short d-c current pulse which will produce a remanent internal magnetic field. In many cases, however, the transducers are used both for transmitting and receiving so that a permanent bias must be provided. This can be achieved either by a *polarizing current* or by means of *permanent magnets* inserted into the flux path of the stacks. The electronic circuits for driving magnetostrictive transducers can be designed according to well-established procedures given in standard textbooks.[29]

The control of directivity Special cylindrical magnetostriction transducers have been developed[30] for non-directional receiving. An example is the laminated ring stack illustrated in Fig. 5.11c. One should not overlook, however, the potential advantages of barium

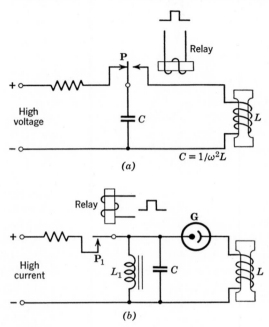

Fig. 5.18. Simple circuits for shock excitation.

titanate cylinders for receivers of uniform azimuthal sensitivity (see Section 4.13).

Underwater sound direction finding and other applications often require the azimuthal sensitivity to be confined to a small angle. The principles underlying the forming of radiation beams are discussed in Chapter 3. They lead to the basic relation for the beam width

[29] F. E. Terman, *Radio Engineers Handbook*, McGraw-Hill, New York, 1948. See also *Radio Amateurs Handbook*, Rumford Press, Concord, N.H.

[30] The description of a small probe microphone is given in the *Final Report on Atmospheric Physics*, Pa. State Coll., 1950. A ring of hard-drawn nickel is supported on a copper wire with a layer of thread interposed for sound insulation. The coil consists of 100 turns of very fine No. 48 enameled copper wire, and the whole assembly is sealed by coats of Glyptal and electrically shielded by a coat of silver paint.

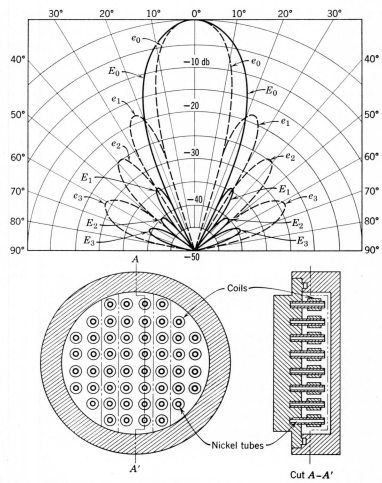

Fig. 5.19.   Underwater sound transducer using an array of nickel tubes.   Two beam patterns are shown; the dashed curve (lobes e_n) corresponds to uniform amplitude distribution; the solid curve (lobes E_n) shows side-lobe suppression due to amplitude shading.

of a circular transducer:

$$\sin \alpha_0 = 1.2\lambda/d \qquad (5.43)$$

For small values of λ/d the angle between the half-power points is approximately:

$$\alpha_{\frac{1}{2}} \simeq 25 \; \lambda/d \quad \text{(degrees)}$$

With increasing frequency, smaller diameters of the unit are needed if one wishes to obtain the same directivity.   For example, a beam angle $\alpha_{1/2}$ of about 2.5° is obtained with $d = 50$ cm at 30 kcps, but with $d = 0.5$ cm at 3 mcps. At low frequencies an array of transducer elements may be needed to cover the required area. The elements can be stacks of ADP crystals as described in Chapter 3, or laminated magnetostrictive stacks, or simply nickel tubes that are partly slotted to reduce eddy currents. Figure 5.19 illustrates an underwater sound transducer composed of such nickel tubes; the corresponding beam pattern is also shown.[31] Whenever high directivity is desired, as in echo ranging, the amplitude distribution across the transducer face is an important consideration since it determines the ratio of the energy contained in the main lobe to the energy in the side lobes. A suppression of the side lobes is often desired. The character of the near field in front of transmitters is also influenced by the lateral amplitude distribution on the transducer face (see Fig. 3.12).

If the piston is composed of several transducer elements, as illustrated by Fig. 5.19, the lateral amplitude distribution can be shaped as desired by adjusting (*shading*) the sensitivity of the individual elements.[32]

There will usually be some optimum design of beam characteristics, and a study of the special requirements will suggest the best compromise between main-beam sharpness and side-lobe suppression. This is of particular importance in underwater sound work.[33]

There are many ways of adjusting the desired amplitude distribution. This can be done electrically by varying the number of turns

[31] L. Batchelder, U.S. Pat. 2,407,643 and 2,407,293, September 17, 1946. See also H. M. Hart, U.S. Pat. 2,407,271, September 10, 1946.

[32] For instance, amplitude graduation across the transducer radius in steps of 1:2:3:4 and in zone widths of 4:3:4:9 will result in a side-lobe suppression of more than 30 db. More detailed information on this technique is given by F. Massa in U.S. Pat. 2,427,062, September 9, 1947, and in the paper by N. Davids, E. Thurston, and R. Mueser, *J. Acoust. Soc. Amer.*, *24* (1952), 50.

[33] H. M. Hart, U.S. Pat. 285,902, July 22, 1939, gives the following design equation for a circular radiator having a radially symmetric amplitude distribution $A(r)$ and an amplitude A_0 at the center:

$$\frac{A(r)}{A_0} = 1 - \frac{12}{7}\left(\frac{r}{R}\right)^2 + \frac{6}{7}\left(\frac{r}{R}\right)^4$$

An alternative design gives a lateral amplitude distribution $A(x)$ symmetrical about a diameter:

$$\frac{A(x)}{A_{av}} = \frac{7}{5} - \frac{32}{15}\left(\frac{x}{R}\right)^2 + \frac{16}{15}\left(\frac{x}{R}\right)^4$$

in which A_{av} is the average value of the amplitude taken over the whole surface and x is the lateral distance of the chord from the diameter of symmetry.

on the driving coils of the appropriate transducer elements, or by connecting these coils to different taps of a common matching transformer.[34]   Or, the amplitude distribution can be shaped by mechanical means if the ratio of the mass of the driving elements to the mass of their associated radiating members is varied.

If the signals obtained from the elements within each row of the transducer array are shifted in phase by an increasing amount, the

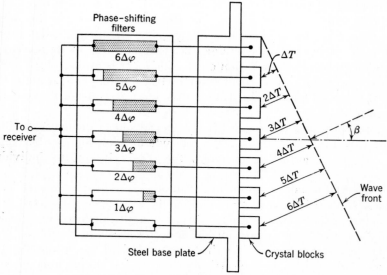

Fig. 5.20.   Beam tilting by means of phasing

whole directivity pattern will be tilted by an angle β, depending on the phase shift between adjacent elements:

$$\Delta\phi = 2\pi\,\frac{\Delta T}{T} = \omega\,\frac{D\,\sin\,\beta}{c} \tag{5.44}$$

where $T = \lambda/c$ is the period of the sound vibration in the medium and D is the spacing of adjacent transducer elements, as shown in Fig. 5.20.   It is possible to build electronic phase-shifting networks that permit a periodic sweeping of the receiver pattern over a wide angle.[35]

[34] E. E. Turner, U.S. Pat. 2,407,329, September 10, 1946.

[35] In a unit developed by the Bell Telephone Laboratories the beam can be shifted from −90° to +90° by a frequency change from 18 kcps to 24 kcps.   Filters of the confluent bandpass type are used which have a uniform phase shift with frequency.   See also L. Batchelder, U.S. Pat. 2,408,028, September 24, 1946, and 2,406,340, August 27, 1946.

CHAPTER 6

Physical Mechanisms for Sonic Processing

6.1 General Considerations

The applications of sonics, as discussed in Chapter 1, are divided broadly in two categories: analysis and processing. This division is analogous to that of electrical engineering, which encompasses communications and power. In the analytical applications, such as flaw detection, underwater signaling, determination of elastic and molecular properties, and viscosimetry, we require only sufficient power to yield an interpretable signal. Usually the desired information can be communicated, above "noise," at intensities so small that they in no way influence the sonic transmission medium. Processing, on the other hand, implicitly demands sufficient power (or intensity, pressure, or particle velocity) to modify the medium in some specified manner, such as degassing, emulsification, coagulation, surface cleaning, or changing the viscosity.

From the physical point of view we might designate these two parts as *small-amplitude* and *large-amplitude* sonics, though we recognize that there will be borderline cases and exceptions, such as the production of cavitation near the face of a high-power projector for underwater signaling. In Chapters 2 and 3 we reviewed the basic principles of small-amplitude sound, its radiation, transmission, reflection, and scattering. Nearly all demands for the generation of small-amplitude sound can be met by electroacoustic transducers as discussed in Chapters 4 and 5. In the present chapter we discuss the behavior of large-amplitude sound and its effects on materials. Later we shall consider the design of generating systems to meet the special demands of sonic processing.

We start with an elementary discussion of aerosols in which the suspended particles execute oscillatory motions under the influence of sound. These motions, under certain conditions, greatly increase the rate of collisions among particles which then cling together and form larger particles that are more readily collected.[1]

We then consider several types of steady forces exerted on particles by a sound field. These produce a steady drift, rather than an oscillation with the sound, and in some cases the particles move in a particular direction with respect to the sound field. These forces can be used to enhance aerosol agglomeration, and they may provide a new tool for sorting and separating fine particles.

Particles suspended in a liquid are also acted on by steady forces of the same type. More generally, any discontinuity within or at the boundary of a liquid is subject to sonic forces. These can produce structural changes in biological tissues, viscoelastic materials, and multiphase chemical systems.

Of particular importance in liquids is the phenomenon of cavitation, and the associated formation, oscillation, and collapse of gas or vapor bubbles. Steady forces and cavitation are aspects of large-amplitude sound that are discussed in detail in this chapter.[2] One cannot over-emphasize the need for a clear understanding of these basic phenomena. The lack of such understanding has been responsible for misconceptions and disappointments in many past attempts in sonic processing.

The choice of sonic variables Up to this point we have spoken of high power and large amplitude in general terms only. We must now become more specific: we must designate those particular variables of the sonic radiation that correlate significantly with the particular processing mechanism, and we must express the correlations as quantitatively as possible. The sonic variables include:

1. System variables
    Frequency
    Total power radiated
    Time of radiation
    Area of radiation
    Amplitude distribution over the radiating area

---

[1] Substances differ widely as to their adhering properties, which depend largely on the microstructure of the particle surfaces. Carbon black, for example, clings readily, wheras some forms of cement dust with smooth hard surfaces do not. It is sometimes possible to treat a non-adhering aerosol with water spray or other agent that increases the adhesion among particles. Such questions of physical or chemical properties of materials to be processed lie beyond the scope of this book. However, they should be studied in detail for any contemplated application because they may have a critical influence on the economic possibilities of the proposed sonic process.

[2] The generation of heat by sound absorption is used in some processes. Absorption phenomena are discussed in Chapter 8 and the appendix.

    Boundary conditions of the container
    Losses in the processed medium
2. Field-point variables
    Particle displacement
    Particle velocity
    Sound pressure
    Acceleration
    Intensity
    Energy density

Interrelations among field variables are discussed in Chapter 2. Most of the processes considered to date can be described adequately with about three of these variables, but the variables required are by no means the same for all processes.

A few processes depend only on the total energy absorbed by a unit volume of the substance. The mechanism is presumably the conversion of sound energy into a particular quantity of heat. This appears to be the principle mechanism in medical therapy, for example.[3] The energy absorbed will depend on the absorption coefficient of the tissue at the frequency of radiation.[4] Knowing this, one can compute the energy that must be supplied. This, in turn, is the product of power and time of irradiation. The frequency is not a primary variable where only heating is desired. However, the range of usable frequencies may be dictated by such considerations as beam sharpness and size of radiator, required depth of penetration, peak pressure limitations for freedom from cavitation, or manufacturing economy.

Many liquid processes depend mainly or solely on cavitation. Below the cavitation threshold there is no useful effect, but once the threshold is reached and maintained there is no appreciable benefit from further increases in the sound pressure. Thus the process can be designed primarily in terms of required sound pressure throughout a given volume of material. The cavitation threshold pressure, in turn, depends on frequency, on temperature, on static pressure, and on properties of the material. In some cases the desired effect is produced only after a certain time of exposure to cavitation. If a continuous flow treatment is involved, it will be necessary to design the flow rate and the area of radiation to satisfy the requirements.

Agglomeration of aerosols depends on particle velocity, frequency, and exposure time. Some of the steady forces that may be involved

[3] H. Schwan and F. Carstensen, *J. Am. Med. Assoc.*, May 1952. R. Pohlman, "Die Ultraschalltherapie," published in 1950 by Huber, Bern, Switzerland.
[4] T. F. Hueter, Naturwiss., *35* (1948), 285.

are related basically to the energy density, but this can be expressed in terms of the velocity and certain constants of the medium and the sound field.   It is important to recognize that particle velocity is not uniquely determined by the sonic power, but depends also on the sound field characteristics (e.g., the amplification at velocity maxima in a standing wave).   Since operating cost depends on watt hours, a quantitative knowledge of the relations among particle velocity, exposure time, product yields, and total power is necessary to design an economically optimized system.

6.2   Sound Fields in Processing Tanks

When the variables essential for a proposed process have been analyzed, along the lines indicated above, and expanded in the following sections, one is in a position to consider transducers and processing

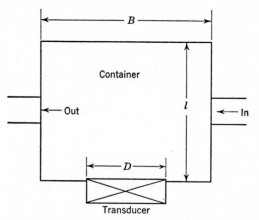

Fig. 6.1.   Schematic diagram of a processing system (see Table 6.1).

tanks.   An illustrative system is shown in Fig. 6.1, consisting of a container, a transducer, and a means for circulating a fluid through the sound field.   We have previously analyzed transducers (Chapters 4 and 5) as isolated components, and have seen that properly designed electroacoustic transducers can have electroacoustic conversion efficiencies of 30 to 50 per cent when radiating into a free field.

We now consider the transducer and associated tank equipment as a system, and extend the concept of efficiency to express the useful yield per unit cost.   For a process which depends directly on particle velocity, the transducer conversion efficiency alone has little practical meaning if the same transducer in two different tanks produces very different values of particle velocity.   Also, a 50 per cent "efficient" electroacoustic transducer would be less useful than a 10 per cent "efficient" fluid-dynamic type, if the system containing the latter gave a greater product yield per unit cost.

A full analysis of a transducer-tank system usually requires an extensive application of theoretical principles and a coordinated program of experiments in scale models. However, a general prediction of the system performance can be given in terms of the idealized behavior of certain limiting configurations, as summarized in Table 6.1. Five types of sound field are listed, together with certain design conditions and sonic variables associated with each. The design conditions indicate limiting ranges only; each type of field can be obtained to some extent with other conditions also, but the behavior and the analysis are then more complicated.

The following considerations have led to the idealized system design conditions given in Table 6.1. To obtain an essentially free field, the tank must be large compared to wavelength (l, $B > 10\lambda$) and the energy that is reflected from the tank walls back to the transducer must be reduced at least by 20 db. This reduction may result either from the attenuation α_m of the medium within the tank ($\alpha_m l > 10$), or from the absorption at the tank surfaces ($\alpha_s > 0.9$). Free field conditions are more easily realized as the wavelength decreases.

A diffuse field also requires short wavelengths ($\lambda \ll l$, B), and the tank surfaces must be irregular in shape.[5] In this case, also, the absorption (α_s and α_m) in the tank must be relatively low. The values given for the rms pressure and other variables in a diffuse field are valid only for space averages throughout the tank. Values at individual points may deviate widely (10 or 20 db) from the average values. The pressure is the variable that is usually measured (as by a standard sound-level meter), and the energy density and intensity can be computed from the given relations.

A standing-wave field is often desired because of the amplification of pressure or particle velocity at the nodes or loops. A one-dimensional standing wave (without crossmodes), can be obtained in a container if its diameter D is much smaller than the wavelength ($B \simeq D < \lambda$). This requirement calls for relatively low frequencies. Alternatively, a plane standing wave can be obtained if the transducer and tank diameters are much larger than the wavelength, and if the surface of the container opposite the transducer is aligned parallel to the transducer face and the distance between the faces is

[5] A detailed discussion of requirements for sound diffusion is given by P. M. Morse and R. H. Bolt, "Sound Waves in Rooms," *Rev. Mod. Phys.*, April, 1944.

Table 6.1

Sound-Field Type	System Design Conditions	Sonic-Field Variables
a, Free wave field (plane waves)	$l, B > 10\lambda, D > \lambda,$ $\alpha_m > 10/l$, or $\alpha_s > 0.9$	$p = \sqrt{\dfrac{4\rho_0 c\,W}{\pi D^2}}$ $E = \dfrac{4W}{\pi D^2 c}$ $\mathit{s} = Ec$
b, Diffuse field	$l, D > 10\lambda,$ $\alpha_m < 1/3l$, and $\alpha_s < 0.2$ Boundary shape irregular	$p = \sqrt{\dfrac{4\rho_0 c\,W}{a_s}}$ $E = \dfrac{4W}{a_s c}$ $\mathit{s} = \dfrac{Ec}{4}$ Values averaged over space
c, Standing wave field (plane waves)	$B, D \ll \lambda$ or $B, D \gg \lambda$ $\alpha_m < 1/\lambda,\ 10/l$ $l \simeq n\lambda/4,\ n = 2, 3, 4, 5, \cdots$ Source impedance matched to line impedance	$p = \sqrt{\dfrac{4\rho_0 c\,W}{\pi D^2}}$ (SWR) at pressure maximum $u = \sqrt{\dfrac{4W/\rho_0 c}{\pi D^2}}$ (SWR) at velocity maximum $\mathit{s} \simeq 0$
d, Pressure field	$l, B, D \ll \lambda, D \simeq B$ Rigid closed container	$p = \dfrac{\rho_0 c^2}{l}\, y_p$ $Z_p = -j\,\dfrac{\pi \rho_0 c^2 D^2}{4 l \omega}$
e, Acceleration field	$l, B, D \ll \lambda, D \simeq B$ Liquid in container with one open surface	$a = \dfrac{4}{\pi D^2 \rho_0 l}\, F_p$ $Z_p = j\,\dfrac{\pi D^2 \rho_0 l \omega}{4}$

Definition of Symbols

ρ_0 = density of medium
c = sound velocity of medium
$\omega = 2\pi \times$ frequency
B = diameter ⎱ of tank
l = length ⎰
D = diameter of piston
y_p = amplitude of piston motion
F_p = Force applied by piston
Z_p = Mechanical impedance seen by piston
SWR = Standing-wave ratio
$\quad = \dfrac{1 + R}{1 - R} = \dfrac{P_{max}}{P_{min}}$
R = Amplitude reflection coefficient

λ = wavelength
α_m = attenuation constant of medium in container (db/m)
α_s = average absorption coefficient of container surfaces
$a_s = \alpha_s S$ = absorptive units in container
S = interior surface area of container
W = acoustic power delivered by source
p = rms pressure in tank
u = rms particle velocity in tank
a = rms acceleration in tank
E = energy density
s = intensity

adjusted to a multiple of half waves. In either case, the transducer will be loaded with an impedance that depends on the length of the container and on the reflection property of the terminating surface. For strong standing waves the terminal impedance must be either much greater than or much less than the characteristic impedance of the medium in the tank.

If the wavelength is much greater than all dimensions of the tank, the entire contents are subjected to an essentially uniform excitation. This is a pure pressure excitation if all bounding surfaces are *rigid* (high impedance). Conversely, if one surface is *soft* (low impedance) compared with the medium, the contents are vibrated with a large velocity and acceleration. In these cases the transducer works into an impedance that is largely reactive, and little power is expended in producing the pressure or acceleration. The power losses in the system are attributable mainly to damping in the container walls or to internal losses in the transducer itself.

The concept of *system gain factors* is often useful in studying the economics of a process. These are dimensionless ratios that relate the values of a particular variable as obtained in two different types of field, as follows:

$$\text{(diffuse-field gain factor)} = \frac{(p^2/W)_{\text{diffuse}}}{(p^2/W)_{\text{free field}}} = \frac{\pi D^2}{\alpha_s} \qquad (6.1a)$$

$$\text{(standing-wave gain factor)} = \frac{(p^2/W)_{\text{standing wave}}}{(p^2/W)_{\text{free field}}} = \text{SWR} \qquad (6.1b)$$

$$\text{(pressure-field gain factor)} = \frac{(p/y_p)_{\text{tank}}}{(p/y_p)_{\text{free field}}} = \frac{1}{kl} \qquad (6.1c)$$

$$\text{(acceleration-field gain factor)} = \frac{(a/F_p)_{\text{tank}}}{(a/F_p)_{\text{free field}}} = \frac{1}{kl} \qquad (6.1d)$$

As an example, consider a diffuse-field tank of proportions $B = l = 2D$, lined with steel having an absorption coefficient $\alpha_s = 0.01$. The gain factor by eq. 6.1a is about 16, so the average sound-pressure level in the tank would be about 12 db higher than in a free plane wave generated by the same amount of power. Again, let a piston vibrating with constant amplitude Y_p radiate into a closed tank of dimensions $l = B = D = \lambda/60$. The pressure will be about ten times that produced in free plane waves by the same piston amplitude. In the latter case plane waves could be produced only in a long tube with a terminating impedance that matched the characteristic impedance of the medium, for the very small piston $(D \ll \lambda)$ would radiate essentially spherical waves into an "infinite" medium.

We note from Table 6.1 that in some important cases (a, b, c) the principle sonic variable depends both on the container characteristics and the power delivered by the source to the system.   Not all this power will be available for processing, but a part of it will be dissipated in various ways before it can reach and affect the whole fluid volume to be processed.   We have already mentioned the attenuation in the medium and the absorption at the container walls.   In media with

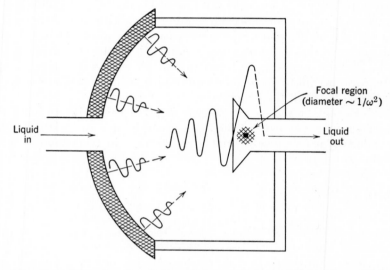

Fig. 6.2.   Focusing system for continuous flow.   Note amplitude decay of individual sound rays in the absorbing medium.   This decay is compensated by focusing, as shown schematically.

high viscosity or inhomogeneity the sound intensity in the regions of the container that are remote from the sonic source will be reduced. This will limit the volume that can be treated at a given time, even if banks of transducers are installed at different locations of the container.   Under these conditions *flow processing* methods (continuous or recirculated) have to be adopted.   Either the fluid is forced through a small gap over the transducer face using low frequencies (case d, pressure field) or it is forced through the focal region of a converging transducer device (case a, free field).   Figure 6.2 illustrates the latter possibility, which is discussed in detail in Section 7.4.   We note that the geometrical increase in energy density makes up for the damping of the individual wave trains.   All the liquid then passes through a small region where the intensity is 10 to 10^3 times larger than at the transducer face, depending on the losses in the liquid and the frequency.

In a processing tank some energy will be transmitted through the container walls to regions outside. Also, there may be some losses through the ports of the container which serve as fluid inlet or outlet in continuous-flow systems. These wall and port losses may bring up a serious noise problem if audible frequencies are used as with most fluid dynamic transducers (sirens, jets). With such systems sufficient sound isolation must be provided to reduce the noise to tolerable levels.[6]

6.3 Fundamentals of Gas Kinetics

Most gas-phase sonic applications are based on specific mechanisms of interaction between a sound wave and a system of particles suspended in a gas. Such suspensions are called "aerosols." In practice the gas may be a mixture, but we shall consider only the case in which all the gas molecules are identical and each has a mass $m_m = M/N$ (M = molecular weight, N = Avogadro's number). If there are n_m molecules per unit volume the density of the gas is $\rho_g = n_m m_m$. We shall also consider the gas to be "ideal": the molecules are very far apart compared to their diameter, they perform perfectly elastic collisions with each other, and their only interaction is a simple exchange momentum. Under these assumptions the simple procedures of kinetic theory lead to approximate expressions for the characteristic properties of the gas. We shall review some of these results,[7] and subsequently apply a similar analysis to the suspended particles in the aerosol.

The molecules, under equilibrium conditions, are moving in a completely random manner, with a wide range of velocities (vectors) that are distributed according to some probability function. The square root of the sum of the squares of all the velocity magnitudes is the rms velocity v_m. In terms of this quantity the internal pressure of the gas is approximately $P_g = \frac{1}{3} n_m m_m v_m^2$. This is the pressure that would be exerted on the walls of a container or on the surface of a pressure gauge placed in the gas. This pressure is simply the

[6] L. L. Beranek *Acoustics*, Chapter 11, McGraw-Hill, New York, 1954.

[7] Kinetic-theory derivations with various degrees of approximation, and discussions of the underlying assumptions and their consequences, can be found in standard works such as E. H. Kennard, *Kinetic Theory of Gases*, McGraw-Hill, New York, 1938; Sir James Jeans, *Dynamical Theory of Gases*, Cambridge, 1930; L. B. Loeb, *Kinetic Theory of Gases*, McGraw-Hill, New York, 1938.

force per unit area arising from the sum of the momentum changes as the molecules strike the surface at a certain rate and rebound with equal and opposite normal velocity (recall Newton's second law).

Combining the above relations we can write

$$v_m = (3P_g/\rho_g)^{\frac{1}{2}} \tag{6.2}[8]$$

This is the same as the equation for the velocity of sound in the gas, but with γ replaced by the constant 3 (which is only an approximation). The velocity of sound is the same order of magnitude as the rms molecular velocity, just a little less. This is quite reasonable, for sound motion is carried by molecular motions.

Next we introduce the effective diameter of the molecule d_m. This is the equivalent diameter of the assumed "billiard ball" molecule but is actually a dimension determined by the repulsive forces rather than the concentration of mass. As the "average" molecule moves, it sweeps out a cylindrical volume of length v_m in 1 sec. The actual cylinder is bent at each collision, but we can consider it straight for the analysis. This cylinder will touch all molecules lying within $d_m/2$ of its surface. That is, the cross-sectional area swept by the moving molecule is πd_m^2. Now, if all the other molecules were stationary, the moving molecule would hit $\pi d_m^2 v_m n_m$ molecules per second. We can use this result in some cases for aerosol particles in a sound field, where larger particles are moving much less rapidly than smaller particles. But in the gas we must take account of the relative velocities, in all directions, of the other molecules. This leads to the following approximate expression for the number of collisions per second experienced by one molecule:

$$Z_m = 4d_m^2 v_m n_m \tag{6.3}$$

The average distance between successive collisions of a given molecule is its mean free path:

$$L_m = v_m/Z_m = \tfrac{1}{4}d_m^2 n_m \tag{6.4}$$

Interestingly, this depends only on the size and number of molecules, not on their velocity. However, the value of the constant in the equation depends on the type of velocity distribution.

Tangential stresses and viscosity Let us consider two plane parallel sheets of area S separated by a distance dy equal to the mean

---

[8] The rms velocity of the molecules can also be expressed in terms of the absolute temperature T.

$$v_m = 3k_B T/m_m)^{\frac{1}{2}} \tag{6.2a}$$

where k_B is Boltzmann's constant (see Table 6.2).

free path of the gas molecules which are contained between the sheets. Let one sheet be fixed and let the other move with a velocity dv_x parallel to it. Each molecule which strikes the moving sheet then rebounds with the velocity dv_x superimposed on the x component it possessed before striking. Its velocity components in the y and z directions are unchanged. In each collision with one of the sheets the molecule experiences a momentum change $m_m\, dv_x$. The result is a retarding force on the moving sheets which is equal to $m_m\, dv_x$ times the total number of impacts per second:

$$F_x = m_m\, dv_x \left(SL_m \frac{n_m}{3} \right) Z_m \qquad (6.4a)$$

where $SL_m n_m$ is the number of molecules contained in the space $S\, dy = SL_m$ between the sheets. Using eqs. 6.3 and 6.4 this force becomes

$$F_x = \left(\frac{n_m m_m v_m L_m}{3} \right) S \frac{dv_x}{dy}$$

$$= \eta S \frac{dv_x}{dy} \qquad (6.4b)$$

in which η is the so-called viscosity coefficient, defined as the tangential stress per unit velocity gradient:

$$\eta = \frac{m_m v_m}{12 d_m{}^2} \text{ (kg/sec/m or centipoise)} \qquad (6.5)$$

One important consequence of viscosity[9] is the *boundary layer* adjacent to any fixed surface in a moving fluid stream. Right at the surface the molecules must be at rest relative to the surface, and out in the stream they must have the mass flow velocity of the fluid (superposed on the molecular velocities). The effective thickness of the boundary layer that is set up by the periodic flow in a sound wave of frequency ω is $t_b = \sqrt{(v_m L_m)/3\omega}$. Beyond this distance the effect of the boundary is not felt by the molecules. This boundary layer should not be confused with the range of vorticity or with a hydro-dynamic flow pattern, in either of which it is possible for the effect of a boundary to be "felt" by a fluid stream at far greater distances than the boundary-layer thickness.

[9] Another consequence of the momentum transfer between molecules is heat conduction. The coefficient of heat conductivity is $k_h = \dfrac{\eta}{\gamma - 1} \dfrac{k_B}{m_m} \mathbf{K}_h$ kilocal/ (m·sec·degree), where $\mathbf{K}_h$ is the mechanical equivalent of heat (kilocalories/joule).

Stokes' law and free-fall velocity   Viscosity is a primary means of coupling the particles in an aerosol to the motions of the gas. If the particle is a rigid smooth sphere of diameter d_p the viscous drag force is given by Stokes' law:

$$F_d = 3\pi\eta d_p v_g \tag{6.6}$$

in which v_g is the velocity of the gas relative to that of the particle. If the particle is allowed to fall freely against gravity its equation of motion is:

$$m_p \frac{dv_p}{dt} + 3\pi\eta d_p v_p = m_p g \tag{6.7}$$

in which m_p is the mass of the particle and v_p its vertical velocity. The steady-state solution $(dv_p/dt = 0)$ yields the free fall at terminal velocity:

$$v_t = \frac{m_p g}{3\pi\eta d_p} = \frac{d_p{}^2 \rho_p g}{18\eta} \tag{6.8}$$

in which ρ_p is the density of the material in the particle. In some cases the purpose of sonic agglomeration may be to increase the average particle size until the free-fall velocity is sufficiently great to meet some requirement for collection rate.

Brownian motion   If the particle is very small (d_p of the order of microns or less) a microscopic examination will reveal random motions of the particles, even in a completely "stationary" gas. These are Brownian motions caused by the unbalanced forces of a relatively small number of gas molecules striking the particle during any small interval of time. Though the particles are still many order of magnitudes larger than the molecules, their motions resemble those of the molecules, and the two can be related by a simple theory. The result is the formula

$$\xi_b{}^2 = \frac{8d_m{}^2 v_m}{9d_p}\tau \equiv \frac{2k_B T}{3\pi\eta d_p}\tau \tag{6.9}$$

in which $\xi_b{}^2$ is the mean squared displacement of the particle along any linear coordinate during a time interval τ. The quantity T is the absolute temperature, and k_B is the Boltzmann constant. The random particle velocities due to Brownian motion are usually much smaller than the velocities of the oscillating motion caused by viscous drag forces which is discussed in Sections 6.4 and 6.6. For example, in a sound field of 160-db intensity and with particles of 1-micron diameter the average Brownian velocity is 10^3 times smaller than the maximum sonic particle velocity. Only for particle diameters below 0.001 microns (10^{-9} m) do the two velocities become comparable.

The gas kinetic constants introduced in the preceding paragraphs and some values of the derived quantities for hydrogen molecules at 0°C and 1 atm pressure are summarized in Table 6.2. We note that

Table 6.2 Gas Kinetic Constants and Derived Quantities

Boltzmann constant	$k_B = 1.38 \times 10^{-23}$ watt·sec/degree
Avogadro's number	$N = 6.02 \times 10^{23}$ molecules per mole
Mechanical heat equivalent	$\mathbf{K}_h = 2.39 \times 10^{-4}$ kilocal/watt·sec
Absolute temperature	$T_K = T°$ Centigrade $+ 273.2°$
	Kelvin (°K)

Some Derived Quantities for Hydrogen molecules (at 0°C 1 atm)

Diameter	$d_m \simeq 10^{-10}$ m
Mass	$m_m \simeq 1.66 \times 10^{-27}$ kg
Mean free path	$L_m \simeq 1.7 \times 10^{-7}$ m
Mean number of collisions per second	$Z_c \simeq 10^{10}$/sec
Viscosity	$\eta = \dfrac{(3k_B T_K m_m)^{1/2}}{12 d_m{}^2}$
	$\simeq 8.4 \times 10^{-6}$ newtons·sec/m^2
	(centipoise)
Kinematic viscosity	$\nu = \eta/\rho \simeq 4.25 \times 10^{-4}$ m^2/sec
Heat conductivity	$k_h = \dfrac{\eta}{(\gamma - 1)} \dfrac{k_B}{m_m} \mathbf{K}_h$
	$\simeq 4 \times 10^{-5}$ kilocal/(m·sec·degree)
Mean molecular velocity	$v_m \simeq 2.5 \times 10^3$ m/sec
Sound velocity	$c = 1.284 \times 10^3$ m/sec
Specific heat ratio	$\gamma = 1.408$

the viscosity turns out to be independent of pressure or density as a result of combining eq. 6.2a with eq. 6.5 and that the ratio $\eta/k_h = (\gamma - 1)m_m/k_B$ is a constant. Another important quantity which occurs in most fluid dynamic equations is the kinematic coefficient of viscosity $\nu = \eta/\rho$. From eq. 6.5 and $\rho = n_m m_m$ it follows that this is simply $\nu = (v_m L_m)/3$.

6.4 Relative Velocity Effects; Particle Agglomeration

We are now ready to consider a simple sonic mechanism for aerosol processing. We have stated that a sound wave incident on a suspension of small particles in a medium will impart vibratory motion to the particles, and that small particles will follow the vibration more readily than large ones. The greater the difference in amplitudes between large and small particles the more often collisions will occur between them. Two particles will frequently stick together upon collision. The total mass will increase as more and more particles collide with the original two particles. We note that by this mechanism the original particle size distribution is changed, the number of small-sized particles being reduced and the number of large particles increased. Such a process we shall call agglomeration or coagulation, and it has been found to occur in aerosols which are suspensions of air particles in a gas, such as in smokes, fumes, and mists.

As an example, let us direct a beam of sonic energy (frequency between 1 and 3 kcps) from a powerful generator though a thin diaphragm into a tank filled with artificial fog such as magnesium oxide. If the intensity of the incident sound reaches a level of about 150 db, intense agitation of the particles is observed for a few seconds. A microscopic inspection under dark-field illumination reveals that particles of a diameter smaller than 2 microns follow the motion of the sound

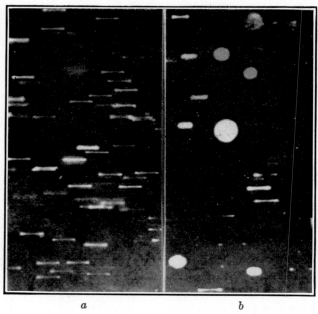

a   b

Fig. 6.3.   Particle motion in 2-kcps sound field.   a, Most particles smaller than 2 microns.   b, Most particles larger than 10 microns.

waves completely, as shown in Fig. 6.3a, while particles larger than 10 microns are almost at rest (Fig. 6.3b). After a while the fog gradually dissipates as the agglomerated particles are settling down on the bottom of the container.

If a fluid of viscosity η flows by a rigid spherical particle of radius r, momentum is transferred to the particle. The transfer of momentum occurs within the boundary layer between the sphere and the fluid. This leads to a force on particles that are much smaller than wavelength. The oscillatory motion of the fluid in a sound wave produces an alternating force according to Stokes' law (eq. 6.6) which is in dynamic equilibrium with the inertial force of the particle. Equation 6.7 is applicable here, if we neglect gravity and substitute for v_p in the inertia term the velocity of the particle $u_p = \omega \xi_P$ and in the viscous term the relative velocity between the fluid and the particle, $u = u_F - u_P = \omega(\xi_F - \xi_P)$.   Equation 6.7 can then be rewritten as:

$$\frac{6\pi\eta r}{j\omega m_p} (\xi_F - \xi_P) = \xi_P \qquad (6.10)$$

Solving for ξ_P/ξ_F and substituting $m_p = \frac{4}{3}\pi r^3 \rho$ (spherical particles) we obtain

$$\frac{\xi_P}{\xi_F} = \frac{1}{1 + j\frac{2}{9}\frac{\rho}{\eta}\omega r^2}$$

We recognize a difference in magnitude and a shift in phase between fluid and particle motion which both depend on ωr^2.   The magnitude of the displacement ratio is

$$\left|\frac{\xi_P}{\xi_F}\right| = \frac{1}{\left[1 + \left(\dfrac{2\rho\omega r^2}{9\eta}\right)^2\right]^{1/2}} \qquad (6.11)$$

From eq. 6.11 follows that for very small particles ($r \to 0$) the ratio ξ_P/ξ_F becomes unity, i.e., that these particles move with the sound wave.   On the other hand, the value of ξ_P/ξ_F decreases as the particle size increases.   This relationship is illustrated in Fig. 6.4a for one particular frequency.

Optimum frequency range   In most aerosols and industrial fogs the particles are distributed in size over some range.   To promote relative displacements among the particles of different size that lead to collisions and subsequent agglomeration, a particular frequency will be most effective.   This is demonstrated by Fig. 6.4b for particles with a peak in the distribution curve at a radius of 5 microns.   The optimum frequency (in this case 2 kcps) is found from eq. 6.11 if we set $\xi_P/\xi_F = 0.5$, which yields:

$$f = \frac{9}{r^2}\frac{\sqrt{3}}{4\pi}\frac{\eta}{\rho}$$

For air at room temperature we obtain:

$$f = \frac{22.4}{\rho r^2} \quad \text{(kcps)} \qquad (6.12)$$

if ρ is expressed in grams per cubic centimeter and r in microns.   This important relationship is plotted in Fig. 6.5.   In using eq. 6.12 we

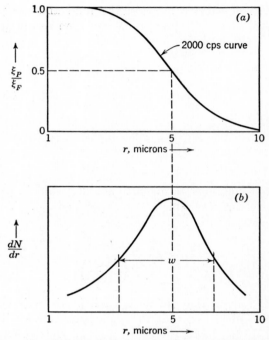

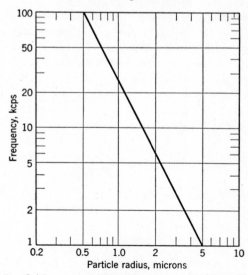

Fig. 6.4.   *a*, Relative displacement between particles of different size.   *b*, Typical distribution of particle sizes.

Fig. 6.5.   Optimum processing frequency versus particle size.

must bear in mind that during sonic processing the particle size distribution is shifted toward larger sizes requiring lower frequencies than indicated by Fig. 6.5 for the initial distribution.

6.5   Large-Amplitude Effects in Gases

This need for a frequency spectrum rather than one single frequency is met to some extent by the fact that for airborne sound of high intensity (150 db ref $2 \cdot 10^{-5}$ newton/m^2) the wave form is distorted from a sinusoidal shape to a sawtooth shape which contains harmonics. At such intensities the particle displacement is not infinitesimal any

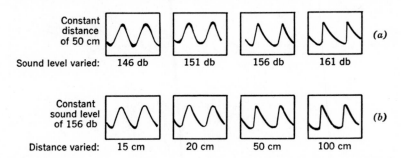

Fig. 6.6.   Development of sawtooth waves in a sound field of high amplitude (wave trains shown travel from left to right).

more, as was assumed in the derivations of Chapter 2.   If the amplitude of particle displacement is finite, the density and compressibility of the gas are no longer constant and higher order terms must be taken into account in the wave equation.[10]   This non-linear behavior is most pronounced in explosion phenomena where shock wave fronts of great steepness are observed which propagate with supersonic velocities and contain a wide frequency spectrum (see Section 8.9).

Let us consider the shape of plane waves produced by a high-intensity generator[11] operating at 15 kcps.   In Fig. 6.6a, the wave forms at a distance 50 cm from the source are traced for four pressure levels from 146 db to 161 db.   In Fig. 6.6b the source pressure amplitude is fixed at 156 db but the distance is varied from 15 to 100 cm.   We note that the wave must travel a certain distance to allow

[10] R. D. Fay, *J. Acoust. Soc. Amer.*, *3* (1931), 223 and G. C. Werth and L. P. Delsasso, *J. Acoust. Soc. Amer.*, *26* (1954), 59.   See also Pa. State Coll., *Final Report on Atmospheric Physics*, 1950, pp. 63 and 246.

[11] Electrodynamic piston, as discussed in Section 7.6 or siren, as discussed in Section 7.8.

for build-up of the distortion.   The distribution of sound amplitudes over the various harmonics in the distorted sound wave is of particular interest.   In Fig. 6.7 the acoustic pressure of the harmonics is plotted versus source amplitude for 15-kcps sound at a distance of 50 cm from the source.   We note that below certain amplitudes the sound

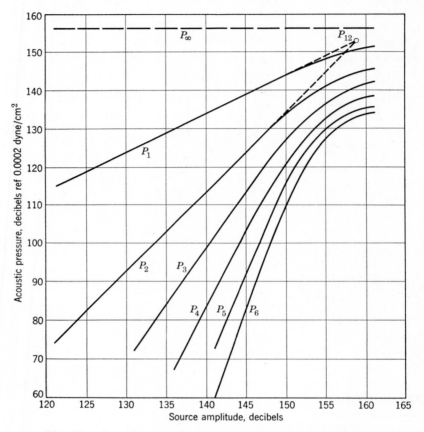

Fig. 6.7.   Acoustic pressure of harmonics versus source strength.

pressure of the nth harmonic rises as the nth power of the source pressure.   At higher source amplitudes the curves bend over and finally reach limiting values.[12]   It turns out that the sound pressure of the fundamental measured on a given point x on the beam axis asymptotically approaches the value $P_{\infty} = \sqrt{2} \cdot P_{12} \simeq 156$ db, where

[12] This holds for the practical case where a gas is blown across the sonic beam for processing.

P_{12} is the point of intersection of the extrapolated low-pressure curves for the fundamental and second harmonic, as shown in Fig. 6.7. The limiting pressure for the nth harmonic is simply P_∞/n, which corresponds to a perfect sawtooth.[13]   The magnitude of the characteristic pressure P_{12} decreases with distance x from the source:

$$\text{for spherical waves} \qquad P_{12} \sim x^{-3/2}$$

$$\text{for plane waves} \qquad P_{12} \sim x^{-1}$$

It follows that one cannot expect more sonic action if he increases the intensity beyond a certain level depending on the distance from the source.   In Fig. 6.8 the source pressure required to produce this

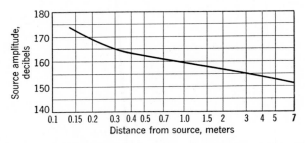

Fig. 6.8.   Source pressure required to give maximum distortion.

"saturation" effect is plotted versus distance from the source for free-field plane wave conditions.   The distance at which a stable sawtooth wave shape is developed is:[14]

$$x = \frac{2c^2}{(\gamma + 1)} \cdot \frac{1}{\omega^2 \xi_0} = \frac{\gamma/\beta_{\text{is}}}{(\gamma + 1)} \cdot \frac{\xi_0}{E_0} \tag{6.13}$$

in which γ is the specific heats ratio, c the sound velocity, β_{is} the isothermal compressibility of the gas, ξ_0 the displacement at the source, and E_0 the energy density at the source.

The presence of harmonics in an intense sound wave widens the range of particle sizes that are likely to be agglomerated.   In Fig. 6.5 the fundamental frequency should thus be chosen from the size of the larger particles in a given distribution rather than from the size that corresponds to the peak in the original distribution as was indi-

---

[13] The Fourier analysis of a sawtooth wave shape leads to:

$$P = \frac{2P_0}{\pi} \left(\sin \omega t + \frac{1}{2} \sin 2\,\omega t + \frac{1}{3} \sin 3\,\omega t + \cdot \cdot \cdot \right)$$

[14] E. Fubini Chiron, *Rev. Acoust.*, *6* (1937), 118.

Table 6.3 Particle Diameters of Common Aerosols

Gas Cleaning Devices				Sonic Agglomerators 1 kcps	10 kcps	100 kcps	
	Cyclones						
		Wash Towers					
			Entrainment Filters				
			Electrostatic Collectors				
Ranges of Common Aerosols	←rain dro	ps→←misty ra	in→←——fog	——→	←to	bacco smoke→	
				←H_2SO_4 mist→			
		←flot	ation ores——	—→	←oil fogs——	—→	
	←foun	dry sand→		←NH_4 Cl	smoke——→		
			←flying ashes→	←SO_3 fog—	→ ←carbon	black→	
		←carbon	dust——→	←milk powder→	←—ZnO	smoke—→	
				←dye stuffs—→			
		←concret	e dust——→				
					←dust in undis	turbed open air——→	
			←dust and sm	okes in steel mi	lls——→		
			←Zn po	wder——→			
				←SiO_2 dust—	—→		
			←spores→				
			←—	—bacteria—→			
Particle diameter in microns	10^4	10^3	10^2	10	1	10^{-1}	10^{-2}
Particle diameter in meters	10^{-2}	10^{-3}	10^{-4}	10^{-5}	10^{-6}	10^{-7}	10^{-8}
Comparable Electromagnetic wavelengths				←sun spectrum→			
	microwaves——→	←infrared——	——	——→	visible light	←ultraviolet→	X-rays

cated in Fig. 6.4. This consideration leads to frequencies between 1 and 10 kcps for most industrial agglomeration work. The ranges of particle sizes occurring in some important aerosols are presented in Table 6.3. While particles above 50-micron diameter can be filtered readily by conventional separators (cyclones, entrainment filters) the smaller particles of sizes down to 0.1 micron require special treatment.[15]

6.6 Steady Sonic Forces on Particles in a Fluid

The interaction between small suspended particles and a sound field leads to other forces in addition to the periodic Stokes-type drag force described above. Both hydrodynamic and viscous mechanisms contribute to these steady forces.

Bernoulli attraction Let us first consider the hydrodynamic attraction that occurs between two spherical particles that are smaller than wavelength and close to each other. If the condition $\xi_P/\xi_F \ll 1$ is met for two such particles a hydrodynamic flow pattern of the type shown in Fig. 6.9 will be set up between them. For laminar flow [particle diameters larger than $\eta/(\rho_0 u)$][16] the continuity of volume flow through the constriction between the two particles leads to an increased flow velocity u. This, in turn, lowers the hydrostatic pressure in the constriction. The resulting pressure difference is obtained from Bernoulli's equation:

$$P = P_0 - P_1 = \tfrac{1}{2}\rho_0(u_1{}^2 - u_0{}^2) \tag{6.14a}$$

in which the subscript 0 refers to the undisturbed region and 1 to the constricted region (see Fig. 6.9), and ρ_0 is the density of the fluid. This net pressure produces a force: $F = PS_e$, where S_e is an equivalent cross section of the particles. Equation 6.14a then can be rewritten in terms of a constriction factor C:

$$F = \tfrac{1}{2}\rho_0 u_0{}^2 C = E_0 C \tag{6.14b}$$

(E_0 = energy density), in which C depends on the geometry of the flow pattern. For two spherical particles of radius r_1 and r_2 spaced a distance d apart, the constriction factor C is:[17]

[15] Collection of very fine particles has been effected for some time by electrostatic methods. Sonic dust collection has been applied since about 1947 to a number of special processes. The choice between the two methods depends largely on the economic considerations that are valid in each particular case (see Section 7.8).

[16] The quantity $R_e = 2ru\rho_0/\eta = 2ru/\nu$ is known as *Reynolds number*; for small spheres in a gas, turbulence is avoided if $R_e < 1$.

[17] W. König, *Ann. Phys.* (Leipzig), *42* (1891), 43.

$$C = 3\pi \frac{r_1^3 r_2^3}{d^4} \tag{6.15}$$

This hydrodynamic force will come into play mainly during the final phase of the sonic agglomeration process.   Maximum relative velocity is obtained when the majority of the particle population has accumulated enough mass to stay fixed in the sound field.

Steady drag forces   The fluid velocity u_0 occurs in eq. 6.14b in quadratic form, so there are steady (rectified) forces of attraction between two particles, in addition to the a-c force associated with the first power of velocity and the Stokes viscous drag.   We now discuss

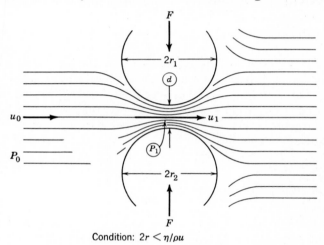

Condition: $2r < \eta/\rho u$

Fig. 6.9.   Flow pattern between two adjacent spheres.

three other quadratic mechanisms that lead to steady forces[18] on single particles:

  a. Radiation pressure, associated with sound scattering.

  b. Average *Stokes* pressure, associated with the dependence of the viscosity on the instantaneous local temperature.

  c. Average *Oseen* pressure, associated with the harmonic wave distortion.

  It will be shown that the relative magnitudes of the three resulting forces differ greatly for progressive waves and low frequencies, but are comparable for standing waves and high frequencies.

Radiation pressure   We saw in Section 2.11 that a force F_R appears within a medium subjected to sound waves whenever there is a discontinuity of energy

[18] P. Westervelt, *J. Acoust. Soc. Amer.*, *22* (1950), 319.

density $E = \mathscr{g}/c$. In that section we limited our discussion to cases where the width of the discontinuity (reflecting or absorbing interface) was much larger than the wavelength. The particles considered here are much smaller than wavelength and can be regarded essentially as sources of scattering according to the discussion in Section 3.7. As is evident from Fig. 3.19 such scattering leads to a non-uniformity of energy density in the immediate vicinity of the particle. The resulting force on a small rigid particle can be evaluated[19] in terms of a surface integral of asymptotic scattering functions.[20] If viscous boundary losses are neglected, the drag coefficient $D = F/E_0S$ (defined in Section 2.12, Table 2.1) for a rigid sphere of mass much greater than the surrounding medium is, for progressive waves:

$$D = 1.2(kr)^4 \tag{6.16a}$$

and for standing waves (maximum value):

$$D = 2.7 \ kr \tag{6.16b}$$

We note that kr occurs in the fourth power in eq. 6.16a, which leads to negligibly small forces for particles smaller than wavelength. In standing waves, however, a maximum d-c force occurs at the positions x_m of maximum energy density E_m:

$x_m = x_{va} \pm \dfrac{\lambda}{8}$, where x_{va} is the coordinate of any particular velocity antinode.

The force is directed toward the velocity antinode. The relative magnitudes of the drag coefficient D for progressive and standing waves are given in Fig. 6.10. We note, for example, that for a sphere of 20 microns diameter at 10 kcps the radiation pressure in the progressive wave lies 180 db below that in the standing wave.

Average Stokes force We have seen that the steady forces due to the radiation pressure on a small rigid sphere in a sound field achieve appreciable magnitude only if standing waves are present. Even then they usually are smaller than the two other types of steady forces associated with the non-linearity of the medium.

It has been mentioned previously that linearity can be assumed only for infinitesimal amplitudes. In general, such quantities as density ρ, sound velocity c, and viscosity η are not constant but depend on the amplitude ξ or particle velocity $u = j\omega\xi$ of the sound wave. This consideration has already been used in Section 2.5 for a simple derivation of radiation pressure. We will now apply a similar approach to Stokes' law. Let us reexamine eq. 6.6 with regard to the instantaneous force F acting on a sphere of radius r:

$$F = 6\pi r \eta_i u \tag{6.17a}$$

[19] P. Westervelt, J. Acoust. Soc. Amer., 23 (1951), 312. See also L. V. King, Proc. Roy. Soc. (London), A, 107 (1947), 215.

[20] $F_R = \dfrac{1}{c}\left[P_d - \displaystyle\int I_\theta \cos\theta \, dA \right]$, where c is the sound velocity in the surrounding fluid, P_d the total power dissipated by scattering and absorption by the object, I_θ the magnitude of the scattered intensity, θ the angle formed by the directions of incident and scattered intensities. For a plane perfect reflector of area S normal to the incident sound beam, we get $P_d = I_0S$, $I_\pi = I_0$, $\cos\theta = -1$, $\int dA = S$. In this special case, the resulting force is $F = 2I_0S/c = 2E_0S$, in accordance with the simple case ($D = 2$) presented in Table 2.1.

in which the instantaneous value η_i of the viscosity coefficient is a function of u. We will see that this dependence leads to a rectified Stokes force as a result of the adiabatic conditions in the sound wave.

In an adiabatic compression the temperature rises by an amount $dT = T_0[(V_0/V)^{\gamma-1} - 1]$, where V is the volume and γ the ratio of specific heats of the gas. From eq. 6.2a and 6.5 it follows that $\eta \sim T^{1/2}$, and hence the viscosity varies between the compressional ($V < V_0$) and dilational ($V > V_0$) phases of the sound wave.

Since η_i is larger during compression ($V < V_0$, $u = U_0 \sin \omega t$) and smaller during dilation [$V > V_0$, $u = u_0 \sin(\omega t + \pi)$], the product $\eta_i u$ will not vanish during one cycle but will have the average value

$$(\eta_i u)_{av} = \frac{\gamma - 3}{4} \cdot \frac{\eta_0}{c_0} \cdot u_0^2 \qquad (6.18)$$

in which η_0 and c_0 are the ambient values for viscosity and sound velocity, and $u_0 = \omega \xi_0$ is the particle-velocity amplitude at the source. Combining eq. 6.17a and 6.18 we obtain for the drag coefficient of the average Stokes force:

$$D = \frac{F}{E_0 S} = \frac{3(\gamma - 3)}{r} \frac{\eta_0}{\rho_0} \qquad (6.18a)$$

This drag causes the particle to drift toward the sound source with a velocity v_d which is determined by the equilibrium condition

$$\eta_0 v_d = (\eta_i u)_{av}$$

Hence we have:

$$v_d = \frac{\gamma - 3}{4} \frac{u_0^2}{c_0} \qquad (6.19)$$

In air ($\gamma = 1.4$) at 20°C and 1 atm the sound velocity is $c_0 = 343$ cm/sec and we obtain $v_d = -1.17 \times 10^{-3} u_0^2$. For example, with a sound-pressure level of 151 db (0.01 atm peak), u_0 will be 2.4 m/sec and $v_d = 0.66$ cm/sec.

Oseen forces   Let us now expand eq. 6.17a to the second order in the velocity:

$$F = 6\pi r \eta u(1 + \delta/u) \qquad (6.17b)$$

An additional force results from the second term of this equation which is independent of the temperature variations in the sound wave. This force arises from the wave-shape distortion associated with large amplitudes. If the particle is much smaller than wavelength, the rate of momentum transfer (See eq. 2.53) is larger during the steep portion of a sawtooth-shaped wave than during the slowly rising portion. This leads to a net pressure proportional to the degree of distortion of the wave. Using an approximation derived by Oseen[21] we may substitute for δ in eq. (6.17b); $\delta = 0.375 \rho_0 r/\eta_i$. The second term of this equation then has an average value:

$$F_0 = 2.25\pi r^2 \rho_0 \left[u|u| \right]_{av} \qquad (6.20)$$

[21] A rigorous derivation of this second-order effect requires a transformation of the wave equation from fixed (Eulerian) to moving (Lagrangean) coordinates. Such analysis is beyond the scope of this book; we give only certain results to enable an estimate of the magnitude of the effects. For further details see P. Westervelt, *J. Acoust. Soc. Amer.*, *22* (1950), 319, and also *Modern Developments in Fluid Mechanics,* ed. by Goldstein, Clarendon Press, Oxford, 1943, pp. 491–492.

in which ρ_0 is the density of the fluid, u is the particle velocity vector, and $|u|$ is its magnitude. For a purely sinusoidal wave the time average of the bracket factor is zero. For a distorted wave there is a time average of $[u|u|]$ which depends on the magnitude u_2 and phase φ of the second harmonic component. The particle velocity of the sound wave then is:

$$u = u_0[\sin \omega t + c_2 \sin (2\omega t + \varphi)] \qquad (6.21)$$

in which $c_2 = u_2/u_0$ is the fractional second harmonic content ($c_2 < 0.5$). Inserting eq. 6.21 into 6.20 and taking the time average we obtain a steady force:

$$F_0 \simeq -3r^2\rho_0 u_0^2 c_2 \sin \varphi = E_0 S \cdot D \qquad (6.20a)$$

in which $D = -(3/\pi)c_2 \sin \varphi)$ is the drag coefficient on a small spherical particle heavy enough to stay fixed with respect to the first-order motion of the medium. We see that there is a maximum positive force (away from the source) for a phase angle $\varphi = -\pi/2$; and a maximum negative force (toward the source) for a phase angle $\varphi = +\pi/2$.

A summary of the four types of forces discussed in this section is given for progressive waves in Table 6.4. The drag coefficient D is

Table 6.4   Steady Forces on a Rigid Inert Sphere in a Sound Field

Type of Force	Physical Cause	Drag Coefficient for Progressive Wave	Direction Force
Radiation	Scattering	$1.2 \, (kr)^4$	Away from source
Average Stokes	Temperature dependence of viscosity	$\dfrac{3(\gamma - 3)}{r} \dfrac{\eta}{\rho}$	Toward source
Oseen	Wave distortion	$\dfrac{3}{\pi} c_2 \sin \varphi$	Depends on phase
Bernoulli	Hydrodynamic flow	$3 \dfrac{r_1^2 \cdot r_2^2}{d^4}$	Attraction between 2 particles

Definition of Symbols

r = particle radius
d = distance between two adjacent particles
γ = specific heat ratio
η = viscosity coefficient of the fluid
ρ = density of the fluid

$k = \omega/c = 2\pi/\lambda$
$c_2 = u_2/u_0$ = fractional second harmonic content
φ = phase shift between fundamental and second harmonic of distorted sound wave

defined as the average force, divided by the energy density E_0 of the sound wave and the cross-sectional area πr^2 of the rigid sphere. The drag coefficient is plotted as a function of the diameter of the sphere, on a logarithmic scale, in Fig. 6.10 (for air). Radiation pressure is lower by several magnitudes than the Stokes, and Oseen pressures. For standing waves the oppositely directed forces due to radiation pressure and average Stokes pressure tend to cancel. For distorted waves with an appreciable second harmonic content ($c_2 \simeq 0.5$) the maximum Oseen forces ($\varphi = \pm \pi/2$), exert by far the largest drag on a particle.

In practical sonic systems of high intensity this means that small suspended particles may assume appreciable drift velocities. It has been shown that even in an undistorted wave a superimposed dc air

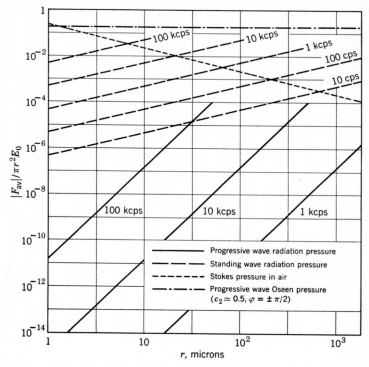

Fig. 6.10.   Drag coefficients for four types of steady forces according to P. Westervelt.

flow will lead to strong Oseen forces. One significant consequence is that the free fall of small particles in an intense sound field will no longer be governed by Stokes' law.

The streaming effects that have been observed in liquids[22] are related to the mechanisms discussed above. These effects, for example, cause violent motion within biological cells subjected to intense ultrasonic irradiation and may give a clue to the biological

[22] E. Eckart, *Phys. Rev.* *73* (1948), 68.   L. N. Liebermann, *Phys. Rev.*, *75* (1949), 1415.

mechanism of reaction to ultrasound.[23]   They are also responsible
for the electrokinetic effects that are observed in electrolytic cells
which are exposed to a sound field (see ref. 53 of this chapter).

6.7 Basic Aspects of Cavitation in Liquids

We shall discuss cavitation in some detail since it plays an important
part in liquid-phase sonic applications.   Cavitation can limit the
sound intensity that can be propagated within a liquid, and cavitation
can also act as a powerful agent capable of producing effects unattain-
able by other means.   In particular, we shall examine some of the
variables that control the onset of cavitation.

If a liquid is exposed to intense sonic vibrations one can usually
observe small gas bubbles formed within the liquid.   Most liquids,
unless they are specially treated, contain dissolved or entrained gases.
The amount of entrained gas depends on the pressure and temperature
of the liquid.   Under normal conditions the gas is very finely dispersed.   It may be present in the form of molecules located at vacant
sites of the quasi-crystalline structure of the liquid (see Appendix,
Section A.5), or the gas may be contained in invisible bubbles of
microscopic dimensions.   Such bubbles constitute weak points within
the liquid; the tensile strength is determined by the largest bubble
present.

Let us recall the behavior of a liquid, in certain familiar static
experiments.   If the temperature of a liquid is raised to the boiling
point at constant pressure, or if the external pressure is lowered at
constant temperature, thermal agitation will override the cohesive
forces in the liquid.   At the boiling point there is a transition from
liquid phase to gas phase which is accompanied by the appearance of
many gas bubbles in the liquid.   As the process continues, the bubbles
grow in size and become more buoyant.   The bubbles grow by collect-
ing dissolved gas in their neighborhood and also by coalescing with
other bubbles.   Near the boiling point the bubbles contain a large
amount of vapor.   In fact, the final phase transition from liquid to
gaseous state occurs wherever, throughout the liquid, a surface is
created by the presence of a bubble.

The role of impurities   If a "clean" liquid, one that has been
freed from impurities and dissolved gas, is slowly heated above its
normal boiling point the phenomenon of superheating occurs.   Under
this condition the external temperature can be raised considerably
above the normal boiling point without the phase transition taking

---

[23] W. J. Fry and R. B. Fry, *J. Acoust. Soc. Amer.*, *25* (1953), 6.   T. F. Hueter,
Chem. Eng. Progress, Symposium Series No. 1, *47* (1951), 57.

place.   If a liquid in this state is disturbed, e.g., by mechanical shock
or an added impurity, it will turn explosively into vapor.   In the
same way liquids can be undercooled without solidification at the
normal melting point.   Thus, extremely purified water is found to
have a melting point below −40°C.   All these findings[24] suggest the
important role that impurities or nuclei play within a liquid by providing weak points in its structure.

If sound waves in a liquid have sufficient intensity to produce pressure amplitudes larger than the hydrostatic pressure, the net external
pressure becomes negative during the dilational phase.   This condition
can be produced in water with average sound intensities greater than
about ⅓ watt/cm^2.

From van der Waals' equation[24a] we know that the cohesive forces
within a liquid are very large, in water of the order of 10^3 atm.   Theoretical considerations show that this value is very little affected by
the presence of *dissolved* gas.   However, in the presence of nuclei
such as small gas bubbles or other impurities, a much smaller tension
will cause rupture in the liquid.   Several investigators[25] have reported
a wide range of rupture thresholds for water, between 1 and 10^2
atm under varying experimental conditions and degrees of con-
tamination.   The presence of sufficiently high negative pressure once
in each cycle of an intense sound wave may then lead intermittently to
phenomena similar to boiling or superheating, as described above.

Recent studies[26] with focusing systems (free-field conditions) suggest
that cavitation has three different aspects: (*a*) quiet degassing; (*b*)
linear resonance of gas bubbles; and (*c*) non-linear collapse of vapor
bubbles.

In a gassy liquid exposed to a strong sound field, two phenomena
have been found to occur.   For instance, in water irradiated at a
frequency of 60 kcps, quiet degassing (*a*) sets in at sound-pressure
amplitudes of about 0.25 atm.   The large visible bubbles that are
formed do not produce noise in a hydrophone.   Once formed, these
bubbles will remain after the sound field is shut off.

---

[24] J. Frenkel, "Kinetic Theory of Liquids," Oxford University Press, 1946.   See
also E. H. Harvey, "Bubble Formation in Liquids," *Medical Physics*, Vol. 2 (1950),
p. 137, Year Book Publishers, Chicago, Ill.

[24a] See Appendix, eq. A.40.

[25] F. G. Blake, Jr., "The Tensile Strength of Liquids: A Review of the Literature," Harvard Univ. Acoustics Research Laboratory, June, 1949, *Rept.*
NR-014-403.

[26] M. D. Rosenberg, *Tech. Mem.* 25, August 8, 1952, Harvard Univ. Acoustics
Research Laboratory.   T. Lange, *Acustica, 2* (1952), AB 75.   G. W. Willard,
J. Acoust. Soc. Amer., 25 (1952), 669.

Cavitation noise If the sound-pressure amplitude is raised to about 1.25 atm, foggy streamers are formed. These consist of much smaller bubbles (b) that fade out after the sound is shut off. These streamers produce noise which is detectable by a hydrophone. This noise has a line spectrum containing harmonics and subharmonics of the exciting sound frequency.

In carefully degassed[27] water a third phenomenon (c), different in aspect from the above mentioned types of gas bubble formation, has been observed. This phenomenon is produced only with difficulty in oil, benzene, and other less polar liquids. As the sound-pressure amplitude is raised to about 4 atm (at 60 kcps), small explosive ruptures can be seen in dark-field illumination. The ruptures produce sharp snapping sounds that have a wide-band noise spectrum.[28] They are caused by the collapse of vaporous bubbles and can be interpreted as a breakdown of small superheated regions. A typical cavitation noise spectrum obtained at 500 kcps with a frequency analyzer is shown in Fig. 6.11.[29] The line spectrum superimposed on the white noise band is due to the harmonics and subharmonics of resonant gas bubbles.

All three effects, quiet degassing, gaseous type, and vaporous type of cavitation, require the presence of small, usually invisible gas bubbles in the liquid. The smaller the bubbles, the larger their internal pressure P_i because of the effect of surface tension

$$P_i = P_0 + \frac{2\sigma}{R} \qquad (6.22)$$

where P_0 is the hydrostatic pressure, σ the surface tension[30] and R the bubble radius.

This high internal pressure tends to force the gas within the bubble into solution in the liquid. In fresh tap water, for instance, there will be more bubbles entrained than in aged tap water. Unless a liquid is supersaturated with gas, it cannot contain gas in the form

[27] The entrained gas can be removed by boiling, spraying into a vacuum, and sonic degassing. It also can be forced into solution by high external pressures.

[28] This noise is similar to the one produced by a hot-wire source under water. See M. F. Osborne and F. H. Holland, *J. Acoust. Soc. Amer.*, *19* (1947), 13.

[29] R. Esche, *Acustica, 2 Akust. Beih.* (1952), AB 208.

[30] This quantity is defined as:

$$\sigma = \frac{\text{work necessary for an increase in surface area}}{\text{amount of increase in surface area}}$$

and has the dimension newtons/m or joules/m^2. For a water-air interface $\sigma = 72 \times 10^3$ (in CGS units: $\sigma = 72$ dynes/cm).

of stable bubbles. All experimental evidence indicates, however, that actual liquids possess weak points in the form of small bubbles. There must then be a stabilizing agent that keeps these bubbles from dissolving. All liquids, even if purified, contain a large number of small dust particles. Their number depends on the heat of wetting, which happens to be particularly high in water. Such dust particles will entrain gas in the form of extremely small bubbles (radius 10^{-5}

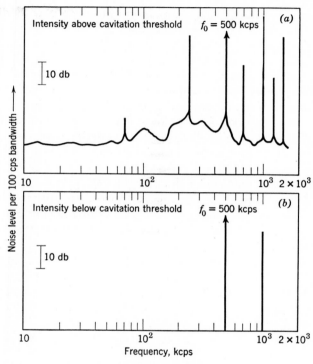

Fig. 6.11.   Cavitation noise spectrum.

to 10^{-4} cm) which are thus stabilized and kept from going into solution. Similarly, gas nuclei will be found in the small surface cracks in the walls of the container or in the face of the transducer.[31]

Gas-bubble dynamics To understand cavitation we must study the dynamic behavior of bubbles in a sound field. Sonic cavitation involves an important parameter, the driving frequency, that is absent

[31] With transducers generating plane waves, cavitation usually occurs first at the transducer face itself, thus limiting the power that can be propagated into the liquid.

in the hydrodynamic cavitation[32] produced in venturi tubes and on ship propellers. Associated with frequency is a critical dimension of the bubble at which bubble resonance occurs. The resonance radius R_0 of a bubble is given to first approximation by:

$$R_0 = \frac{1}{\omega} \sqrt{\frac{3\gamma P_0}{\rho}} \approx 326 P_0^{1/2}/f \text{ (cm)} \qquad (6.23a)$$

if $P_0 \gg 2\sigma/R$, and by:

$$R_0 = \frac{1}{\omega} \sqrt{\frac{6\gamma\sigma}{\rho R_0}} \approx \left(\frac{3.9}{f}\right)^{2/3} \text{ (cm)} \qquad (6.23b)$$

if $P_0 \ll 2\sigma/R_0$, where γ is the specific heat ratio of the gas, P_0 the total external pressure (in atmospheres), and ρ the density of the

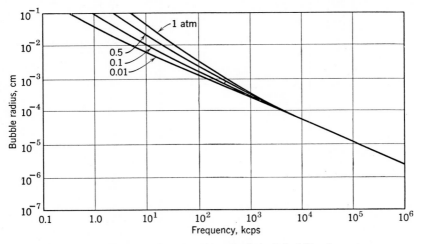

Fig. 6.12. Resonance radius of oscillating air bubbles in water.

liquid (in g/cm^3). In Fig. 6.12 the resonance radii of oscillating air bubbles in water are plotted versus frequency with the hydrostatic pressure as parameter. We note that the diameter of a resonating bubble is two orders of magnitude smaller than the wavelength in the liquid at the particular frequency. Above 1 mcps ($R_0 \sim 4$ microns) such bubbles can be detected only by dark-field illumination, unless they occur in very large numbers as clusters or streamers.

A theoretical treatment by Noltingk and Neppiras[33] has revealed

[32] M. Harrison, *J. Acoust. Soc. Amer.*, *24* (1952), 776.

[33] B. E. Noltingk and E. A. Neppiras, *Proc. Phys. Soc.* (*London*) *B*, *63* (1950), 369.

that only the bubbles which are smaller than resonant size are capable of rupture and subsequent collapse before the end of the pressure cycle. Experimental evidence indicates that the smallest stable bubbles have radii of the order of 5×10^{-7} m (0.5 microns). As the frequency is increased, fewer and fewer bubbles are available that are small enough for rupture. According to eq. 6.23b, a frequency of approximately 10 mcps constitutes a limit above which vaporous-type cavitation is unlikely to occur. This is borne out by experiments,[34] as shown in

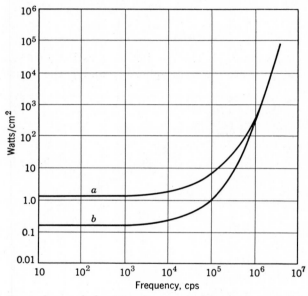

Fig. 6.13. Dependence of the intensity required to produce cavitation on frequency, for (a) degassed water, (b) aerated water, both at room temperature.

Figure 6.13. The sound pressure necessary for vaporous-type cavitation (characterized by a white noise spectrum) increases rapidly above 100 kcps and becomes as high as 100 atm at 5 mcps. Figure 6.13 also demonstrates that degassed water exhibits a higher cavitation threshold than aerated (tap) water. In aerated liquids, of course, quiet degassing will be the most pronounced of the three effects mentioned.

Relative radius versus time curves of a small bubble of initial radius R_0 in a sound field of 4 atm pressure amplitude, ($P_0 = 1$ atm) are given in Fig. 6.14 for two frequencies, below and above bubble resonance. At the higher frequency (f_2, solid line) a complex wave shape is observed that will give rise to a line spectrum. The dashed line

[34] R. Esche, *Acustica loc. cit.;* see footnote 29.

corresponds to the lower frequency (f_1) and indicates the presence of very high radial velocities (collapse), which leads to a broad noise spectrum.

The higher the ratio of the maximum bubble radius R_m to the initial radius R_0 the more violent is the collapse. For a given initial radius R_0 the ratio R_m/R_0 increases with the sound-pressure amplitude

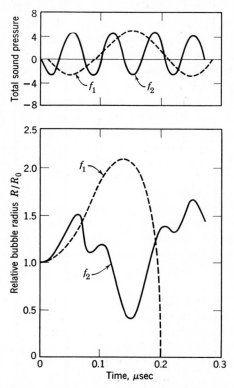

Fig. 6.14. Radius-time curve of a small bubble at two frequencies f_1 and f_2. The upper drawing shows the variation with time of the total pressure (sound plus ambient pressure) in atmospheres.

at constant frequency, and decreases with increasing frequency at constant sound pressure. If both sound pressure and frequency are kept constant the ratio R_m/R_0 increases if the initial bubble radius R_0 is reduced. Thus vaporous-type cavitation is most pronounced at low frequencies and high sound pressures if the bubble nuclei are very small.

During collapse, the walls of the bubble rush inward until the cushioning action of the gas within the bubble stops the radial motion.

At the end of the collapse the contents of the bubble are highly compressed and high instantaneous temperatures[35] may occur within the bubble, depending on the degree to which adiabatic conditions prevail. These high local temperatures, which are confined to the gas and vapor content of the bubble, may lead to ionization effects as evidenced by luminescence[36] and formation of OH radicals and peroxide. This mechanism is believed to be responsible for some of the chemical and biological effects that have been observed in the presence of cavitation.

In the liquid itself, temperature effects will be negligible, the main effect being caused by the shock waves that emanate from the cavitation centers. The peak pressures of such shock waves have been measured[37] with small crystal probes. At 10 kcps, with an initial bubble radius of about 100 microns and a sound-pressure amplitude of 1 atm, the shock waves have a peak pressure of 200 to 500 atm at a distance 0.1 cm from the bubble center.

Limitations of power transmission   Processing systems based on the occurrence of strong vaporous-type cavitation must be designed to give large ratios R_m/R_0. However, attempts to raise the sound pressure in a given region of the treated liquid much above the cavitation threshold value will generally fail. In such a case, cavitation is bound to occur somewhere along the path of sound transmission before the desired location is reached. This limits the sound pressure that can be transmitted beyond the point where cavitation first occurs since the bubbles present will scatter and dissipate a part of the sound energy.[38]

Pulsating bubbles lose their energy both by radiation and by internal damping. The latter is essentially a thermal damping due to heat conduction. The bubbles that have resonant size (see eqs. 6.23) are mainly responsible for the dissipation of the energy in a sound beam. Because of the amplification of their radial motion at resonance, a larger area of the sound field is affected. In other words, bubbles in resonance have an increased effective "cross section" for scattering and absorption. Approximate expressions, valid in the frequency

[35] Assuming strictly adiabatic conditions, B. E. Noltingk and E. A. Neppiras, *loc. cit;* (see footnote 33) have determined the gas temperature at minimum radius to be $T = T_0(P/3Q)/3(\gamma - 1)$, where T_0 is the absolute temperature of the surrounding liquid, P the net external pressure, and Q the internal gas pressure at maximum bubble radius. In a liquid at room temperature and $P_0 = 1$ atm, and if $Q \simeq 0.01$ atm, the internal temperature of a collapsed bubble would reach the order of $10^4°$C.

[36] J. Frenkel, *Acta Physiochim.*, U.R.S.S., *12* (1940), 1.

[37] H. G. Moeller and A. Schoch, *Akust. Z.*, *6* (1941), 165.

[38] Z. Soneyosi, *Tokyo Electrotech. J.*, *5* (1941), 49.

range 10 kcps to 500 kcps, will be given for the effective cross sections of bubbles in water.   In this range the Q of a resonating bubble is determined essentially by the thermal damping.   The scattering cross section is[39]

$$\sigma_s \simeq \frac{f}{k_h(\gamma - 1)^2} \qquad (6.24a)$$

in which k_h is the coefficient of heat conductivity in the gas and γ the ratio of specific heats.   The absorption cross section of resonance bubbles in the specified frequency range is:

$$\sigma_a \simeq 0.5 \frac{\lambda}{(\gamma - 1)} \left(\frac{f}{k_h}\right)^{\frac{1}{2}} \qquad (6.24b)$$

in which λ is the wavelength in the liquid.   Above and below this frequency range the thermal damping decreases, and reaches the value of the radiation damping at about 2 kcps and 2 mcps.   At these two frequencies the absorption cross section reaches a maximum:

$$(\sigma_a)_{max} = \lambda^2/4\pi \qquad (6.24c)$$

This equation gives the maximum absorption cross section of resonators in general: it is valid for electromagnetic and acoustic cavity resonators as well as for the capture of neutrons in nuclear reactions.[40]

Pressurization   Cavitation can be suppressed by applying an increased hydrostatic pressure P_0 to bias the sound pressure $P_s \sin \omega t$. Cavitation occurs only if the net pressure $P_n = P_0 + P_s \sin \omega t$ at its greatest negative value $(P_0 - P_s)$ reaches the cavitation threshold. Cavitation cannot, however, be made more *violent* simply by increasing P_0 and then bringing P_s up to the value necessary to reach the threshold.   The violence of collapse is determined by the ratio of radii R_m/R_0.

In focusing systems, pressurization of the coupling medium has certain advantages if the following arrangement is used.   A focusing (curved) transducer is located in a chamber that is filled with liquid at high pressure.   In this chamber, then, a high intensity of sound can be maintained without cavitation and without the associated dissipation of sound energy.   The convergent beam passes through a sound-transparent window into a second chamber that contains the liquid to be processed.   Here the beam comes to a focus with a very large value of P_s, while the liquid is at normal pressure.   In this

[39] M. L. Exner, *Acustica, Akust. Beih. 1* (1951), AB 25.

[40] J. C. Slater, *Microwave Transmission*, McGraw-Hill, New York, 1952, p. 245; also U. Jngard, *J. Acoust. Soc. Amer.*, *25* (1953), 1037.

region, the high concentration of energy leads to a high rate of rupture and collapse of cavitating bubbles. A more detailed discussion of focusing systems is given in Section 6.5.

6.8   Factors Determining the Threshold of Cavitation

We have discussed several aspects of cavitation in a rather qualitative way. The factors that determine the onset of cavitation are interrelated in a very complicated manner, and there is as yet no unified quantitative theory of cavitation. We can, however, present some quantitative information relevant to the design of sonic systems. We have already noted the physical analogy between boiling and the rupture that occurs in a liquid that is superheated or subjected to high sonic tension. In a two-phase system (liquid-gas) there is, as we might expect, a functional relationship among the cavitation threshold pressure P_c, the boiling point T_p, and the ambient temperature T. An empirical formula of limited validity is:

$$P_c = 0.7(T_p - T) + 1 \text{ (atm)} \tag{6.25}$$

in which T_p is the boiling-point temperature at the ambient pressure P_0. This formula has been obtained from measurements of cavitation threshold at 60 kcps in partially degassed water.[41] The relationship of eq. 6.25 is plotted in Fig. 6.15, for water and for a frequency of 60 kcps. At higher frequencies the slope of the lines of constant hydrostatic pressure will be steeper and they will intersect the abscissa somewhat above the boiling point.

There is some indication that this relationship is not universally applicable. We shall mention two phenomena which are not fully explainable by eq. 6.25. Metal surfaces exposed to high sonic amplitudes have been found to exhibit a maximum of cavitation erosion at a certain temperature, depending on the hydrostatic pressure. This is exemplified in Fig. 6.16 by a curve obtained on the weight loss due to cavitation pitting of a brass surface, at a frequency of 20 kcps and $P_0 = 1$ atm. We note that the amount of erosion owing to cavitation reaches a maximum at about 60°C, whereas eq. 6.25 predicts that erosion should continue to increase above this temperature.

Again, eq. 6.25 implies that the cavitation threshold decreases continuously as the hydrostatic pressure is lowered. This trend is reversed under certain conditions if P_0 is reduced below a critical value. This anomaly has been reported only for degassed water at

[41] F. G. Blake, *Tech. Memo.* 12, Acoustics Research Laboratory, Harvard Univ., September 1949.

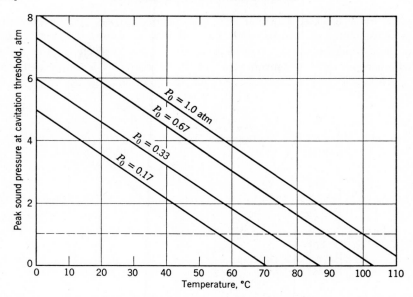

Fig. 6.15.   Temperature dependence of cavitation threshold in water at 60 kcps.

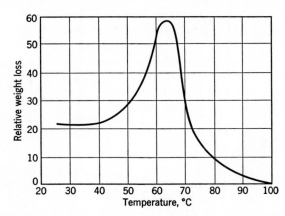

Fig. 6.16.   Relative weight lost by cavitation pitting of a brass surface as a function of temperature (frequency 20 kcps).

$P_0 < 0.4$ atm.   The effect is illustrated in Fig. 6.17 for a frequency of 575 kcps at room temperature.   The trends apparent in both Fig. 6.16 and Fig. 6.17 may have a similar physical cause; as the boiling point is approached, either by a reduction of external pressure or by an increase of ambient temperature, there occurs a point at which the effects of vaporous-type cavitation become most pronounced.

In most liquids, however, eq. 6.25 seems to predict the pressure dependence of cavitation with a fair degree of approximation. This is illustrated for partly degassed castor oil and kerosene in Fig. 6.18, which represents measurements[42] at 25 kcps and at a temperature of

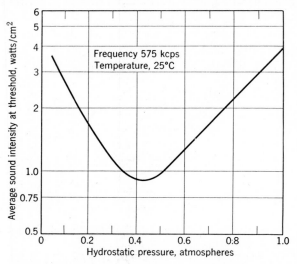

Fig. 6.17.   Dependence of cavitation threshold on hydrostatic pressure in degassed water.

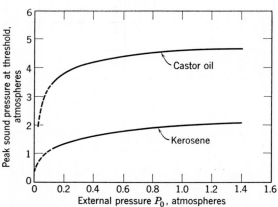

Fig. 6.18.   Dependence of cavitation threshold on hydrostatic pressure.

25°C. We note that the two liquids differ considerably in their "resistance" to cavitation. It has been found also that sea water

42 H. B. Briggs, T. B. Johnson, W. P. Mason, *J. Acoust. Soc. Amer.*, *19* (1947) 664.   See also U.S. Pat. 2,436,377, February 24, 1948, issued to these authors.

cavitates more easily than degassed castor oil. This difference is advantageous in underwater sound transmitters of the type shown in Fig. 4.26. The oil filling of the transducer housing makes it possible to operate the crystals at higher intensities without cavitation.

We have been considering cavitation thresholds under continuous radiation of sound waves. Measurements with pulses of varying length have revealed that there is a time delay between the application of sonic power and the onset of cavitation. The longer a liquid is

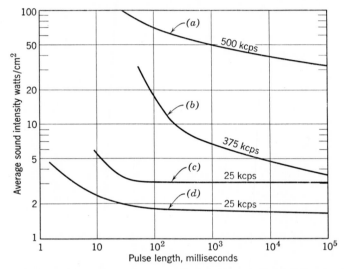

Fig. 6.19. Dependence of cavitation threshold on pulse length. (a) degassed water; (b) tap water; (c) degassed castor oil; (d) degassed transformer oil. The difference in threshold levels of the curves shown is due to: gas content for (a) and (b); viscosity for (c) and (d); frequency for (a), (b) and (c), (d). It follows from Fig. 6.13 that for 25 kcps the water curves would lie below curve (d).

exposed to intense sound, the lower is the threshold pressure at which cavitation occurs. This dependence is shown in Fig. 6.19 for some liquids under different conditions. The trend to higher thresholds as the frequency increases is apparent and was discussed above (see Fig. 6.13). A comparison between curves a (highly cleaned water) and b (tap water) indicates that the pulse-time effect is more pronounced if the conditions are such that gaseous-type cavitation prevails. The time element can then be explained in terms of the finite speed of bubble growth by diffusion. Curves c (degassed castor oil) and d (degassed transformer oil) are substantially flat down to pulse lengths of 100 millisec. Below this value the sound intensity necessary to produce cavitation increases rapidly.   This phenomenon also can be used to advantage in sonar applications.[43]

Correlation between cavitation threshold and the properties of a liquid   The simple qualitative picture of the mechanism of cavitation which was given above suggests some generalizations on the influence of such liquid properties as surface tension, vapor pressure, and viscosity.   We note first, from eq. 6.23b, that the internal pressure in a gas bubble depends largely on the surface tension σ if the bubble is very small.   Expansion of the bubble requires an amount of work of about 7.2×10^{-6} watt-sec per unit area of the increased surface. When the bubble collapses the potential energy of the bubble surface

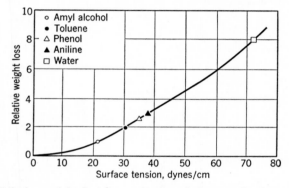

Fig. 6.20.   Relative weight lost by cavitation pitting on aluminum surface as a function of surface tension.

is concentrated into a very small volume.   The higher the surface tension, the greater the amount of energy released in the collapse. Therefore, it is not surprising that the pitting action of ultrasonic cavitation increases with surface tension.   This is demonstrated in Fig. 6.20 in which the weight loss of aluminum samples (in arbitrary units) is plotted versus surface tension for several liquids at constant vapor pressure (10 mm Hg).   Water is particularly well suited for the production of violent cavitation, owing to its very high value of surface tension.

On the other hand, the vapor pressure of the liquid also influences the cavitation process very strongly.   The maximum radius to which the bubbles expand and the smallest radius which the bubbles reach in the collapse both depend on the vapor pressure of the liquid.   In a liquid of high vapor pressure, or in water containing a small percentage of a substance that has high vapor pressure, such as acetone or ether,

[43] W. P. Mason, *loc. cit.* (see footnote 42).

the effects of cavitation are relatively small. For example, chemical oxidation and bacterial destruction are produced readily by cavitation in pure water but are suppressed if some amount of ether is added.[44]

There appears to be some optimum relationship among surface tension, vapor pressure, and temperature. In water-alcohol mixtures,

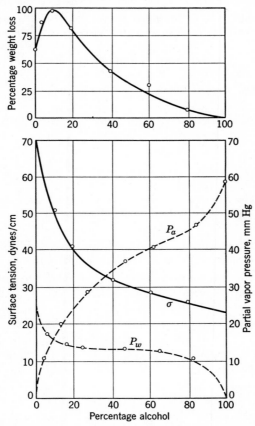

Fig. 6.21. Cavitation pitting on aluminum surface in water-alcohol mixture, as compared with surface tension and partial pressures.

cavitation pitting occurs most readily at a mixture ratio of 10 per cent alcohol and 90 per cent water.[45]

In Fig. 6.21 the surface tension σ and the partial pressures P_w and P_a

[44] Prudhomme and Grabar, *C. r. acad. sci.* (Paris), *226* (1948) 1821, have shown that the oxidation of cellular extracts can be inhibited if as little as one drop of ether is added per 50 cc of suspension.

[45] H. Nowotny, *Werkstoffzerstoerung durch Kavitation*, V.D.I. Verlag, Berlin, 1942, reprinted by Edwards Bros., Ann Arbor, Mich.

are plotted against the percentage alcohol of a water-alcohol mixture at 25°C.   The relative weight loss of aluminum samples is also shown. This behavior is in agreement with the temperature dependence of cavitation pitting in water which was illustrated in Fig. 6.16.   The same trend is apparent from the data in Table 6.5.   In cyclohexane,

Table 6.5   Weight Loss of Aluminum Samples at Constant Surface Tension ($\sigma \simeq 22 \times 10^{-3}$ newton/m) and Viscosity ($\eta \simeq 6 \times 10^{-3}$ poise)

Liquid	Surface Tension (newton/m $\times 10^3$)	Viscosity (poises)	Temperature (°C)	Vapor Pressure (mm Hg)	Relative Weight Loss
Amyl alcohol	26	9×10^{-3}	0	0.6	0.6
Octane	22	6×10^{-3}	15	9	0.65
Hexane	20	4×10^{-3}	0	46	0.7
Methyl alcohol	23	7×10^{-3}	20	96	0.85
Ethyl alcohol	20	8×10^{-3}	40	140	0.9
Cyclohexane	24	7×10^{-3}	40	180	1
Cyclohexane	22	6×10^{-3}	50	280	0.55
Cyclohexane	20	$>6 \times 10^{-3}$	60	440	0.33

for example, the surface tension and viscosity do not change very much as the temperature is decreased from 60°C to 40°C, but the large reduction in vapor pressure is accompanied by a pronounced increase in pitting action.   All the liquids listed in Table 6.5 have rather low viscosity.   The small bubble nuclei which serve as centers of cavitation can move about easily in such relatively inviscid liquids. This allows them to collect dissolved gas from the regions through which they pass.   Some of the bubbles that have thus grown by diffusion will break up into many small nuclei during cavitation collapse, and more centers for cavitation are created throughout the liquid.[46]

We thus have a qualitative explanation for the dependence of the apparent cohesive strength on the previous history of a liquid.   Once cavitation has been induced, the liquid will cavitate at a lower acoustic pressure (pulse length effect; see Fig. 6.19) and a certain length of time is required for the liquid to return to its original state.

When the mobility of bubble nuclei is small, as in liquids of large viscosity, bubble growth and reproduction of nuclei are relatively slow.   Viscous liquids, such as oils, solutions of high polymers, and biological fluids, therefore have high cavitation thresholds, and their thresholds increase as the magnitude of their viscosity increases. Empirical evidence for this behavior is given in Fig. 6.22, which presents threshold pressures of ten liquids which were cavitated at

[46] G. W. Willard, paper C1 presented at 47th Meeting of the Acoust. Soc. of Amer., June 23, 1954 in New York.

25°C with a frequency of 25 kcps.   The numbers in Fig. 6.22 refer
to the substances listed in Table 6.6

The cavitation threshold increases rapidly in the frequency range
between 10^2 and 10^3 kcps.   Visible bubble formation under such

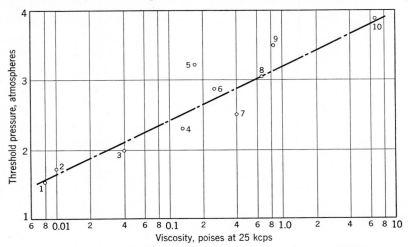

Fig. 6.22.   Cavitation threshold versus viscosity according to H. B. Briggs et al.
(see footnote 42).

conditions and at moderate sound intensities (1 to 10 watts/cm^2)
is often referred to as "cavitation," but should rather be described
as degassing.   The visible bubbles that are liberated at higher ultra-

Table 6.6   Cavitating Sound Intensity at 25 kcps versus Viscosity.

No.	Substance	Viscosity at 25°C (poises)	Sound Velocity (m/sec)	Density (kg/m³)	Threshold Intensity (watt/cm²)
1.	Xylene hexafluoride	0.0084	879	1370	0.9
2.	Carbon tetrachloride	0.0098	926	1595	1
3.	Kerosene	0.04	1324	810	1.9
4.	G.E. Transil	0.131	1350	880	2.3
5.	Dimethyl phthalate	0.178	1463	1176	3
6.	Sperm oil	0.25	1440	880	3.3
7.	Linseed oil	0.38	1468	921	2.1
8.	Corn oil	0.63	1463	914	3.5
9.	Olive oil	0.84	1431	912	5
10.	Castor oil	6.3	1477	969	5.3

sonic frequencies are unable to produce the striking effects associated
with the collapse of vaporous cavities.[47]

[47] For a review of physicochemical effects by ultra-sonic cavitation, see *Chem.
Eng. Progress Symposium Series* 1, *47* (1951), 22.

6.9 Processing by Cavitation

We have presented a rather detailed picture of the phenomena associated with cavitation since some of the most promising practical uses of sonic energy depend on its occurrence. Homogenization and dispersion,[48] emulsification,[49] extraction of enzymes and vaccines from cell aggregates,[50] and in some cases depolymerization of high polymers[51] by means of cavitation have made ultrasonic apparatus a very useful addition to many biochemical and physicochemical laboratories.

Large-scale industrial applications of ultrasonic cavitation have been developed for cleaning of small parts,[52] such as ball bearings, lenses, shaving heads for electric razors, small motor armatures, valves, jewelry screws, and many other high-precision products. Here the liquid medium must be compatible both with the materials of the work piece and with the requirements of cavitation. Fluids suitable for sonic cleaning must satisfy simultaneously two conditions: (a) they must have ordinary cleaning requirements (e.g., ability to dissolve fats, detergency, etc.); and (b) they must have properties favorable to cavitation (e.g., optimal values of surface tension, vapor pressure, and viscosity). The information given above on these parameters will assist in making the right choice. Successful sonic cleaning has

---

[48] L. A. Chambers has reported on homogenization of milk in *J. Dairy Sci.*, *19* (1936), 29. See also U.S. Pat. 2,091,267 (1934). K. Soellner discusses ultrasonic dispersion of solids in liquids in *Trans. Faraday Soc.*, *34* (1938), 1170. See also B. Claus and E. Schmidt, *Kolloid-Beih.*, *45* (1935), 202. H. Freundlich and K. Soellner describe thixotropic changes in irradiated gels: *Trans. Faraday Soc.*, *32* (1936), 966. Mercury dispersion in water is analyzed by E. C. Marboe and W. A. Weyl in *J. Appl. Phys.*, *21* (1950), 937. J. Santet et al. have dispersed DDT: *C. r. acad. sci.* (Paris), *224*, (1947), 66.

[49] Detailed reviews of ultrasonic emulsification have been given by K. Soellner in *Chem. Rev.*, *34* (1944), 371, and by N. Marinesco, Chimie et Ind. (France), *55* (1946), 263.

[50] Ultrasonic effects on serum proteins are discussed by R. O. Prudhomme and P. Grabar, *Bull. soc. chem. biol.* (France), *29* (1947), 122; by M. Royer and P. Grabar, *Ann. inst.* Pasteur, *73* (1947), 215; and by F. Kress, "Der Ultraschall i.d. Medizin" (*Erlangen Cong. Rept.*, published by S. Hirzel, Switzerland), 1949, p. 225. Ultrasonic extraction is discussed by P. K. Stumpf, D. E. Green, and F. W. Smith, *J. Bacteriol.*, *51* (1946), 487. See also U.S. Pat. 2,230,997 (1941). Results on the killing of bacteria by ultrasound are given by J. P. Horton, *J. Acoust. Soc. Amer.*, *25* (1953), 480.

[51] G. Schmid and O. Rommel, *Z. phys. Chem.*, 85*A* (1939), 97. E. Wada and H. Nakane, *J. Sci. Research Inst.* (Tokyo), *45* (1951), 1236. A. J. Weissler, *J. Appl. Phys.*, *21* (1950), 177.

[52] G. E. Henry, *General Electric Rev.*, *55* (1952), 60. F. Massa, *Electrical Manufacturing*, March 1950, p. 106. T. F. Hueter, *Elektrotech. Z.*, October 1953, p. 336.

been achieved with trichlor-ethylene, cyclohexane, Varsol, and Alcalock.

In some installations the parts are carried on a conveyor chain through the sonic treatment bath at rates of 1 to 10 ft/min. Not only removal of grease, dirt, and grinding grits has been accomplished but the pitting action of sonic cavitation is powerful enough to break off scale oxide layers and to speed metal pickling processes.

Whereas the usefulness of sonic cavitation effects for the cleaning of metal surfaces has now reached widespread industrial recognition,

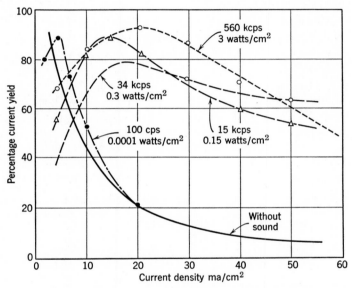

Fig. 6.23.   Electrochemical effects of sonic irradiation, according to A. Roll.

their potential application to electrochemistry is still the subject of laboratory studies.   If we keep in mind that gas bubbles at electrode interfaces play an important role in electrolytic processes, for example in electroplating, we can easily visualize interactions between a sound field and the gas bubbles.   Mechanisms of this kind, as well as sonically induced streaming, will counteract the depletion of the diffusion layer between electrode and electrolyte of ions which ordinarily limits the current yield.[53]   This is illustrated in Fig. 6.23 for

[53] Major contributions in this field have recently been made by A. Roll, *Metalloberflache*, B, 4 (1952) 49, 65, 81; and Z. *Metallkunde*, *41* (1950), 339, 413; *42* (1951), 238, 271; and by E. Yaeger et al., *J. Acoust. Soc. Amer.*, *25* (1953), 443, 456, 461, and 443.

a combination of nickel anode and brass cathode in an electrolytic solution of 40 g nickel sulfate, 35 g sodium citrate in 1 liter water (pH value of 6, temperature 20°C).   In this example sonic irradiation is applied parallel to the cathode face at four different frequencies. An increase of nickel current yield is obtained if the current density is higher than 10 milliamp./cm^2.

Because of the frequency dependence of cavitation thresholds, sonic treatment of metal surfaces is most efficient at lower frequencies. On the other hand, the discomfort of intense audible vibrations makes it expedient to use frequencies above 20 kcps.   Hence the optimum frequency range for cavitation effects is approximately 20 to 200 kcps. Suitable devices are discussed in Chapter 7.

CHAPTER 7

Devices and Techniques for Sonic Processing

7.1 Criteria for Transducer Selection

The field of sonic processing encompasses a wide range of diverse applications. The required sonic variables depend on the particular mechanisms involved, some of which we discussed in Chapter 6. Also, the scale of application may vary, involving power levels from a few watts, as in medical therapy by ultrasound, to 10^3 watts, as in liquid processing. Many of these demands can not be met by piezo-electric or magnetostrictive transducers, but there are several other types of sound generators that may be employed. Some of the sources, such as sirens, jets, and whistles, operate on fluid dynamic principles, while others are driven by mechanical forces or by heat.

The main criterion for the choice of a transducer is the frequency at which the particular processing mechanism works optimally. Once the frequency range is fixed, a selection between several available transducer types (electroacoustic, fluid dynamic, mechanical) can be made on the basis of operating efficiency and equipment cost. The general range of transducer types is outlined in Table 1.1. Often these ranges overlap, so other engineering considerations will determine the final choice.

We shall give some general rules in this section, and a few important exceptions will be discussed in the later paragraphs. The optimum frequencies for most power applications fall in the range between 1 kcps and 20 kcps for gases and in the range between 10 kcps and 400 kcps for liquids (and melts). The processing of solids, on the other hand, usually involves local action of a vibrating tool, and no general rules can be given with regard to an optimum frequency. Oil-well drilling may require vibrations of 20 to 50 cps, but cutting of small dies may work best at 20 to 50 kcps. Frequencies as high as 1 mcps are indicated only in applications where small localized regions are to be affected in liquids or viscoelastic materials, or where

245

the heating due to sound absorption plays an important role, as in ultrasonic therapy.

It appears that gas-phase processing is best carried out with fluid-dynamic transducers. These are capable of generating at low frequencies the high displacement amplitudes which are required to deliver high power to low-impedance loads. Furthermore, such transducers operate without electronic equipment which is relatively costly and usually requires a good deal of maintenance. In this respect they have a particular advantage over electromechanical devices.

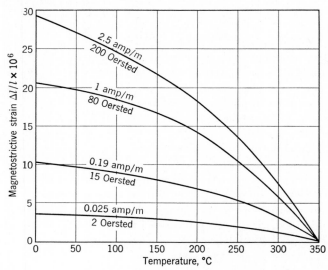

Fig. 7.1.   Decrease of magnetostrictive strain with temperature.

In liquid-phase processing (including cleaning of solid surfaces immersed in a liquid) electromechanical devices compete with fluid dynamic transducers of the whistle type. Both types are capable of producing cavitation, which is the mechanism responsible for most of the successful applications which have been reported. Liquid whistles and modulated jets operate between 1 kcps and 10 kcps and have the advantage of ruggedness and low cost.

Magnetostrictive transducers operate in the range between 10 kcps and 100 kcps and are superior to other devices at elevated temperatures. The Curie temperature of nickel is 358°C; as the temperature approaches this point the activity of the magnetostrictive element drops to zero. The amount of decrease of the induced magnetostrictive strain with temperature depends on the internal polarization.

This dependence is shown in Fig. 7.1 for various polarizing fields. Compared with quartz, which has its Curie point at 576°C, but fails mechanically under relatively small local temperature gradients, magnetostrictive materials like nickel are much more resistant to mechanical and thermal strain. For example, the irradiation of metal melts at temperatures exceeding 800°C can be effected with the use of cooled ceramic coupling pieces between transducer and liquid (see Section 7.5).

Limitations of piezoelectric crystals   The basic variables of a potential sonic application are usually evaluated by experiments with small-scale laboratory equipment of the piezoelectric type. In an effort to obtain similar results at a production level, attempts are sometimes made simply to scale up such laboratory equipment. However, there are some basic physical limitations which make it difficult to increase the power output from piezoelectric transducers above certain limits. Some general information on these limitations, such as safe ranges of temperature and humidity, dielectric loss factor, and dynamical breaking stress is given in Table 7.1.

Table 7.1   Physical Limitations of Piezoelectric Materials

Crystal Material	Temperature Limits (Centigrade)	Safe Humidity (Unprotected Crystal) (%)	Dielectric Loss Factor (tan σ)	Breaking Stress [X_{max} (newton/cm^2)]
Quartz	Non-piezoelectric above 576°. Above 250° slow decrease of piezoelectric activity.	Excessive moisture may cause external electrode short circuiting.	0.02 %	$76 \cdot 10^6$
ADP	Melting point at 190°. Above 100° ammonium evaporates from surface.	Maximum tolerable value 94 %; leakage negligible below 50 %.	~1 %	$20 \cdot 10^6$
Rochelle salt	Decomposition at 55°. Electric leakage above 45°. Dielectric Curie points at +24° and −18°.	Maximum tolerable value 84 %. Minimum safe value 30 %.	~5 % between Curie points; at 30°C 0.5 %.	$15 \cdot 10^6$
Lithium sulphate	Decomposition above 75°.	Maximum tolerable value 95 %. Leakage negligible below 50 %.	(No data available)	$20 \cdot 10^6$
Barium titanate	Depolarization occurs above 120°. Polarization decreases above 100°. activity reduced at lower Curie point: +5° for pure BaTiO₃; −40° for BaTiO₃ with 5 % CaTiO₃	Excessive moisture may cause short circuiting	1 % at 50°C. 2 % at 100°C.	$45 \cdot 10^6$

We note from Table 7.1 that of all crystals quartz is the material of greatest stability and strength. In fact, intensities up to 10^3 watts/cm^2 have been radiated into water from quartz transducers operated at a frequency of several megacycles. At frequencies of the order of 100 kcps and lower, however, their electric impedance becomes very large (see Fig. 4.4), so that bulky matching networks and excessively high driving voltages are required. For example, to obtain an intensity of 4 watts/cm^2 at 50 kcps a rms voltage of 40 kv is required. It is difficult to prevent electrical breakdown at such high voltages, particularly at the edges of the electrodes. For CW operation it has been found that dielectric breakdown of the insulating medium at the transducer edges rather than mechanical breakdown of the quartz limits the maximum intensity to about 50 watts/cm^2.[1]

The dielectric strength of quartz is about thirty times higher than that of insulating oils, whose dielectric strength also depends on moisture content, amount of dissolved gas, the form of the electrodes, and the duty cycle. The mechanical breaking strength of quartz would permit operation at intensities which are much higher than 50 watts/cm^2. The maximum intensity at resonance depends on the impedance $\rho_0 c$ of the loading medium:

$$ \mathcal{I}_{\max} = \frac{1}{2} \rho_0 c \left(\frac{X_{\max}}{\rho_m c_m} \right)^2 \tag{7.1} $$

where $X_{\max}$ is the breaking stress and $\rho_m c_m$ the specific acoustic impedance of the crystal. Using the values given in Table 7.1 we find that, for quartz, $\mathcal{I}_{\max} \simeq 2000$ watts/cm^2, for ADP $\mathcal{I}_{\max} \simeq 500$ watts/cm^2 if the transducer radiates into an oil or water load. These maximum values can be approached only with pulses which are short enough that neither dielectric breakdown nor cavitation limiting occurs. With gas loading, however, little driving voltage is required to produce high internal stresses, because of the high transducer Q. In this case, the maximum intensity is determined entirely by eq. 7.1 and becomes for quartz $\mathcal{I}_{\max} \simeq 0.5$ watts/cm^2, for ADP $\simeq 0.13$ watts/cm^2.[2]

In view of these electrical limitations and the relatively high cost of large crystal slabs, quartz transducers are not as suitable for most power applications as might be expected from their other advantages. Lithium sulfate and Rochelle salt can not be used for high-power generation because of their limited temperature range. Of the

---

[1] L. F. Epstein, W. M. A. Andersen, and L. R. Harden, *J. Acoust. Soc. Amer.*, *19* (1947), 248.

[2] T. F. Hueter, *J. Acoust. Soc. Amer.*, *23* (1951), 590.

remaining two materials listed in Table 7.1, barium titanate ceramic has the great advantage of mechanical ruggedness and of availability in all kinds of shapes. Ceramic transducers also require less effort in assembling and mounting than do ADP stacks which must be built up from individually electroded slabs. The use of barium titanate is therefore indicated, whenever the application at hand calls for a piezoelectric processing system. Some features of focusing systems using barium titanate are discussed in Section 7.4.

An over-all comparison of the relative merits of barium titanate transducers and magnetostrictive transducers shows about equal suitability for power applications. However, the optimum frequency range for thickness-type barium titanate units is 100–400 kcps, while the optimum frequency range for magnetostrictive units is 10–60 kcps. A decision between the two types will depend mostly on the availability of the basic transducer materials and on the geometrical dimensions of the processing system.

7.2 Special Properties of Barium Titanate

We shall discuss only those features which distinguish barium titanate ceramic from ordinary piezoelectric materials. Barium titanate is commonly called *ferroelectric* since it exhibits certain dielectric properties that are analogous to the special magnetic properties of ferromagnetic materials (see Chapter 5). In both groups of materials, spontaneous polarization occurs within small regions or "domains." The electric dipoles in ferroelectric materials, or the elementary magnets in ferromagnetic materials, are in parallel alignment within each domain. Detailed theories on the ferroelectric effect have been given in the literature.[3] For our purpose a qualitative understanding of the ferroelectric behavior of barium titanate is sufficient.

Barium titanate is representative of a class of crystals of special structure, called *perovskite*. This structure is characterized by the formula ABO_3. The interaction between the ions in the crystal lattice and an electric field depends on the degree to which the ions can be displaced from their equilibrium positions, which in turn is a function of the relative size of the ions. Electromechanical coupling occurs if the ionic radii of the components A and B have specifically related values.

The right conditions exist in the titanates of some alkaline earths and also in certain columbates and tantalates. The crystal structure of barium titanate is shown in Fig. 7.2, in which the titanium atom is taken as the center of symmetry. Because of its small size relative to the surrounding ions, the titanium atom is easily displaced by an electric field. In the tetragonal phase of barium titanate the titanium atom tends to move towards one of the face-centered oxygen atoms, owing to the potential distribution between two opposite oxygen atoms. Each crystal cell, therefore, has a dipole moment which may be oriented toward any one

[3] H. Mueller, *Phys. Rev.*, *58* (1940), 565, 805. W. P. Mason, *Phys. Rev.*, *73* (1948), 1398. J. C. Slater, *Phys. Rev.*, *78* (1950), 748. E. T. Jaynes, *"Ferroelectricity,"* Princeton University Press, Princeton, 1952.

of the six oxygen atoms.   Since the orientation of the dipole moment within one cell is influenced by the orientations in the neighboring cells, there are regions of parallel alignment, called "domains."

The dielectric constant of barium titanate has a value of 1200 to 1500 at room temperature and shows a pronounced peak at 120°C.   At this "Curie point" the dielectric constant may be as high as 9000.[4]   X-ray studies have shown that barium titanate changes from tetragonal to cubic structure if the temperature is raised above this Curie point.   Figure 7.3 shows the dimensions of the crystal cell below and above the Curie point.   In the tetragonal phase the axis in the direction of the titanium displacement (c axis) is 1 per cent longer than the other two axes (a axes).   It is evident that mechanical distortion within the crystals will result

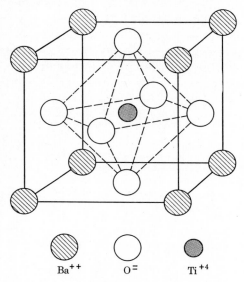

$$Ba^{++} \qquad O^= \qquad Ti^{+4}$$

Fig. 7.2.   Crystal structure of barium titanate.

if two neighboring cells are polarized at 90° to each other.   When regions of parallel alignment (domains) are formed, this mechanical distortion within the crystal is considerably reduced and the crystal is in a more stable state.

If a strong electric field is applied, the electric axes of the domains oriented at

[4] Pure barium titanate has a second Curie point near 5°C.   The piezoelectric response has a minimum at this temperature, but reaches a rather high level below it.   It was found that the lower Curie temperature can be shifted upward if a few mole per cent of zirconium oxide (ZrO_2) are incorporated into the barium titanate.   For instance, 2 mole per cent ZrO_2 will bring the lower transition point up to about +20°C.   On the other hand, addition of 7 per cent calcium titanate shifts the second transition point to −40°C.   These effects are important wherever large variations of sensitivity with temperature in the operating range are to be avoided.   See D. A. Berlincourt and F. Kulcsar, *J. Acoust. Soc. Amer.*, *24* (1952), 709.   Other promising titanate compositions are discussed by B. Jaffe, R. S. Roth, and S. Margullo, *J. Appl. Phys. 25* (1954), 809.

right angle to the field are turned into the direction of the field and a uniaxial crystal is created in which all c axes are parallel to the field.   If all the domains are aligned in this manner the dielectric constant in the c direction is much smaller than in the a direction (300 as against 1500 at room temperature).   Alignment of the longer c axes in the field direction also causes the crystal to become thicker than it is without the field.   If the field is reversed, the c axes will eventually switch around 180° and again the crystal will be thicker.   A *large* a-c field will therefore cause a vibration of twice the driving frequency, which means that the strain is proportional to the square of the electric field strength.   If a strong d-c bias is once applied some of the induced domain alignment persists.   This remanent polarization provides an internal field with the result that a *small* a-c field will now

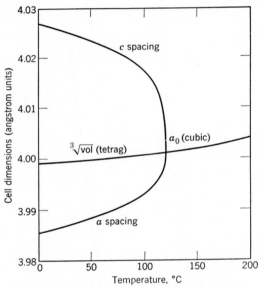

Fig. 7.3.   Dimensions of crystal cell versus temperature, for barium titanate.

cause a thickness vibration of the same frequency.   The internal field, therefore, acts in much the same way as the d-c polarizing current in a magnetostrictive transducer (see Chapter 5).

In a barium titanate ceramic many small crystallites are baked together and each crystallite is subdivided into dielectric domains.   A large biasing field will switch the domains into some degree of alignment with the field vector.   This process is called prepolarization.   A schematic picture of the polarization process in barium titanate ceramic is shown in Fig. 7.4.

Polarization and losses   A dense ceramic is made by pressing and baking, which locks the individual crystallites into positions that are randomly oriented with respect to their longer c axes.   Because of this interlocking, elastic forces must be overcome to switch the domains into alignment with the polarizing field, and the thermal vibrations within the ceramic assist an external d-c bias in this switching.   The strength of the d-c field required for polarization is about 12 kv/cm (30 volts/mil). At room temperature polarization takes approximately 2 hours. The fact that heat facilitates domain switching can be used to shorten this time. In this case the ceramic is first heated in an oil bath to a temperature above its Curie point (up to 150°C). Then a field is applied to the ceramic during the cooling period. Both the necessary field strength and polarization time are reduced if hot polarization is used.

A driving voltage applied to a polarized barium titanate disc near its resonance frequency will make the domains whose c axes are in the field direction grow at the expense of neighboring domains whose c axes are at angles to the electric field vector. As a result, a disc of the material becomes thicker when the driving field is parallel to the direction of the inner polarizing field and becomes thinner when

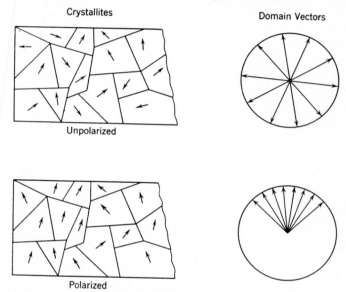

Fig. 7.4. Domain alignment by polarization in barium titanate.

it is antiparallel. In addition, the domains that are in perfect alignment with the field will stretch or contract, depending on the field direction.

The driving field and the resulting dielectric displacement are not completely in phase, so there is a hysteresis loop with accompanying losses[5] (see Fig. 5.8). The loss tangent of barium titanate is of the order of 2 per cent, about 10^2 times larger than for quartz. If such transducers are driven too hard, excessive heat will be generated within the ceramic. This may raise the temperature up to the Curie point and thus completely depolarize the material. In CW operation, sound intensities larger than 3 watts/cm² cannot be generated safely unless effective cooling of the transducer is provided by forced air or by liquid circulation. In pulse operation the sound intensity at the transducer can be increased in inverse proportion to the duty cycle, and levels of 10^2 watts/cm² and more have been

[5] K. Kambe, I. Nakada, and H. Takahasi, *J. Phys. Soc. Japan, 8* (1953), 9; T. F. Hueter, D. P. Neuhaus and J. Kolb, *J. Acoust. Soc. Am., 26* (1954), No. 6.

reached.   If a d-c bias is maintained across the transducer sound intensities of
up to 10 watts/cm^2 can be radiated continuously even if the temperature reaches
the Curie point.   Higher intensity levels can be achieved by focusing techniques
which also circumvent the limiting effect of cavitation at the transducer face.

7.3   Principles of Ultrasonic Applicator Design

We shall describe a few prototypes which are being used successfully
in power applications of relatively small scale: cup-shaped units for

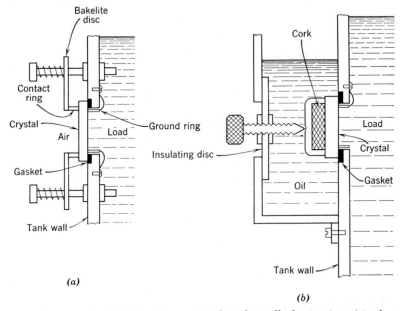

Fig. 7.5.   Method of mounting a crystal to the wall of a treatment tank.

the immersion of small parts as in ultrasonic surface cleaning and
self-contained units for the application of ultrasonic energy to biological specimens as in medical therapy.   These examples will allow
us to discuss some design considerations of general validity.

Means for immersion treatment of small objects   Let us consider a quartz or barium titanate transducer which is to be mounted
in the side or bottom wall of a processing vessel.   A mounting consistent with pressure and insulation requirements is shown in Fig. 7.5a.
The crystal is pressed tightly against a rubber gasket around the
opening in the wall.   The leads are connected to contact rings on
either side of the crystal.   If the driving field is below approximately
8 kv/cm, air will provide sufficient insulation and, at the same time,
optimum acoustical backing.   This is generally the case with barium

titanate. With quartz crystals driven at higher driving fields an arrangement of the type shown in Fig. 7.5b must be used where the high-voltage side of the crystal is immersed in oil. Pressure-release backing of the crystal is then obtained by a special back electrode filled with a porous air-containing material such as cork.[6]

A design which is often used for the irradiation of small samples of material is shown in Fig. 7.6. An open oil container holds the crystal, which is clamped between two contact rings R_1 and R_2 which are fitted

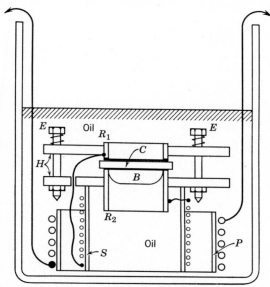

Fig. 7.6. Beaker-type mounting; sound is radiated from the crystal C in the upward direction.

into two round ceramic plates H. The plates are held against each other by the bolts and springs E. In the lower cylindrical ring an air bubble B is trapped which serves as pressure-release backing. The cylinder R_2 could also be sealed at the bottom and completely filled with air or cork. The same oil container can also accommodate a matching transformer, as shown by the two coils P and S. In this case the RF power can be fed to the transducer container through a low-impedance cable which permits more flexibility of operation. In the simplest arrangement of this type, the use of a cable is avoided altogether by mounting the transducer and container directly on a floor-model transmitter.[7]

[6] W. J. Fry, *J. Acoust. Soc. Amer.*, *22* (1950), 871.
[7] G. E. Henry, *General Electric Rev.*, March 1952, p. 60.

We shall now consider the design of magnetostrictive transducers for purposes similar to those of the crystal units described above. Two possible forms will be discussed which operate in the frequency range from 10 to 30 kcps at cavitation levels.

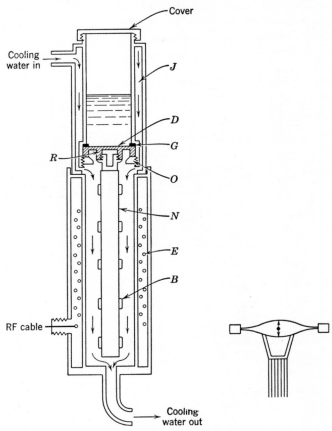

Fig. 7.7.   Magnetostrictive rod coupled to a small treatment chamber.   Courtesy of Raytheon Manufacturing Company, Waltham, Mass.

The magnetostrictive transducer unit illustrated in Fig. 7.7 provides a cup-shaped treatment chamber which is directly coupled to a laminated nickel rod N. For example, a rod of 13-cm length and 4-cm^2 cross section will resonate at 20 kcps. The design is simplified by the use of bolts B to hold the laminations together and by omitting a return path for the magnetic flux which is produced by the excitation coil E. The information in Section 5.6 can be used to determine the electrical data for this type of transducer.

The effective radiating area of the rod is increased by coupling through a cylindrical ring R to a flexible diaphragm D, which is clamped at its periphery by the ring nut O and the gasket G. By proper choice of the diameters of both the ring and the diaphragm with relation to the driving frequency the diaphragm can be made to resonate.[8] In this way the vibration amplitude at the center of the diaphragm is increased, as shown in the insert of Fig. 7.7. If 100

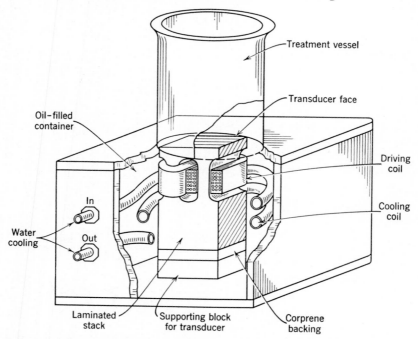

Fig. 7.8.   Magnetostrictive transducer for cleaning of small parts.   Courtesy of Massa Laboratories, Hingham, Mass.

watts are available to drive the rod of our example, the rod amplitude is about 1.5×10^{-4} cm while the amplitude at the center of the diaphragm may be about three times higher.

The conversion efficiency of a device of this type is about 30 per cent, and effective cooling is required to remove the heat (in our example about 70 watts) generated in the transducer.   In the unit illustrated in Fig. 7.7 tap water is flown through the jacket J into the space between the rod and the driving coil.

Another form of a magnetostrictive transducer for the treatment

[8] R. A. Fryklund, U.S. Pat. 2,498,990, February 28, 1950.

of small objects immersed in a beaker-type vessel is demonstrated in Fig. 7.8.   Here a closed magnetic loop is provided according to the design considerations given in Section 5.7.   The laminations are cemented together, and the radiating transducer face is flush-mounted into the plane cover plate of an oil-filled container.   Radiation from the back end of the magnetostrictive stack is prevented by a Corprene layer.   With this arrangement one can obtain sufficient power to produce violent cavitation throughout the liquid, providing, of course, that intimate contact is maintained between the transducer and the flat-bottomed vessel.[9]

Power requirements   In a unit of the type shown in Fig. 7.8 the electric power required for effective sonic cleaning of parts which are immersed into the treatment vessel depends on the following parameters:

a. *The overall conversion efficiency from electric power to sonic power within the vessel.*

It is determined by the losses in the matching network and in the transducer, by the degree of coupling from the transducer to the liquid, by the phase angle of the radiation impedance, and by the efficiency of the driving amplifier.   From Table 5.3 the transducer efficiency at 30 kcps is of the order of 50 per cent.   The plate efficiency of a Class C amplifier is about 70 per cent.   Under these conditions about one-third of the electric power drawn from the line appears as sonic power in the vessel.

b. *The threshold of cavitation in the cleaning fluid and at the frequency of operation.*

From Fig. 6.13 we obtain a value of approximately 1 watt/cm^2 for water at 30 kcps.   Cavitation will first occur at the interface between the bottom of the vessel and the liquid.   To affect regions above this interface higher intensities are necessary.   Experience has shown that 3 to 5 watts/cm^2 are sufficient in most cleaning fluids at this frequency.   At a frequency of 400 kcps, intensities of about 10–20 watts/cm^2 are required.[9a]

c. *The relative dimensions of the parts to be cleaned with respect to wavelength.*

The surfaces of an immersed object which do not directly face the sonic source are reached by the diffracted sound only (see Section 3.6).   If the object is large compared with wave-

[9] F. Massa, *Elec. Mfg.*, May 1951, p. 106.
[9a] T. J. Kearney, *Jour. Acoust. Soc. Amer.*, 26 (1954), 244.

length ($ka \gg 1$) there is shadow formation.   At 30 kcps parts up to a size of about 1 in. can be thoroughly cleaned by stationary immersion at the intensity levels indicated above.   Larger parts must be rotated in the sound field and may also call for an increase of the size of the treatment vessel and of the intensity level.

From these considerations we can find the electric power consumed by an ultrasonic cleaning unit of the type shown in Fig. 7.8.   For example, to produce intensities of about 5 watts/cm^2 over an area of

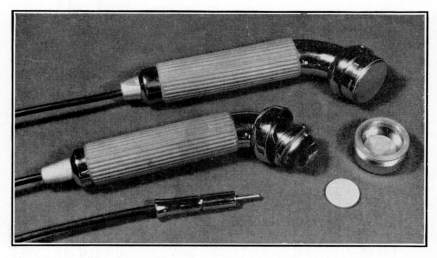

Fig. 7.9.   Applicator for ultrasonic therapy.   *Top*, assembled applicator; *center*, exploded view of crystal head; *bottom*, cable connector to driving unit.   Courtesy of Siemens-Reiniger Werke, Erlangen, Germany.

about 25 cm^2 within the treatment vessel a total transducer output of about 150 watts is required, assuming a transmission loss (coupling and radiation) of about 15 per cent.   This corresponds to a plate output of the amplifier of about 300 watts and to a required line power of about 450 watts.

Applicators for medical treatment   Self-contained transducers of 10 to 50 watts output are used in medical treatment with ultrasonic waves.   In this application a lightweight compact applicator with a flat radiating surface is desired.[10]   Figure 7.9 shows such a unit, consisting of a sealed irradiation head, handpiece, and cable, which can be operated safely under water.   Figure 7.10 illustrates three

[10] E. Skudrczik, *Elektrotech. u. Maschinenbau* (Vienna), *68* (1951), 202.

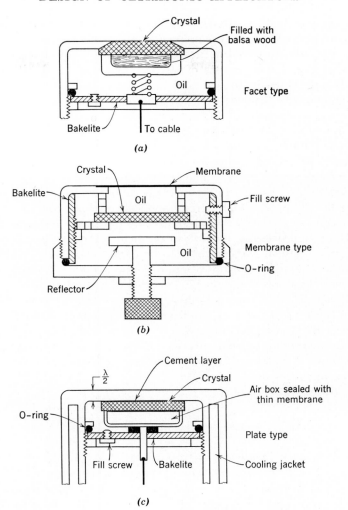

Fig. 7.10. Three typical designs for ultrasonic crystal heads. *a*, facet-type mounting. *b*, membrane-type mounting. *c*, plate-type mounting (most commonly used).

possible designs: (*a*) a faceted crystal cemented into a properly shaped hole in the housing; (*b*) a sound-transparent window provided in the housing; (*c*) a crystal cemented to a tuned half-wave plate. Three different possibilities of back-electrode design are also demonstrated in Fig. 7.10.

The facet-type mounting can be used only if the crystals are relatively thick ($t > 0.2$ cm) and if the driving field is not very high.   If frequencies much above 1.5 mcps are desired, a thicker crystal can be used which is excited at its odd harmonics.   The back electrode shown in Fig. 7.10a consists of an open pill box, filled with cork or balsa wood, which is pressed against the crystal by a spring.   If the driving field is sufficiently low, no oil filling is required.   If oil is used, it must be well degassed.

In units of the type shown in Fig. 7.10b a membrane, for example, of copper bronze, is soldered into a recess around the opening of the casing.   The crystal is supported between a ground ring in front and an insulated ring in back.   The crystal can either be completely surrounded with oil as illustrated, or it can be used with a box-type back electrode.   The oil which serves as transmitting medium must be thoroughly degassed, otherwise air bubbles may form under the membrane and decrease the output of the unit considerably.   A liquid backing is useful if the crystal is to be cooled effectively, which may be important with barium titanate ceramic discs.   In this case a pressure-release backing can be provided if a solid reflector plate is positioned an odd integral number of quarter waves from the back of the crystal.   This is an application of impedance transformation in a transmission line, as discussed in Chapter 2.

Transmittivity of thin plates   If sound passes through a plate of thickness d at normal incidence, the energy-transmission coefficient is given by:

$$T_E = \frac{\mathcal{I}_t}{\mathcal{I}_0} = \frac{1}{1 + \left(\dfrac{m^2 - 1}{2m}\right)^2 \sin^2 (kd)} \tag{7.2}$$

in which $\mathcal{I}_0$ is the incident wave intensity, $\mathcal{I}_t$ the transmitted intensity, $m = \rho_p c_p / \rho_0 c$ is the ratio of the impedance of the plate to the impedance of the medium, and $k = 2\pi/\lambda_p$.   Complete transmission occurs in a lossless plate whenever $d = n\lambda_p/2$.   In the long-wave limit ($d \ll \lambda/2$) the plate reacts as a pure mass and eq. 7.2 reduces to:

$$T_E \simeq 1 - \left[\frac{m^2 - 1}{m} \pi \frac{d}{\lambda_p}\right]^2 = 1 - \mathbf{R}_E \tag{7.3}$$

where $\mathbf{R}_E$ is the coefficient of energy reflection of a thin membrane.[11]

[11] For transmission of airborne sound through panels we have $m \gg 1$ and $kd \ll 1$. The reflected pressure amplitude then is $P_r = P_0 \mathbf{R}$.   It follows from eq. 7.2 that at low frequencies the amplitude reflection coefficient $\mathbf{R} = \mathbf{R}_E^{1/2}$ is proportional to $\rho \omega d = M\omega$, where M is the mass per unit area of the panel.   This relationship is known as the "asymptotic mass law."

Figure 7.11 shows the relationship T_E versus d/λ for two membrane materials, aluminum ($m = 11$) and Lucite ($m = 2.2$), with water as surrounding fluid. We note that for 80 per cent transmission an aluminum membrane must have a thickness $d \simeq \lambda/30$, while for a Lucite membrane the required thickness is $d \simeq \lambda/10$.

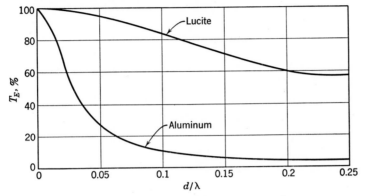

Fig. 7.11.   Sound transmission through membranes.

The elastic constants determining transmission are given in Table 7.2 for several membrane materials. At frequencies higher than 1-mcps membranes of a thickness required for high transmittivity are quite fragile and tuned half-wave plates are preferable.

Table 7.2   Transmission through Membranes

Membrane Material	Density ρ (kg/m³)	Young's Modulus Y_0 (kg/m²)	Poisson's Ratio σ	Bulk Velocity* c_b (m/sec)	Characteristic Impedance ρc_b (kg/m²/sec)	Impedance Ratio m ref water
Steel	$7.7 \cdot 10^3$	$21 \cdot 10^{10}$	0.28	$5.85 \cdot 10^3$	$45 \cdot 10^6$	31
Copper	$8.9 \cdot 10^3$	$12.5 \cdot 10^{10}$	0.35	$4.7 \cdot 10^3$	$42 \cdot 10^6$	27
Brass	$8.1 \cdot 10^3$	$9.6 \cdot 10^{10}$	0.3	$4 \cdot 10^3$	$32.5 \cdot 10^6$	23
Zinc	$7.1 \cdot 10^3$	$10.5 \cdot 10^{10}$	0.25	$4.17 \cdot 10^3$	$29.5 \cdot 10^6$	20
Glass	$\sim 3 \cdot 10^3$	$\sim 6 \cdot 10^{10}$	0.25	$\sim 4.8 \cdot 10^3$	$\sim 14.4 \cdot 10^6$	12
Aluminum	$2.7 \cdot 10^3$	$7 \cdot 10^{10}$	0.34	$6.3 \cdot 10^3$	$17 \cdot 10^6$	11
Polystyrene	$1.06 \cdot 10^3$	$0.35 \cdot 10^{10}$	0.37	$2.4 \cdot 10^3$	$2.55 \cdot 10^6$	1.7

* The normal transmission through membranes and plates is controlled by the bulk velocity.

$$c_b = \left(\frac{Y_0}{\rho} \frac{1 - \sigma}{(1 + \sigma)(1 - 2\sigma)} \right)^{\frac{1}{2}}$$

A crystal mounted on a half-wave plate is shown in Fig. 7.10c. The plate may be made of brass or aluminum. The half-wave resonance is quite sharp, so it is important in designing this type of applicator to have precise knowledge of the sound velocity in the material. A design of this kind provides excellent protection of the crystal.

A good bond between the crystal and the plate can be obtained by using DeKhotinsky cement, thermosetting resins, or a polymerizing cement like Araldite. The adhesive layer should be as thin and uniform as possible and completely free of air bubbles. Cements that contain a liquid thinner are not suitable because their hardening depends on diffusion of the solvent through the interface between crystal and plate. Furthermore, such adhesives have been found to shrink during drying, thereby reducing the area of contact between the crystal and the plate.

Figure 7.10 also shows another type of back electrode consisting of an air box sealed with a thin metal foil. This design keeps the current density low because of the large area of contact. An electrode arrangement of this kind corresponds to a condenser with a three-layer dielectric: the cement, the crystal, and the oil film between

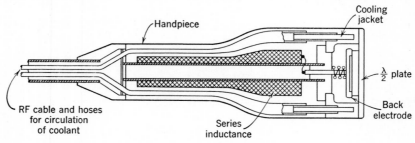

Fig. 7.12.   Ultrasonic applicator containing a matching coil.

crystal and air box. Since the two outer layers are extremely thin, almost all the voltage is developed across a crystal of low dielectric constant, as with quartz. With barium titanate, however, which has a dielectric constant about 300 times that of quartz, a considerable drop in voltage would occur across the cement layer. In this case a more intimate electric contact with the electrodes is required. This can be obtained by leads soldered directly to the metallic electrodes covering the barium titanate or by conductive paint.

With a unit of this type no oil filling is required if the driving voltage does not exceed the breakdown value in air. With barium titanate ceramic discs, which tend to heat up because of their higher losses, some means of cooling must be provided. This may be achieved by a cooling jacket around the casing through which water is circulated, as shown in Fig. 7.10c. The heat developed in the transducer disc will then flow through the metal plate to the cooled walls of the case.

It is possible to incorporate a matching coil (see Section 4.5) within the handpiece of the applicator, as shown in Fig. 7.12. This is of advantage with quartz crystals which require high driving voltages. The transformation of the electric impedance by the coil allows one to feed the RF to the unit at low voltage through a lightweight flexible cable.   Applicators of this type are available commercially at frequencies between 0.7 and 2 mcps, with a power output of 10 to 40 watts.   They permit radiation of average intensities at levels from 1 to 4 watts/cm^2.[12]

7.4 Focusing Systems

We mentioned in Sections 6.2 and 6.7 that in liquid-phase processing it is difficult to affect all regions of a large treatment tank if the attenuation in the material is high, or if cavitation is required in the process. In such cases a method using continuous flow through the high-intensity region of a focused sound field is indicated.   We shall discuss various possibilities of focusing sound in a liquid medium by means of reflection (mirrors), refraction (lenses), and diffraction (curved transducers).   Solid focusing devices, as in the form of exponentially tapered rods, can be used to provide concentrated local action.   Some special applications will be mentioned.

Paraboloid reflectors   A plane wave can be converted into a spherical wave converging on a focal point F by means of a parabolic reflector.   A high coefficient of reflection $\mathbf{R}_E$ can be obtained from either a rigid or a soft reflector.   For example, the reflecting surface can be machined into a thick steel block ($\mathbf{R}_E = 88$ per cent) with back surfaces shaped so as to diffuse the sound which is not reflected at the front.   A lighter structure is obtained with a reflecting layer of Corprene or with a properly shaped thin foil ($t \ll 0.03\lambda$) backed by air.   The geometry of a paraboloid reflector is illustrated in Fig. 7.13. From the equation for a paraboloid

$$z^2 + y^2 - 2px = 0 \qquad\qquad (7.4)$$

we find that the focal point F is located at $x = p/2$ and that the radius a of the mirror aperture is related to the mirror depth h by $a = \sqrt{2ph}$. We also note from Fig. 7.13 that the waves that are reflected twice from the mirror are parallel with the incident waves, provided that the incident beam is confined to an annular area whose outer radius is a and whose inner radius is $b = p^2/a$.   This suggests the use of a ring-shaped transducer located at such a distance from the front plane of the reflector as is required to produce standing waves in the system.

---

[12] These levels are considered to be both safe and effective for purposes of medical therapy; see *Physical Medicine in General Practice*, 3rd edition, 1952. Harper, New York, pp. 276–296.

The gain factor of the focusing system illustrated in Fig. 7.13 is:

$$\Gamma = \frac{\text{peak pressure at focus}}{\text{peak pressure in free field}} = \Gamma_g \cdot \Gamma_s$$

in which Γ_g is the geometrical gain factor of the mirror and Γ_s the standing-wave gain factor. The geometrical gain factor can be determined from diffraction theory.[13] For $\lambda \ll a$ it is:

$$\Gamma_g = kp \ln (2h/p) \qquad (k = 2\pi/\lambda) \qquad (7.5a)$$

where p is twice the distance F–P, as shown in Fig. 7.13.

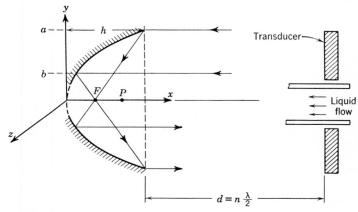

Fig. 7.13.   Paraboloid reflector. The focal point F is located at $x = p/2$, if p is the distance from the origin to the semi-latus rectum P.

It follows from eq. 7.5a that for a given wavelength the gain is a maximum if $h = 3.7p \simeq 1.4a$. For example, at 300 kcps the optimal dimensions of a mirror of aperture diameter $2a = 55$ cm are $p = 10$ cm and $h = 35$ cm. Assuming linearity of the medium one obtains for the maximum geometrical gain:

$$\Gamma_{g \max} \simeq 4.6a/\lambda \qquad (\lambda \leq 10a) \qquad (7.5b)$$

For the mirror of our example the wavelength is $\lambda = 0.5$ cm and hence $\Gamma_{g \max} \simeq 250$. In practice the gain is limited by losses in the medium, as well as bubble formation and cavitation. Also, the dimensions of both the focusing reflector and the associated transducer become too large to be practicable if one attempts to obtain

[13] M. D. Rosenberg, *Internal Rept.*, Harvard Univ. Acoustics Research Laboratory, July 1952.   C. W. Horton and F. C. Naral, *J. Acoust. Soc. Amer.*, *22* (1950), 855.

pressure gains higher than 50 at frequencies lower than 100 kcps. As we shall see, the same limitations apply to all kinds of focusing devices.[14]

Ultrasonic lenses   The refraction of a sound wave passing through media of differing sound velocity can be used for focusing.   However, when the refractive index $n = c_1/c_2$ differs from unity, there is usually a discontinuity of impedance $m = \rho_1 c_1/\rho_2 c_2$ which leads to a reflection coefficient R_E.   The conditions desired for an efficient lens material are: $n \neq 1$ and $m \simeq 1$.   This pair of conditions is approximated by only a few combinations of media, some of which are shown in Table 7.3.

Table 7.3   Performance of Ultrasonic Lenses

Lens Medium (1)	$\rho_1 \times 10^3$ (kg/m³)	$c_1 \times 10^3$ (m/sec)	n	m	R_E (%)	Surrounding Medium ($\rho_2 c_2$)
Carbon tetrachloride	1.59	0.938	0.73	1.1	1	Water
Steel	7.7	5.85	4.1	2.25	16	Mercury
Lucite	1.18	2.8	1.9	2.2	14	Water
Polystyrene	1.1	2.4	1.6	1.7	12	Water
Glass	~2.3	~4.9	3.3	~7.4	60	Water
Aluminum	2.65	6.3	4.3	13	74	Transformer oil

Planoconcave lenses of Polystyrene have been used successfully to produce high local ultrasonic intensities in biological materials whose specific acoustic impedance is approximately equal to water.[15]   Polystyrene is superior to Lucite for higher power levels since its sound absorption is lower.   The lens can be mounted with its plane side flush on the transducer face.   For a simple spherical lens of small aperture the radius of curvature of the concave face is

$$r = f\left(\frac{n-1}{n}\right) \qquad (7.6)$$

in which f is the focal length and n the index of refraction.   The pressure gain at the focus is proportional to $(f/\lambda) \cdot \tan(\alpha/2)$ where α is the angle of convergence ($\alpha < \pi/2$).   The focal pressures which can be produced by a plastic lens also depend on the reflectivity and absorption of the lens material.[16]

[14] Other types of focusing reflectors are discussed by A. Barone, *Acustica, Akust. Beih. 2* (1952), 221. See also: T. F. Hueter German Pat. 760,163, *Class 42s*, issued November 23, 1944, and C. Kleesattel, *Acustica, 3* (1953), 407.

[15] G. D. Ludwig, *J. Acoust. Soc. Amer., 22* (1950), 862.   P. D. Wall, D. Tucker, F. J. Fry, and W. H. Mosberg, *J. Acoust. Soc. Amer., 25* (1953), 281.

[16] D. Sette, *Ricerca Sci., 18* (1948), 831.

Curved transducers It is possible to obtain direct focusing action from a curved transducer. Spherical or cylindrical shapes can be constructed from a multiplicity of transducer elements (piezoelectric or magnetostrictive mosaics), or from a single block of piezoelectric material ground to the desired curvature. The grinding of curved quartz crystals is rather difficult because of the fixed natural orientation of their piezoelectric axes.[17] With barium titanate ceramic, however, almost any desired shape can be obtained by casting or molding and subsequent firing, grinding and polarizing.[17a]

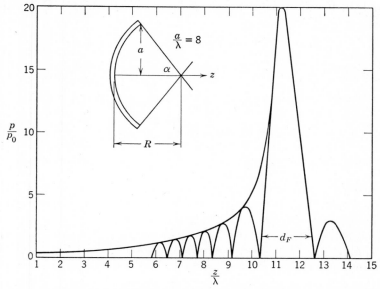

Fig. 7.14. Axial pressure distribution for a transducer bowl, according to O. Mattiat.

In any type of focusing device the sharpness of the focal point is proportional to the ratio of the aperture of the device to the wavelength, a/λ. The field of a focused beam has diffraction characteristics similar to the ones encountered in the transition region between the Fresnel zone and the Fraunhofer zone of a plane transducer (see Section 3.4).[18]

The pressure distribution on the axis of a bowl-shaped spherical segment $(a/\lambda = 8)$ with an angle of convergence $\alpha = 90°$ is shown in Fig. 7.14. The ordinate in the graph is p/p_0, and the abscissa is

[17] G. W. Willard, *J. Acoust. Soc. Amer.*, *21* (1949), 360.

[17a] O. Mattiat, *J. Acoust. Soc. Amer.*, *25* (1953), 241.

[18] H. T. O'Neil, *J. Acoust. Soc. Amer.*, *21* (1949), 516.

z/λ, in which p_0 is the pressure at the transducer face, z the axial distance from the face of the transducer, and R the radius of curvature. At the focus ($z/\lambda = 11.3$) the peak sound pressure is about twenty times greater than the average sound pressure at the surface of the bowl. The field shown in Fig. 7.14 corresponds to the bowl dimensions $R = 17$ cm, $a = 12$ cm at 100 kcps, and to $R = 5.6$ cm, $a = 4$ cm at 300 kcps if the ratio a/λ is to be 8 in both cases.

Several interference maxima and minima occur along the axis in the near field. The lateral width of the focal spot is determined by the same directivity function that controls the beam width of a circular piston source (see Chapter 3, Table 3.1 (5) and eq. 3.13), namely, $2J_1(x)/x$. For a spherical bowl the argument is $x = (2\pi a/\lambda) \sin \theta$, in which θ is the angle between the beam axis and the line connecting the center of the transducer with any point in the focal plane normal to the beam axis. As in beams formed by a plane circular piston, there is a main lobe ($x < 3.83$) surrounded by several side lobes. The main lobe, however, carries about 84 per cent of the energy radiated by the transducer. In the focal plane the radius r_F of the circular cross section of the main lobe is determined by the condition $J_1(x) = 0$, which yields:

$$r_F \simeq [R \sin \theta]_{(x=3.83)}$$

$$\simeq \frac{3.83}{2\pi} R \frac{\lambda}{a} = 0.61 \frac{R\lambda}{a} \tag{7.7}$$

If the total power output of the transducer is W, the average intensity of the main lobe in the focal plane is:

$$\mathcal{I}_F = 0.84 \frac{W}{\pi r_F{}^2} = 0.71 W \left(\frac{a}{\lambda R}\right)^2 \tag{7.8}$$

The power W is related to the effective intensity $\mathcal{I}_0$ at the transducer face by $W = \mathcal{I}_0 S_0$, where S_0 is the total radiating area of the curved transducer:

$$S_0 = 2\pi R^2 \left(1 - \cos \frac{\alpha}{2}\right)$$

in which α is the angle of convergence. Thus we can rewrite eq. 7.8 in the form

$$\frac{\mathcal{I}_F}{\mathcal{I}_0} = 1.42\pi \left(1 - \cos \frac{\alpha}{2}\right)\left(\frac{a}{\lambda}\right)^2 \tag{7.8a}$$

The peak pressure gain Γ_g of a focusing bowl is $2.2(\mathcal{I}_F/\mathcal{I}_0)^{\frac{1}{2}}$, in which the factor 2.2 relates *average* pressure to *peak* pressure at the center of the focal area.   For a half sphere ($\alpha = \pi$, $a = R$) the peak pressure gain is

$$\Gamma_g = 4.4R/\lambda \qquad (7.9a)$$

and for a 90° bowl-shaped spherical segment $\left(\alpha = \dfrac{\pi}{2},\ a = 0.71R \right)$:

$$\Gamma_g = 2.6a/\lambda \simeq 1.8R/\lambda \qquad (7.9b)$$

We note that almost twice the gain factor is obtained from a half sphere as from an optimal paraboloid reflector (see eq. 7.5b).

As an example, consider a transducer bowl of $R = 6.3$ cm, $a = 1.4$ cm, $\alpha = 25°$, radiating a power $W = 7$ watts into water at 5 mcps. From eq. 7.8 we find $\mathscr{I}_F = 3.25 \times 10^2$ watts/cm^2.   The radiating surface of this transducer is 6.3 cm^2, and hence $\mathscr{I}_0 = 1.1$ watts/cm^2. This leads to an intensity amplification $\mathscr{I}_F/\mathscr{I}_0 = 295$, and the peak intensity at the center of the focus is

$$\mathscr{I}_{\text{peak}} = (2.2)^2 \cdot 295\mathscr{I}_0 \simeq 1300\mathscr{I}_0 \simeq 1400 \text{ watts/cm}^2$$

The peak pressure gain factor is in this case $\Gamma_g \simeq \sqrt{1300} = 36$.   At the frequency of 5 mcps this corresponds to peak accelerations at the center of the focus of 14 million times gravity and peak pressures of about 46 atm.[19]

A commercial transducer for generation of focused sound at relatively small scale is illustrated in Fig. 7.15.   With a radius of curvature of $R = 6.3$ cm and an aperture $a = 4.5$ cm, the pressure gain factor at a frequency of 400 kcps is $\Gamma_g = 31$.   Assuming an intensity $\mathscr{I}_0 = 2$ watts/cm^2 at the transducer face, which is a safe level for barium titanate operated without a permanent bias, the theoretical peak focal intensity is $\mathscr{I}_0 \cdot \Gamma_g{}^2 \simeq 2000$ watts/cm^2.   Unless the unit is pressurized, however, cavitation will occur in regions between the transducer and the focus, so the actual intensity at the focus will be much reduced.

Curved mosaics   It follows from eqs. (7.9) that bowl-shaped transducers of substantial gain ($\Gamma_g > 30$) have to be rather large at frequencies below 10^5 cps.   The heat which is generated within such large bodies of ceramic by dielectric and mechanical losses can not be removed sufficiently by surface cooling.   This difficulty is considerably reduced by breaking the transducer up into a multiplicity of mosaic

---

[19] G. W. Willard (*loc. cit.;* see footnote 17) has produced 15 kw/cm^2 at 5 mcps in water.   At such high intensities radiation pressure effects lead to rapid streaming of the liquid at the focal point, and this streaming raises the cavitation threshold.

elements. The resulting increase in surface facilitates sufficient heat transfer to a cooling liquid.

The use of larger wavelengths has the advantage of a larger volume of the focal region. For example, in liquid-flow processing the volume that can be treated per unit time is proportional to $Cr_F{}^2\pi v_F$, in which r_F is the radius of the focal core and v_F is the flow velocity. The factor

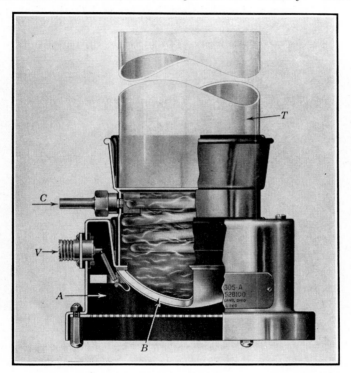

Fig. 7.15. Commercial focusing transducer bowl. A, air-filled box; B, ceramic bowl; C, inlet for cooling liquid; V, connector for driving voltage; T, treatment chamber. Courtesy of Brush Development Company, Cleveland, Ohio.

C expresses the effect of a non-uniform intensity distribution in the focal core. From cavitation experiments with pulsed sound (see Section 6.8) we know that a given liquid volume must be exposed to the intense sound field of the focal region for some minimum time t_m to produce violent cavitation. Hence, we find for the maximum flow velocity:

$$v_{F\mathrm{max}} \simeq d_F/t_m$$

in which d_F is the axial depth of the focal core as indicated in Fig. 7.14.

For a 90° bowl ($a = 0.71R$) diffraction theory yields $r_F = 0.86\lambda$ (see eq. 7.7), $d_F \simeq 4.2\lambda$, and $C \simeq 0.1$; hence, the maximum flow volume which can be cavitated efficiently per second is:

$$Q_F \simeq C r_F{}^2 \pi \frac{d_F}{t_m} \simeq \frac{\lambda^3}{t_m} \ [\text{cm}^3/\text{sec}] \qquad (7.10)$$

in which λ is the wavelength in centimeters and t_m the time of cavitation onset in seconds. The importance of using large wavelengths in focusing systems for liquid-flow processing is apparent from eq. 7.10.

Fig. 7.16.   Focusing mosaic operating at 100 kcps.   Courtesy of Brush Development Company, Cleveland, Ohio.

For example, a reduction of frequency from 400 kcps to 100 kcps amounts to an increase of maximum volume flow rate by a factor of 65.

The minimum time t_m is a function of sound intensity and the properties of the liquid as shown in Fig. 6.19. At frequencies near or below 100 kcps, t_m for water is about 0.1 sec if the intensity just exceeds the cavitation threshold value of about 1 watt/cm². At the highest intensities of the order of 10^3 watts/cm² which can be generated at the focus of a barium titanate bowl in this frequency range, t_m may be considerably shorter.

A ceramic transducer for a focusing system operating at 100 kcps is shown in Fig. 7.16. The radiating area is built up as a mosaic of several hundred hexagonal barium titanate elements. To facilitate the cooling which is necessary at surface intensities above 2 watts/ cm^2, gaps are provided between the individual elements. The cooling oil enters through the holes in the curved base plate and then flows through the gaps. Between each individual mosaic element and the base plate there is a reflecting layer of Corprene. All the mosaic

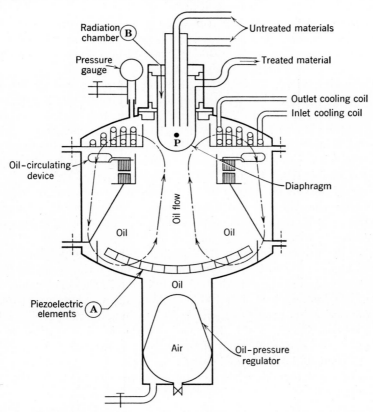

Fig. 7.17. Schematic diagram of flow processing system. The focus of the transducer mosaic A is located in chamber B at point P. Courtesy of Brush Development Company, Cleveland, Ohio.

elements may be connected in parallel as shown in Fig. 7.16 or partly in parallel and partly in series, depending on the matching requirements.

A diagrammatic sketch of a system designed to mix or emulsify two liquids by continuous flow through a focal cavitation region is given in Fig. 7.17. The system consists of a transducer mosaic mounted in an oil-filled pressurized container. The oil is kept in circulation by rotary blades and passes through a heat exchanger cooled by tap water. The radiation chamber is separated from the transducer tank by a thick stainless-steel diaphragm (see Section 7.3). The type of feeding of the two liquid components to the high-intensity regions shown in this diagram represents only a schematic illustration. In most processes a certain amount of premixing is required to obtain an optimum efficiency of sonic processing.

Focusing cylinders Equation 7.10 gives an upper limit of flow-velocity allowable for cavitation processing in a focusing system. Usually a somewhat lower velocity, providing a longer exposure of each volume element to the focused sound, is necessary to obtain a high reaction yield. Adequately long exposure at reasonable flow rates can be obtained in tubular transducers which focus the ultrasonic radiation along the axis. The volume velocity then becomes approximately $Q_F \simeq \pi(\lambda/2)^2 l/t_m$ if l is the length of the cylinder. Cylindrical-tube transducers operated in the thickness mode near 400 kcps can be made with diameters of reasonable size and with lengths up to many wavelengths. In this case $Q_F \simeq n\lambda^3/t_m$, in which n is the number of wavelengths $(l/n = \lambda)$. Comparing this result with eq. 7.10 we see that the exposure time of each volume element, for a given flow rate, can be made about n times larger in focusing cylinders than in focusing bowls.

It has been shown (Section 4.13) that there are three possible fundamental modes of vibration in a cylinder. A diffraction-type line focus can be generated at the cylinder axis only by excitation of the thickness mode. At frequencies below 100 kcps however, which are most favorable for cavitation processing, the cylinder dimenions required for this mode become impractical. The preferred mode of operation in this frequency range is the radial mode. For a cylinder which is filled with a liquid and surrounded by air both the diameter and the wall thickness are determined by the standing-wave condition within the cylinder.

Let us now consider a *solid* ceramic cylinder, which is analyzed by a differential equation in cylindrical coordinates (see Chapter 3, footnote 17) whose solutions are Bessel functions. The radial modes of a cylinder of infinite length and radius b are given by:

$$f_r = \frac{\psi}{2\pi b} c_b$$

in which ψ is determined by the roots of the equation $J_0(\psi) + \dfrac{2\sigma - 1}{1 - \sigma} J_1(\psi) = 0$.

For barium titanate this condition leads to $\psi = (\omega/c_b)b \simeq 2.1$ for the fundamental radial mode of a solid cylinder, hence:

$$f_r b = \frac{2.1}{2\pi} c_b = 1.67 \times 10^3 \text{ m/sec}$$

or
$$b = 63/f \text{ inches, if } f \text{ is in kcps}$$

The pressure has a maximum P_a at the cylinder axis, and its radial distribution is approximately:

$$P_r \simeq P_a J_0(\beta_r) \qquad (\beta_r = 2\pi/\lambda_b = \omega/c_b) \qquad (7.11a)$$

The radial particle velocity in the solid is obtained by combining eq. 2.32 and 7.11a:

$$U_r = \frac{1}{j\omega\rho} \frac{\partial p_r}{\partial r} \simeq -j \frac{P_a}{\rho_b c_b} J_1(\beta r) \qquad (7.11b)$$

From this we determine the radial distribution of impedance in the solid cylinder:

$$Z_b = P_r/U_r \simeq j\rho_b c_b J_0(\beta r)/J_1(\beta r) \qquad (\beta = \omega/c_b) \qquad (7.12)$$

On the other hand, the radial impedance of a cylindrical column of liquid is given by:

$$Z_l = j\rho_l c_l \frac{J_0(kr)}{J_1(kr)} \qquad (k = 2\pi/\lambda_l = \omega/c_l) \qquad (7.13)$$

If the liquid is water we have $c_l/c_b \simeq 0.3$, and the first nodal radii in eq. 7.12 and 7.13 are related as $r_{l_1}/b \simeq 0.3$. The condition $J_0(kr) = 0$ is again satisfied for a second nodal radius of the water column $r_{l_2} \simeq 2.3 r_{l_1} \simeq 0.7b$, which also falls within the first nodal radius of the solid cylinder. Between the radii r_{l_1} and r_{l_2} the impedance reaches a maximum at $kr \simeq 3.8(J_1(kr) = 0)$. It follows that there is a specific radius r_i at which the impedances of the liquid column and the solid cylinder are equal. The boundary conditions for cylinder resonance are then still met if the core of the solid cylinder is replaced by a water column of radius $a = r_i$. A high axial impedance and a zero outside impedance are maintained in the composite cylinder, and the resonance frequency is unchanged. Combining eq. 7.12 and 7.13 with the condition $Z_b = Z_l$ we obtain:

$$\frac{\rho_b c_b}{\rho_l c_l} \simeq \frac{J_0(ka)J_1(\beta a)}{J_0(\beta a)J_1(ka)}$$

The ratio given by this equation is equal to 18.25 for a barium titanate tube filled with water, in which case the solution of the equation yields: $fa \simeq 0.92 \cdot 10^3$ m/sec, or $a \simeq 36/f$ inches, if f is in kcps. This corresponds to the following thickness to diameter ratio:

$$\frac{t}{d_0} = \frac{b-a}{2b} = \frac{1.67 - 0.92}{3.84} = 0.225$$

From Fig. 4.35 we find the respective electromechanical coupling factor $k_c \simeq 6\%$.

A possible design of a tubular ceramic transducer is illustrated in Fig. 7.18. The liquid to be treated flows through a thin-walled stainless-steel tube which is mounted along the transducer axis. The space between the ceramic and the steel tube is filled with degassed pressurized castor oil which may be circulated through a heat exchanger for cooling. For operation at 30 kcps, for example, the outer diameter of the ceramic is $d_0 = 2b = 4.2$ in., and the wall thickness is 0.9 in.[20]

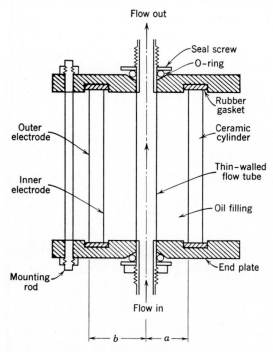

Fig. 7.18. Tubular ceramic transducer for flow processing.

7.5 Sound Conduction through Solid Rods

There are certain applications which do not permit the use of a liquid as transmitting medium. In this section we discuss three typical devices in which the sound is conducted through solid rods. Another special device which employs a resonant bar for oil-well drilling is discussed in Section 7.9. Since waves in rods are, in general, dispersive (see Sections 2.7 and 3.5) certain relationships between diameter and wavelength must be observed in the design of such rod conductors.[21]

Tapered cones for drilling Cutting and drilling of small holes of any desired shape can be accomplished if the vibrations of a suitable transducer are funneled through a tapered cone to a cutting tool

[20] O. Mattiat, *J. Acoust. Soc. Amer.*, *25* (1953), 291.
[21] T. F. Hueter, *Z. Angew. Phys.*, *1* (1949), 274.

attached to the tip of the cone.   The driving element can be a magnetostriction laminated stack, a stack of ADP crystals, or a barium titanate tube excited to lengthwise vibrations.[22]   If the cross-sectional diameter of the tapered cone is at all points smaller than half a wavelength, the particle velocity increases in inverse proportion to the cone diameter.   For example, a decrease in cone diameter from 5 cm at the base to 1.25 mm at the tip corresponds to an amplitude amplification of 40.   Satisfactory performance is obtained if the taper is exponential:

$$S_x = S_0 e^{-sx}$$

in which S_0 is the cross-sectional area at the base of the cone and s is the flare constant.   This condition together with the reasoning used in deriving eqs. 2.24 and 2.25 (see also Fig. 2.17) leads to the following wave equation for the particle velocity in an exponential cone:

$$\frac{\partial^2 u}{\partial x^2} - s\frac{\partial u}{\partial x} + k^2 u = 0 \qquad (k = \omega/c_c) \qquad (7.14)$$

The solution for a cone of length $x = l$ is:

$$u_l = e^{sl/2} U_0 \cos\left(\frac{2\pi}{\lambda_c} l\right)$$

in which $\lambda_c = \dfrac{c_c}{f} = \dfrac{1}{f}\dfrac{c_l}{(1 - s^2 c_l^2/4\omega^2)^{1/2}}$ $(c_l^2 = Y_0/\rho)$ (7.15)

If the length of the cone is made an integral number of half wavelengths, $n\lambda_c/2$, at the resonance frequency of the driving element, the interface between the base of the cone and the transducer is located at a pressure node while the tip of the cone vibrates with maximum amplitude.   If the tip is pressed against a hard surface in the presence of an abrasive (usually a mixture of Carborundum powder and oil) it acts like a miniature trip hammer.[22a]   The abrasive is pounded against the work many thousand times per second, thus chipping off microscopic flakes.   The work material may be glass, steel, or even tungsten carbide; but care must be taken to adjust the static pressure of the vibration tool to a medium level, at which its amplitude is only moderately damped.

A device of this kind, driven by a magnetostriction type transducer,

[22] W. P. Mason and R. F. Wick, *J. Acoust. Soc. Amer.*, *23* (1951), 209.
[22a] L. Balamuth, U. S. Patent No. 2,580,716.

is illustrated in Fig. 7.19.[23] Both the laminated stack and the tapered cone are supported at their velocity nodes. The lower half-wave section of the cone is detachable to facilitate exchange of tools. The drilling or cutting bit is brazed to the tip of the cone since a simple-screw type connection would be shaken loose by the intense vibrations at this end.

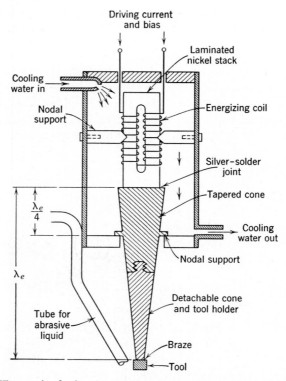

Fig. 7.19. Ultrasonic device for cutting and drilling. Courtesy of Raytheon Mfg. Company, Waltham, Mass.

Ultrasonic soldering Similar transducers are used for removal of oxide scale in aluminum soldering.[24] The sonic vibrations have an effect on the surface of the work which is similar to cavitation at liquid-solid interfaces. Once the oxide scale is loosened the liquid

[23] This figure is based on information given by the Raytheon Manufacturing Company, Waltham, Mass. See also A. S. Cohan, *Metals*, March 1951, p. 216 and L. Balamuth, paper C9 delivered at 47th meeting of Acoust. Soc. in New York, June 23, 1954. Devices of this kind may be used for dental drilling.

[24] H. Barwich, German Pat. 720,629 (Siemens Company, 1938). P. Wenk and U. Nuendel, *Siemens Z.*, *25* (1951), H. 2.

tin will bond readily with the clean aluminum surface without need
for fluxing or pickling agents.   Microscopic tests of ultrasonically
soldered aluminum joints have revealed that beyond the removal of
oxide scale some amount of aluminum is dissolved into the tin layer.

Figure 7.20 shows a commercial device operating at 22 kcps with an
electric input power of 50 watts.[25]   The soldering bit may be heated
directly as shown in Fig. 7.20, or the heat may be supplied to the
work from a hot plate, which is more efficient and reduces the problem
of cooling the transducer.   Another possibility is to irradiate sonic

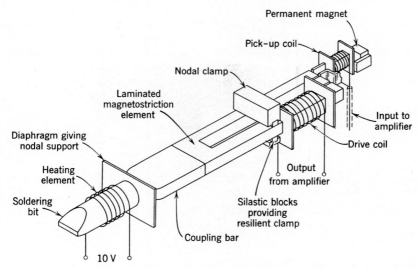

Fig. 7.20.   Ultrasonic vibrator for aluminum soldering.   Courtesy of Mullard
Ltd., London, England.

energy from a magnetostrictive stack through a tuned coupling member of heat-insulating material (porcelain or ceramic) to a pool of hot
molten tin, into which the parts are dipped for tinning.

Irradiation of metal melts   At this point we shall mention
briefly a related application, namely, the irradiation of solidifying
metal melts with high frequency sonic energy.   Experiments at
laboratory scale have shown that a finer texture and a more uniform
alloying can be obtained by this procedure.[26]   Also, molten glass has
been degassed and dispersions of lead into aluminum and of iron into

[25] Courtesy Mullard Ltd., London, England.
[26] G. Schmid and L. Ehret, *Z. Electrochem.*, *43* (1937), 869.   G. Schmid and
A. Roll, *Z. Electrochem.*, *45* (1939), 769.   H. J. Seemann and H. Menzel, *Metall 1*
(1947), 39.

tin have been achieved by ultrasonic irradiation. A system for the irradiation of metal melts at a somewhat larger scale is shown schematically in Fig. 7.21.[27]

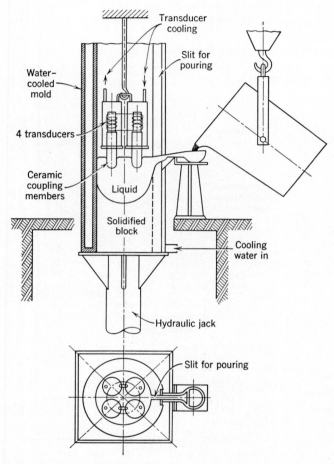

Fig. 7.21. System for the irradiation of melts. Courtesy of Atlas Werke, Bremen, Germany.

The melt is poured into a special water-cooled mold which is lowered as the material solidifies so that the transducers are always coupled to the upper portion of the liquid phase. To protect the transducers from the heat they are encased in a jacket through which a coolant is circulated and are insulated from the melt through tuned ceramic

[27] Courtesy of Dr. H. Thiede, Atlas-Werke, Bremen, Germany.

conductors.   Special ceramics e.g., Ardostan, are available which are
both heat resistant and chemically inert.   The radiating faces of the
conductors have to be rounded to reduce the possibility of cracks
due to very high temperature gradients.   It is evident that, under
the extremely difficult conditions encountered in melt processing, a
compromise must be made between the acoustic requirements of
transducer design and the external processing conditions.

7.6   Electrodynamic Vibrators

The dividing line between sonics and vibration engineering is not
clearly defined (see Table 1.1).   The general design principles of

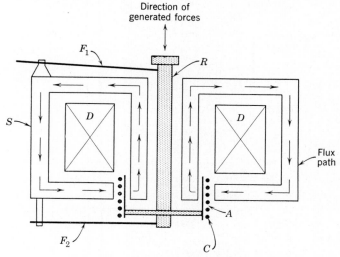

Fig. 7.22.   Electrodynamic generation of large forces.

vibration exciters and the fundamentals of vibration analysis do not
fall within the scope of this book; the reader is referred to standard
publications in this field.[28]   Nevertheless, in some forms of sonic
processing such as shaking, settling of powdery substances, and the
production of high-amplitude effects (see Section 6.5) in relatively
small volumes of gas, transducers of the electrodynamic vibrator
type are useful.   We shall discuss some of their features in this
section to assist potential users in the evaluation of their performance
characteristics.

A schematic arrangement for electrodynamic generation of large
forces is shown in Fig. 7.22.   A stiff rod R is mounted on two flexural

[28] J. P. den Hartog, *Mechanical Vibrations*, 3rd edition, McGraw-Hill, New
York, 1947.   See also R. C. Lewis, *Product Eng.*, McGraw-Hill, November 1950.

members F_1 and F_2. The mechanical resonance frequency is determined by the mass M of the rod and the bending stiffness $2K_f$ of the two flexural strips. For one flexural strip of width w, thickness t, and effective length l, the stiffness becomes: $K_f = \frac{1}{4}Y_0 w(t/l)^3$, where Y_0 is Young's modulus. Hence the resonance frequency of the vibrating armature is:

$$\omega = (2K_f/M)^{\frac{1}{2}} = (Y_0 w/2M)^{\frac{1}{2}}(t/l)^{\frac{3}{2}} \qquad (7.16)$$

Commercial vibrators of this type that are capable of delivering forces up to 10^4 newtons (2500 lb) are available with mechanical resonances up to several kcps, and a usable over-all frequency range from 2 cps up to 20 kcps.[29]

Referring again to Fig. 7.22, we note that the force on the rod is derived from a current through the moving coil C which is located in the air gap A of a stationary magnetic structure S. If MKS units are used the force can be determined by eq. 5.1, while for pound-inch-second units this converts to:

$$F \text{ (lb)} = 0.885 \cdot 10^{-7} N B \text{ (maxwells/in}^2) \cdot l_a \text{ (in.)} \cdot i \text{ (amp)}$$

in which l_a is the length of a single armature turn, N the number of turns in the flux gap, and B the flux density. The maximum acceleration which an electrodynamic shaker can deliver without overheating depends on the load which is added to the armature. For example, a shaker of 600 lb (2500 newtons) force rating and an armature weight of 10 lb (4.5 kg) produces accelerations of 60 g unloaded, and of 10 g with a 50-lb load, which at 100 cps corresponds to a displacement amplitude of 0.1 in. (0.254 mm) and a velocity amplitude of about 6 in./sec (15 cm/sec). From an economic point of view shaking equipment of this type is sometimes disadvantageous in that the generation of high field currents requires heavy and costly rotary power supplies. We shall discuss in Section 7.9 a purely mechanical power oscillator operated on fluid dynamic principles which is superior in this respect.

Another version of the transducer illustrated in Fig. 7.22 can be used for the transmission of sound into large solid bodies at a frequency of several kcps. This device has been designed particularly for geophysical studies and is described in Fig. 7.23.[30] It appears to have potential usefulness for special sonic shaking purposes.

[29] The MB Manufacturing Company, New Haven, Conn., *Bull.* I-VE. The Calidyne Company, Winchester, Mass., *Bull.* 6405.

[30] F. F. Evison, *Proc. Phys. Soc.* (*London*) B, *64* (1951), 311. See also L. Howell, C. Kean, and R. Thompson, *Geophysics, 5* (1940), 1.

Briefly, the transducer consists of a mass, formed by a heavy (about 600 lb) magnetic core M coupled through springs S to a base plate B which is connected rigidly to the load.   The core is magnetized by a d-c coil D imbedded in it.   A single-turn moving coil is provided by

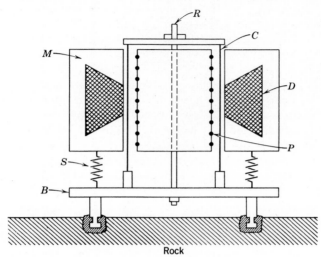

Fig. 7.23.   Electrodynamic generator for the transmission of sound to large solid bodies.

the copper cylinder C which is rigidly clamped to the base plate. The current is induced in the cylinder by a primary winding P of T turns supported by the central clamping rod R.

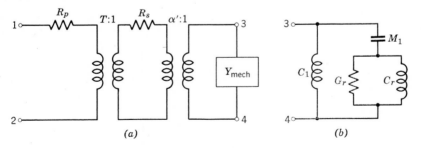

Fig. 7.24.   Equivalent network of vibrator shown in Fig. 7.23.

To find the motional impedance we can apply the analysis given in Section 5.1 to the equivalent mechanical network of the vibrator shown in Fig. 7.24a.   We note that the electric input terminals 1 and 2 are connected through an electric transformer T:1 and an electromechanical transformer $\alpha':1$ to the mechanical terminals 3 and 4. The losses in the primary and secondary of the driving coil are represented by R_p and R_s. In this circuit the mechanical admittance Y_{mech} appears across the terminals 3 and 4. The equivalent circuit for Y_{mech} is given in Fig. 7.24b, in which C_1 is the compliance of the springs S (which may consist, for example, of slender rods), M_1 is the mass of the magnet, G_r is the radiation conductance, and C_r is the radiation susceptance.[31]

Electrodynamic vibrators have found applications as a sonic aid to laundering. In this case the magnet is clamped and a diaphragm is attached to the moving coil which is coupled to the magnetic structure by relatively soft springs. A device of this type if shown in Fig. 7.25.[32] The magnetic driver is contained in the case on top. The disc-shaped diaphragm is connected to the driver by a slender rod mounted in a tube through which an air stream is injected into the liquid load to decrease its mass reactance and to enhance gaseous-type cavitation.

Electrodynamic resonator   The moving-coil principle which is employed in the electrodynamic devices discussed above has been utilized for the generation of high-amplitude sound (see Section 6.5) in small-scale gas-phase processing. Conventional loudspeakers, with compliant diaphragms, are limited in power output by three factors: at low frequencies by the finite displacement of the coil; at resonance by the low Q of the diaphragm; at high frequencies by the mass reactance of the system. The power capabilities have been considerably increased in the very high-Q resonant device shown in Fig. 7.26.[33]

The moving element is a solid aluminum bar B, which is mounted at its midplane so that it can vibrate longitudinally in its fundamental resonant mode. For operation at 15 kcps the length of the bar is 16.5 cm (6.5 in.) and good radiation characteristics are obtained by a diameter of about 10 cm (4 in.) corresponding to a value of $ka \simeq 14$.

---

[31] In geophysical applications where the base plate of this device is rigidly attached to rock-like materials, one operates almost under clamped conditions ($Z_{\text{mech}} \simeq \infty$) and the efficiency is low. For example, at a frequency of 600 cps with solid chalk as a load, an electric input of 2 kw produces a total sonic output of about 0.03 watts, corresponding to a displacement of the ground of about 0.7 mm and an efficiency of 0.025. This is about $\frac{1}{40}$ of the conversion efficiency obtained in surface explosions of dynamite. This method, however, produces signals which yield more readily to analysis than those obtained by explosions.

[32] The magnet is fed directly from the electric line and the device operates at twice the line frequency.

[33] H. W. St. Clair, *Rev. Sci. Instr.*, *12* (1941), 250; see also F. Canac and V. Gavreau, *Acustica 1* (1951), 2.

The bar carries a small mounting ridge S around its periphery and a cylindrical ring C at its bottom end. Both structures S and C are machined out of the bar itself. The circular ridge S is attached to the flexible wall of a supporting ring R, which in turn is rigidly clamped between the flanges D of the transducer housings H_1 and H_2. This

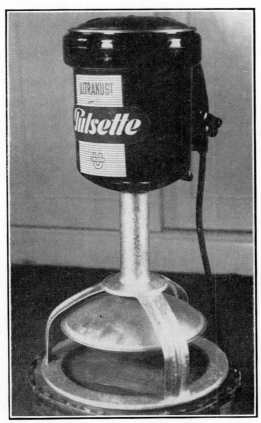

Fig. 7.25.   Sonic laundering aid.   Courtesy of Ultrakust Company, Germany.

type of mounting permits the bar to contract and expand freely in the lateral direction and at the same time provides the necessary support in the nodal plane of the longitudinal resonance.

The ring C projects into the voice-coil gap of a heavy-duty loud-speaker pot magnet M, and serves as a single moving turn, fed by induction from primary coil P (30 to 40 turns), which is attached rigidly to the central pole piece. Eddy-current losses are reduced by several thin radial slots cut into the edge of the pole piece. The field coil F of the magnet is wound in honeycomb fashion to permit efficient cooling by forced air, thus allowing continuous operation at full power (about 60 watts to field coil, 600 watts to primary driving coil, in this particular design). Feedback for maintaining the transducer at resonance is obtained from an electrostatic pick-up E built as

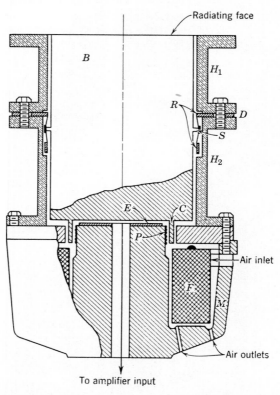

Fig. 7.26. Generator for large amplitudes in gases, according to H. W. St. Clair.

part of the driver. The pick-up consists of a condenser formed by the lower face of the bar and an insulated metal plate mounted on the central portion of the magnet.

The damping caused by the internal losses in the aluminum bar and by the carefully designed nodal mounting is so small that the Q of the device is of the order of 20,000, which corresponds to a band-width of less than 1 cps at 15 kcps. The efficiency of power conversion is about 6 per cent. With 600 watts electric input about 36 watts of sonic power can be radiated from an area of about 100 cm^2.

This generates free field pressures in air of the order of 2×10^3 newtons/m^2 or an intensity level (see Section 2.13) of 160 db.[34]

7.7 Fluid Dynamic Systems

We mentioned in the first two sections of this chapter that most electroacoustic transducers are of limited usefulness for the generation of sonic power in gases. Although the electrodynamic resonator described in Section 7.6 is capable of producing intensity levels of 160 db in air its maximum total power output is small. Liquid-phase processing is readily accomplished with piezoelectric or magnetostrictive devices, although in some cases the same result can be achieved more economically by *fluid dynamic* transducers such as whistles or jets.

These transducers are generally better suited for gas-phase processing because of their inherently low driving impedance, which facilitates optimum power transfer to gases. They were, in fact, the first transducers used for sound generation in the early days of acoustics. The most common sonic sources of this type were the whistle and the organ pipe.

Vortex formation in constricted flow Whistle sounds are generated essentially by vortices which occur if a fluid flows through an orifice or passes an edge.[35] A "string" of vortices moving through an otherwise undisturbed fluid will cause periodic local pressure changes that propagate into the medium as a sound wave. The frequency of this sound is given by the number of vortices that pass a given point per unit time. This corresponds to the translational velocity of the vortices relative to the surrounding stationary medium divided by the distance l between two successive vortices:

$$f = u/l \qquad (7.17)$$

The relative vortex velocity u is proportional to the flow velocity U of the driving fluid. The total momentum ρU of the fluid is distributed by approximately equal parts into rotational motion and translational motion of the vortices, so $u \simeq 0.5U$. The vortex spacing l depends on the geometry of the constriction that forms the vortex. The vortices originate in the viscous boundary layer (see Section 6.2) at the inner surface of the constriction.

Let us consider a circular orifice of about equal diameter d and thickness s, as shown in cross section by Fig. 7.27. Due to the sharp

[34] 2×10^4 dynes/cm^2 or 0.02 atm, measured at a distance of 0.5 m from the source.

[35] G. B. Thurston and C. E. Martin, Jr., *J. Acoust. Soc. Amer.*, 25 (1953), 26.

edge at A, the fluid streaming next to the boundary separates from the interface and rolls up to form a closed loop or vortex as point B is reached. If the boundary layer along $s = AB$ is thus rolled into successive rings of toroidal shape, the ring diameter will be approximately s/π and the distance l between the centers of successive vortices will be nearly equal to s. The shedding of each vortex from point B into free field causes a small pressure pulse which travels back to A with sound velocity and again causes enough instability for the fluid in the boundary layer to separate from the interface A-B.

This is a simplified account of the feedback mechanism that leads to pulsations of the fluid due to periodic vortex shedding from an

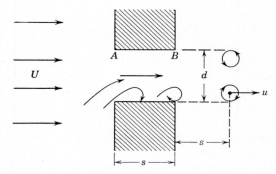

Fig. 7.27.   Vortex formation at an orifice.

orifice and also from a jet edge.[36]   The stability of such a generator is increased considerably if larger feedback is provided. This can be done in two ways, either by coupling a resonating cavity to the orifice or by placing a sharp edge at a distance W in front of a slit-shaped constriction.

Hartmann generators   A special device of the first kind is the Hartmann Generator[37] shown schematically in Fig. 7.28a. Let us first consider the jet operating in a free field without the cavity. The flow through the constriction at **A** leads to a Bernoulli effect and the flow velocity becomes supersonic ($U/c \geq 1$) for upstream pressures P_e greater than 0.9 atm (13.6 psi) in excess of the ambient atmospheric

[36] H. von Gierke, *Z. angew. Phys.*, *2* (1950), 97.   A. B. C. Anderson, *J. Acoust. Soc. Amer.*, *25* (1953), 541.   H. Medwin and I. Rudnick, *J. Acoust. Soc. Amer.*, *25* (1953), 538.

[37] T. Hartmann, *J. Sci. Instr.*, *16* (1939), 146.   See also M. Palmé, *Nuovo Cimento*, *7* (1952), Suppl. 2, p. 260.

pressure.[38] The resulting pressure distribution in the free jet stream is shown in Fig. 7.28b. At point S_1 the pressure drops to a minimum, which causes a pile-up of the gas beyond this point. Hence, a shock wave front indicated by the dashed line is formed. This effect repeats itself in regular intervals at S_2, S_3, etc.

The pile-up regions are unstable and can be used to maintain oscillations of a resonant cavity which is positioned at **B** opposite the jet

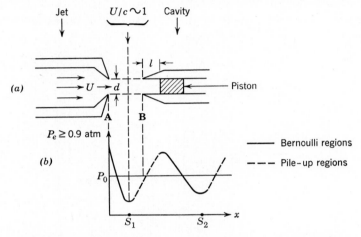

Fig. 7.28.   Hartmann generator operating at supersonic flow velocities.

a small distance beyond one of the points S. The air in the cavity will then pulsate with a frequency:

$$f = \frac{c}{\lambda} = \frac{c}{4(l + 0.3d)} \tag{7.18}$$

in which c is the sound velocity in the gas and l, d the cavity dimensions as indicated in Fig. 7.28a. The conversion efficiency is of the order of 5 per cent, and the power output of such a resonant jet is:

$$W = 3d^2(P_e - 0.9)^{\frac{1}{2}} \text{ watts} \tag{7.19}$$

where d is the diameter of both the jet and the resonator in millimeters and P_e is the upstream pressure in atmospheres ($P_e > 0.9$ atm). For example, at a frequency of 10 kcps and an input pressure of $P_e = 3.4$ atm a sound energy of about 100 watts can be generated ($d \simeq 4.5$ mm).

[38] See eq. 6.14a. With $u_0 \simeq 0$, $u_1 = U \geq c$, $P_0 = P_e$, and $P_1 \simeq 0$ we obtain $P_e \geq \frac{1}{2}\rho_0 c^2 \geq 0.8$ atm (12 psi). Due to the particular shape of an open constriction a correction must be applied to the simple Bernoulli equation which leads to $P_e \geq 0.9$ atm as the condition for supersonic flow (Mach number ≥ 1).

We shall see later that more power and higher efficiencies can be obtained with sirens, which therefore have a greater potential for large-scale industrial gas-phase processing.

Jet-edge generators   The jet-edge generator is a fluid dynamic device, involving vortex formation, in which stabilization is achieved by hydrodynamic feedback between a jet and an edge.   Such transducers appear to be very promising for liquid-flow processing at cavitation levels.[39]   We shall outline briefly the basic ideas underlying the analytic treatment of their properties for operation in gases. A discussion of some special features of the liquid jet will follow.

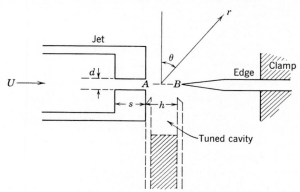

Fig. 7.29.   Jet-edge system for gases.

For a straight jet edge, which is illustrated in Fig. 7.29, we can rewrite eq. 7.17 in the form:[40]

$$f \simeq \frac{nU}{h}\left[a + \frac{b}{R_e}\right] \tag{7.20}$$

where n ($= 1, 2, 3, 4$) characterizes the particular stage of operation (see following discussion) of the jet, a and b are constants, and R_e is "Reynolds number."[41]   In the case considered here R_e is of the order of 10^4 and large compared to b, so that only the first term of

[39] W. Janovsky and R. Pohlman, *Z. angew. Phys.*, **1** (1948), 222.   See also J. V. Boyoucos and W. L. Nyborg, *J. Acoust. Soc. Amer.*, **26** (1954), 511.

[40] Lord Rayleigh, *Theory of Sound*, Dover Publications, New York 1945, Vol. II, p. 410.   See also D. Blokhintzev, *The Acoustics of an Inhomogeneous Moving Medium*, Lebedev Physical Institute, Moscow (U.S.S.R.), 1945, English translation by R. T. Beyer and D. Mintzer of Brown University, Providence, R. I.

[41] V. Strouhal, *Wiedemann's Ann.*, **5** (1878), 216.

Reynolds number is defined as the work required to accelerate the fluid divided by the work against viscous drag: $R_e = sU\rho/\eta$ in which s is a characteristic dimension of the orifice.

eq. 7.20 need be used. The constant a depends slightly on the jet width d and on the stage of operation. For example, if $d = 0.2$ cm and $h = 0.4$ cm, we get $a = 0.44$ if $n = 1$, and $a = 0.58$ if $n = 2$.

The feedback action of the vortices formed with the frequency $f \simeq naU/h$ at the edge (point B in Fig. 7.29) causes an oscillation of the fluid stream.[41a] Successive vortices will flow by the edge on alternative sides. The streaming sheet of fluid between points A and B acts like a membrane oscillating with an amplitude of about $d/2$ and an area of about $S \simeq hl/3$, where l is the height of the jet orifice.[42] The sound pressure generated by this equivalent membrane at distance r and angle θ for the first stage of operation ($n = 1$) becomes:

$$P_r \simeq \frac{2.36}{rc}\, \rho_0 d S^{3/2} f^3 \cos \theta \qquad (7.21)$$

in which all quantities are in MKS units. The sound output of such a generator can be increased considerably if a tuned cavity is coupled to the gap between jet and edge.[43] Even so, we shall see that in air much higher intensities can be generated by sirens.

The dynamic conditions of the fluid that are required for the generation of stable edge tones of a frequency $f = naU/h$ are met only if both U and h lie within certain limits for each stage (n) of operation. This phenomenom is illustrated for stage 1 edge tones (no cavity) in Fig. 7.30. These edge tones will be excited only for combinations of U and h which designate a point within the marked region. Each straight-line section represents a different frequency, in steps of 0.5 kcps. Let us, for example, increase the flow velocity at a constant nozzle-to-edge distance of $h = 2$ mm. No edge tones are excited below $U = 4$ m/sec and above $U = 33$ m/sec. The frequency range available at this setting of h is from 1 to 7.4 kcps. If the flow velocity is increased much above $U = 33$ m/sec, the jet will begin to operate in the next higher stage.

Jet systems for liquids As mentioned before, jet-type sonic generators appear to be most promising for liquid-phase processing. The resonant features required for high stability and output at cavitation levels can be obtained in a liquid jet system by a rectangular

[41a] W. L. Nyborg, *J. Acoust. Soc. Amer.*, *26* (1954), 174.

[42] This semi-quantitative approach is due to H. Von Gierke, *Z. angew. Phys.*, *2* (1950), 97, who finds it in good agreement with experimental data.

[43] W. L. Nyborg, M. D. Burkhard, and H. K. Schilling, *J. Acoust. Soc. Amer.*, *24* (1952), 293. A typical set of operating conditions as used by these authors is: jet cross section 0.5×6.3 mm², 5° wedge, $h = 5$ mm, flow velocity 100 cm/sec, and a square cavity of 15-mm length at 5 kcps.

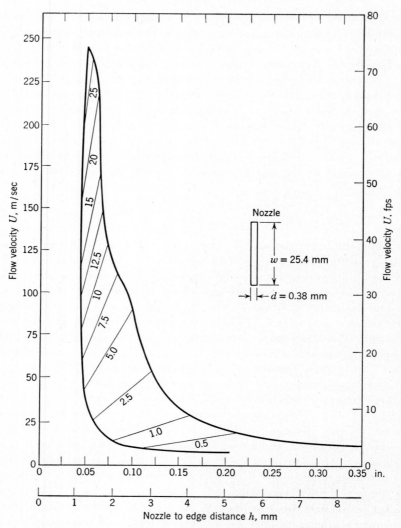

Fig. 7.30. Stability region for stage 1 edge tones in air.

plate which vibrates in flexure. Two types of mounting of such a plate are possible: cantilever clamping and half-wave nodal support.

In the first case a rigid and massive clamping block is required and the fundamental flexural frequency is

$$f_c = \frac{\pi}{2} \frac{(0.597)^2}{\sqrt{12}} \frac{t}{l^2} \sqrt{\frac{Y_0}{\rho}} = 0.162 \frac{t}{l^2} c_l \qquad (7.22)$$

in which t is the thickness and l is the length of the plate, Y_0 is Young's modulus, ρ is the density, and c_l is the "bar velocity." For half-wave nodal support, on the other hand, the mounting is provided by two pairs of stiff and short pins which are held in position a distance $\lambda_f/2$ apart. In this case the fundamental frequency is

$$f_h = \frac{\pi}{2} \frac{2.5^2}{\sqrt{12}} \frac{t}{l^2} \sqrt{\frac{Y_0}{\rho}} = 2.82 \frac{t}{l^2} c_l \qquad (7.23)$$

In eqs. 7.22 and 7.23 we have neglected the damping of the plate by the surrounding fluid, which tends to lower the frequency, and the effects of the wedge-shaped taper at the plate edges, which raises the frequency slightly.[43a]

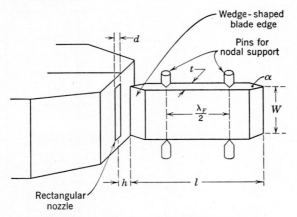

Fig. 7.31.   Jet-edge generator for liquids.

In both types of mounting the sharp front edge of the plate is aligned with the jet nozzle so as to split the stream. The arrangement for a half-wave supported flexural plate which offers the least amount of obstruction to the liquid flow is shown in Fig. 7.31. The dimensions indicated in this figure must meet the following conditions: wedge angle $\alpha \simeq 30°$; nodal spacing $\lambda_F/2 = 0.49l$; $d \leq t$, and $l \geq 2W$.

The frequency of the edge tone produced by a liquid jet is again determined by eq. 7.20. It has been established empirically that the term b/R_e in eq. 7.20 can be neglected, in both liquid and air jets, and that in liquids the constant a is approximately equal to 0.5. For the first stage of operation $(n = 1)$ we then have:

$$f_J \simeq 0.5U/h \qquad (7.24)$$

[43a] A. Leitner and E. A. Hiedemann, *J. Acoust. Soc. Amer.*, *26* (1954), 509.

Combining eqs. 7.24 and 7.23 we obtain a condition of resonance, which corresponds to maximum power conversion, and is specified by:

$$0.5 \frac{U}{h} \simeq 0.282 \frac{t}{l^2} c_l$$

The resulting characteristics are plotted in Fig. 7.32 for a system of the type shown in Fig. 7.31 with a nozzle width $d = 0.02$ cm, a nozzle to edge distance $h = 0.15$ cm, and a plate which resonates at 2.5 kcps.

We note that between A and B the response of the system corresponds to pure edge-tone generation, while at a flow velocity of about

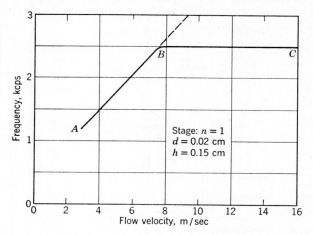

Fig. 7.32.   Frequency characteristics of a liquid jet employing a flexural plate tuned to 2.5 kcps.

8 m/sec (25 fps) the plate resonance takes over and controls the frequency between B and C. It is also apparent from Fig. 7.32 that a certain minimum flow velocity, in this case about 3 m/sec ($\simeq$10 fps), is necessary to establish the fluid dynamic conditions required for vortex shedding.

In a system of this kind some sound is radiated from the vibrating plate, but the zone of greatest intensity is located on either side of the wedge-shaped front edge of the plate. Here the cavitation may be so strong that even plates made of hardened steel are damaged by cavitation erosion. If a probe hydrophone is inserted near the front edge of the plate, a noise spectrum of the type described in Section 6.5 is received.

A commercial device for liquid-flow processing is depicted in Fig. 7.33. The distance between plate and nozzle can be adjusted by turning the knob at the extreme right.   If plates of different size are used the frequency can be adjusted in the range between 1 and 5 kcps. At higher frequencies, the efficiency drops.   The plate length then becomes comparable with the blade width, under which condition detrimental crossmodes appear.

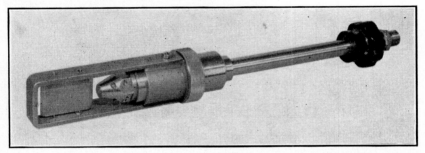

Fig. 7.33.   Commercial jet transducer.   Courtesy of Siemens-Schuckert Werke, Germany.

In Table 7.4 a set of typical data for liquid jet performance is given for three values of upstream pressure.   Columns 1 and 2 represent the relationships

$$U \simeq (2\,P_e/\rho)^{1/2} \quad \text{and} \quad U/h \simeq 2f$$

Column 3 expresses the power requirement W_i in terms of upstream pressure P_e, nozzle cross section S and the volume velocity Q_0 according to

$$W_i = P_e Q_0 \quad \text{and} \quad Q_0 = UCS$$

The factor C represents the fact that the effective cross section of a nozzle is reduced by flow constriction.   In Table 7.4 a value $C = 0.6$ is assumed.

The most promising application of such liquid jet transducers is in emulsification.   They are superior to the electronically operated magnetostrictive and piezoelectric systems with respect to cost, maintenance, and ruggedness.   Emulsification of two liquid components can be achieved in two ways: (1) by immersion of the transducer into a tank filled with the one component and injection of the other component through the jet; or (2) by simultaneous injection of both components after some amount of premixing.   In some cases it has been found convenient to start by injection of one component into the other until a tankload of sonically premixed material is obtained, and then to recirculate this load for some time through the jet.

Table 7.4   Typical Data for Liquid Jet Performance

P_e	Unit	h (2 keps)	h (5 keps)	h (10 keps)	Unit	Quantity	W_i = 0.2 hp	0.5 hp	0.75 hp	1 hp	1.5 hp	Unit
						W_i	150	370	560	746	1120	watts
125	psig	0.43	0.15	0.075	in.	S	1.1×10^{-2}	3×10^{-2}	4×10^{-2}	6×10^{-2}	—	sq in.
						Q_0	2.6	7	10	14	—	gal/min
8	atm	1.1	0.38	0.19	cm	S	7.1×10^{-2}	1.9×10^{-1}	2.6×10^{-1}	3.9×10^{-1}	—	sq cm
						Q_0	0.16	0.44	0.63	0.88	—	ltr/sec
250	psig	0.55	0.22	0.11	in.	S	4×10^{-3}	9.5×10^{-3}	1.4×10^{-2}	2×10^{-2}	2.8×10^{-2}	sq in.
						Q_0	1.4	3	5	7	9.5	gal/min
16	atm	1.4	0.55	0.28	cm	S	2.6×10^{-2}	6.1×10^{-2}	9×10^{-2}	1.3×10^{-1}	1.8×10^{-1}	sq cm
						Q_0	0.088	0.19	0.31	0.44	0.6	ltr/sec
500	psig	0.77	0.32	0.16	in.	S	—	3.4×10^{-3}	4.8×10^{-3}	7×10^{-3}	10^{-2}	sq in.
						Q_0	—	1.65	2.4	3.5	5	gal/min
32	atm	1.94	0.8	0.41	cm	S	—	2.2×10^{-2}	3.1×10^{-2}	4.5×10^{-2}	6.5×10^{-2}	sq cm
						Q_0	—	0.1	0.15	0.22	0.31	ltr/sec

Column headings: 1 — Upstream pressure P_e; 2 — Distance h required for a frequency of; 3 — Nozzle cross section S and volume flow Q_0 for an input Power W_i of.

In estimating the potential use of a sonic jet system for emulsification, the following rationale should be applied. Whenever some amount of emulsification can be achieved by conventional means under the influence of detergents or catalysts there is a chance that sonic processing will yield an emulsion of better stability in a shorter time and with less than the usual amount of emulsifying agent. On the other hand, experience has shown that components which prove immiscible by conventional means will not mix much better under the influence of sound.[43b]   Besides emulsification there are other processes such as homogenization of milk, aging of alcohols, dispersion of dyes, cold reaction of rubber monomers, which hold some promise.[44]

7.8   Sonic Siren Generators

In Chapter 6 we have discussed several mechanisms of interaction between small suspended particles and a sound wave of high amplitude. In gases these effects can be most efficiently produced by a siren generator.   Although powerful commercial sirens have been available for some time, the practical significance of sonic aerosol processing is still somewhat controversial.   There certainly is a need in industry for a type of energy which is capable of influencing the interaction among small solid particles suspended in air.   But the complexity of variables, such as temperature, moisture, grain loading, particle-size distribution, volume flow, has so far restricted the applications to the pilot stage.

A study of the available reports on sonic aerosol processing reveals two main points: First, the occurrence of the basic effects predicted by theory, such as particle collisions and particle motions due to drag forces, has been established experimentally.   Second, a commercially satisfactory exploitation of these effects for purposes of dust collection and fume separation has been achieved in only a few instances.[45]

In most sonic aerosol applications explored to date, the degree of final separation of the particles from the carrier gas has been only marginally improved over conventional cyclonic or electrostatic separation.   There appear to be, however, some promising applications of sonic effects other than dust collection or fume precipitation.   These

---

[43b] One notable exception is the mixing of mercury and water: C. Bondy and K. Soellner, *Trans. Faraday Soc.*, *32* (1936), 556.

[44] Some results are discussed in: *Dairy Sci.*, *19* (1936), 29; *Dairy Industries*, *17* (1952), 1039; *Food Processing*, March 1953, p. 54.

[45] H. W. Danser, Jr., *Chem. Eng.*, May 1952, p. 158.   See also *Chem. Eng. Progress* (Symposium Series) No. 1, *47* (1951), 4, 11, 86.   Estimates of the relative operating costs of sonic versus electrostatic gas cleaning systems are given by H. Schnitzler, *Arch. Eisenhuetenwesen* *24* (1953), 199.

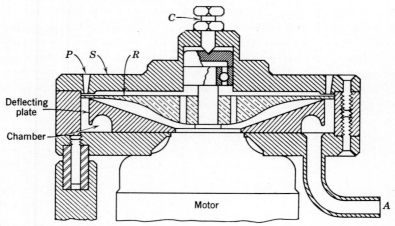

a, Cross-sectional view of a siren after C. H. Allen and I. Rudnick.

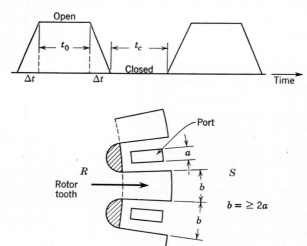

b, Relation between the dimensions of stator ports and rotor teeth, and the flow modulation.

Fig. 7.34.

include the stabilization of combustion processes and the acceleration of gaseous reaction rates. To aid in further exploitation of such applications, we shall present a brief discussion of siren generator performance.

A schematic drawing of a typical siren is shown in Fig. 7.34. In any siren there are the following components: a source or air A, a rotor R which interrupts the air flow at the desired frequency, and ports P in a stator S through which the air escapes.[46] The air is supplied by a compressor whose capacity depends on the power rating of the siren, and may vary between 50 and 2000 cu ft/min, delivered at a pressure of 5 psig ($\sim\frac{1}{3}$ atm). As an example, for a sound output of 300 watts at 10 kcps, an air flow of approximately 150 cu ft/min ($\sim$4.2 m³) is required, and this may be obtained from a compressor driven by a 5 hp electric motor. In order to open and close this air

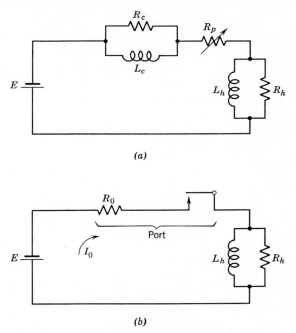

(a)

(b)

Fig. 7.35. Simplified equivlaent circuit for a siren.

stream through a 100-port stator, a rotor drive motor is used, which consumes about 0.7 hp.

The dimensions of the rotor teeth and the stator ports are so chosen that the opening and closing times Δt are less than half the time t_0 or t_c during which the port is fully open or fully closed. In this case a square wave modulation is approximated, as shown in Fig. 7.34b. The adjacent plane faces of the rotor and stator must be machined and lapped to high precision to reduce the gap to less than 0.03 mm ($\sim$0.001 in.). The clearance is adjusted by means of the screw C

[46] C. H. Allen and I. Rudnick, *J. Acoust. Soc. Amer.*, **19** (1947), 857. See also H. Schiesser, *Akust. Z.*, **3** (1938), 363.

shown in Fig. 7.34a such as to reduce air leakage to a minimum. The outer openings of the ports P feed into a tapered horn structure to improve radiation at the lower end of the frequency range.[47]

Equivalent circuit for the analysis of siren efficiency Let us now consider the performance of a siren with square wave modulation, which turns out to be the most efficient kind of operation. For an approximate analysis of the efficiency we can use the equivalent circuit presented in Fig. 7.35a.[48] Here the voltage source E represents the driving pressure P_e delivered by the compressor; the components R_h and ωL_h represent the impedance offered to each port by the throat of the siren horn; ωL_c and R_c represent the impedance of the inner siren chamber; and R_p is the variable flow resistance of the ports. For the frequency range between 2 and 20 kcps an approximate analysis of the network is possible if we set $L_c \simeq 0$ and if we make the simplifying assumptions for the horn impedance $\omega L_h \gg R_h$. The equivalent circuit then reduces to the form shown in Fig. 7.35b with the remaining components:

$$R_p \begin{cases} = R_0 \text{ for open ports} \\ = \infty \text{ for closed ports} \end{cases} \tag{7.25a}$$

$$\left. \begin{aligned} L_h &= \frac{\rho_0 l}{S} \\ R_h &= \frac{\rho_0 c}{S} \end{aligned} \right\} \begin{aligned} &\text{for a } conical \text{ horn section associated} \\ &\text{with each port.} \end{aligned} \tag{7.25b}$$

in which l is the distance from the throat to the virtual apex of the horn and S is the throat area of the horn section. The value of the flow resistance R_0 of an open port can be determined as follows: The volume flow during the open part of the cycle is $Q_0 = US$, and the excess chamber pressure which drives the flow is $P_e = \frac{1}{2}\rho_0 U^2$, in which U is the linear particle velocity through the constriction of the port. The acoustic impedance of the port then becomes

$$R_0 = \frac{P_e}{Q_0} = \frac{1}{2}\frac{\rho_0 U}{S} = \frac{1}{2}\rho_0 \frac{Q_0}{S^2} \tag{7.26}$$

To the load impedance composed of R_h and L_h in parallel, the interrupted flow appears as a square wave modulation of an amplitude $I_0 = Q_0/2$ superimposed on a constant current $I_0 = Q_0/2$. When the

---

[47] L. E. Kinsler and A. R. Frey, *Fundamentals of Acoustics*, John Wiley & Sons, New York, 1950, p. 298

[48] R. Clark Jones, *J. Acoust. Soc. Amer.*, *18* (1946), 371.

port is open the current through R_h will be $+I_0$, and when the port is closed it will be $-I_0$, while the constant current $+I_0$ is drawn by the inductance L_h. The total current through the port, then, is $2I_0 = Q_0$ during the opening period and zero during the closing period, as required by eq. 7.25a. The total potential difference across R_0 and R_h is then

$$E = 2I_0R_0 + I_0R_h \qquad (7.27)$$

We now substitute eq. 7.26 in eq. 7.27 using $Q_0 = 2I_0$:

$$E = 2\rho_0 \frac{I_0^2}{S^2} + I_0R_h \qquad (7.27a)$$

Solving this equation for I_0 we have:

$$I_0 = -\frac{R_hS^2}{4\rho_0} \pm \left(\frac{R_h^2S^4}{16\rho_0^2} + \frac{S^2E}{2\rho_0}\right)^{\frac{1}{2}} \qquad (7.28)$$

Let us rewrite this equation in terms of a parameter $y = 4\rho_0E/R_h^2S^2$ using only the positive root:

$$I_0 = -\frac{E}{R_h}\frac{1}{y} + \left(\frac{E^2}{R_h^2}\frac{1}{y^2} + 2y\frac{E^2}{R_h^2}\frac{1}{y^2}\right)^{\frac{1}{2}}$$

$$= \frac{E}{R_h}\frac{(1 + 2y)^{\frac{1}{2}} - 1}{y} = \frac{E}{R_h}\varphi(y) \qquad (7.28a)$$

The efficiency of a square wave modulated siren may now be calculated from the ratio of the total acoustic output power $I_0^2R_h$ to the compressor output power EI_0:

$$\eta \simeq \frac{I_0R_h}{E} = \varphi(y) \qquad (7.29a)$$

The parameter y can be evaluated from the relationships $E = P_e$, $R_h = \rho_0c/S$ (see eq. 7.25b) and $\rho_0c^2 = \gamma P_0$ (eq. 2.31) which yield

$$y = \frac{4}{\gamma}\frac{P_e}{P_0} = \frac{4}{\gamma}f$$

in which γ is the ratio of specific heats ($\gamma \simeq 1.4$) and f the ratio of excess pressure to ambient atmospheric pressure. It has been established empirically that for driving pressures P_e which satisfy the condition $f \lesssim \frac{1}{3}$ the dissipation of energy by turbulence in the ports is minimized. For $f = 0.35$ the parameter y becomes unity and the efficiency is $\eta = \varphi(y) = 73\%$. For $f \to 0$ the efficiency function

$\varphi(y)$ approaches 1, but the input power $EI_0 = SP_e^2\varphi(y)/\rho_0 c$ decreases as P_e goes to zero.

In practice, sirens are usually operated in the neighborhood of $y = 1$; but the simplifying assumptions $\omega L_h \gg R_h$ and $L_c \simeq 0$ used in our analysis of the efficiency do not fully represent the actual conditions. A better approximation is given by:

$$\eta \simeq \frac{\varphi(y)}{1 + 0.5(ka)^2 + 0.84a/l} \tag{7.29b}$$

in which a is the radius of the ports, and l defines the taper of the radiating horn.[49]

For example, for $a = 0.2$ cm and $l = 40$ cm, the efficiency becomes $\eta \simeq \varphi(y)/1.0064$, at a frequency of 2 kcps, and $\eta = \varphi(y)/1.244$ at a frequency of 20 kcps. We note that the efficiency drops as the ratios a/λ and a/l increase. Measurements on various commercial sirens in this frequency range have shown that total acoustic efficiencies between 60 and 70 per cent can be obtained if the pressure ratio $f = P_e/P_0$ is kept below 0.3 and if square wave modulation is used. In a square wave, however, only the fraction $8/\pi^2 = 0.81$ of the output power is present in the fundamental component; also high-amplitude effects must be considered, which lead to a sawtooth-shaped wave front (see Section 6.5) with a concomitant transfer of energy from the fundamental to the higher harmonics. Consequently, the efficiency of power conversion for the fundamental siren frequency lies below 50 per cent for low amplitudes and becomes still smaller in the presence of high-amplitude effects. The maximum efficiency of a siren with sinusoidal modulation, on the other hand, is only one-half the efficiency of a square-wave siren; e.g., for $y = 1$ and 2 kcps $\eta \simeq 36\%$.

A view of a commercial siren of 300 watts output is shown in Fig. 7.36. From bottom to top we recognize the following components: the exponential horn radiator, the rotor-stator compartment, the variable-speed transmission, the rotor-drive motor and frequency-control unit. The gas flow is supplied from a 5-hp compressor, and the rotor is driven by a 1.5-hp variable-speed motor. The frequency range is 1 to 20 kcps and the maximum intensity level at 5 kcps on the center axis 50 cm from the horn throat is about 160 db. The siren itself weighs about 120 lb.

[49] For a conical horn, l is the distance from the throat to the virtual apex of the cone. For an exponential horn $l = 2/s$, in which s is the flare constant of the horn (see eq. 7.14).

For gas-flow processing special treatment chambers are required whose general design is based on the discussions of Section 6.2.   The chamber dimensions depend on the volume velocity of the irradiated gas stream and on the contact time necessary to produce a specified number of collisions per unit volume of the gas stream.   The contact time, in turn, depends on the number of particles carried by the gas and on the distribution of particle sizes.   Typical values occurring in

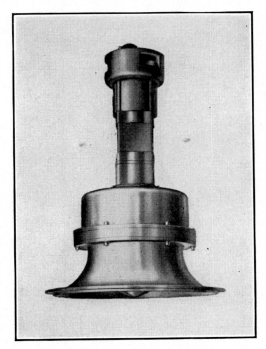

Fig. 7.36.   View of a commercial 300-watt siren.   Courtesy of Ultrasonics Corporation, Cambridge, Mass.

aerosol processing are: a particle density of 2 to 7 g/m³ (1 to 3 grains/cu ft), a particle size from 0.5 to 5 microns (10^{-4} to 10^{-3} cm), a volume flow of 50 to 500 m²/min (2000 to 20,000 cu ft/min), and a contact time of 1 to 5 sec.[50]   The corresponding treatment chambers have a diameter of about 1 m (3 ft) and a length of 2 to 5 m (6 to 15 ft).   Sound insulation constitutes a major problem at intensity levels as high as 160 db (1 watt/cm²).   Relatively thick chamber walls

[50] H. W. St. Clair, M. J. Spendlove, and E. V. Potter, *U. S. Bur. Mines Dept. Invest.* 4218 (1948).

are required since the amplitude reflection coefficient is proportional to the mass per unit area:[51]

$$R \simeq 1.25 \times 10^{-3} \omega M \text{ (kg/sec m}^2) \quad (7.30)$$

7.9   Sonic Oscillators Operated by Hydrodynamic Valve Action

An application of the siren principle to liquid media would lead to difficulties because of undesirable hydrodynamic effects associated with high-speed rotation in an incompressible fluid. A more appropriate method of generating intense sonic vibrations uses the action of a reciprocating valve to modulate the liquid flow in a pipe.

A system of this kind is capable of generating self-excited oscillations if its dimensions are such that part of the hydrodynamic energy in the pipe is fed back to the valve. In rather uncontrolled form, this effect has been known for a long time, under the name *water hammer*, as an unwanted source of high-amplitude shock waves in pipe systems.[52] Since about 1950, this principle has been used to produce self-generating oscillations of satisfactory stability in liquids at high sound-pressure levels. It is expected that further developments will establish this type of sound generation as a means particularly suited for liquid processing. Hence, a brief discussion of the operating mechanism of self-excited hydrodynamic oscillators is in order.[53]

Let us consider a liquid-filled loop-shaped pipe of length L, as shown schematically in Fig. 7.37. One end of the loop (I) carries a rigid seat B for an elastically supported valve V. A circular diaphragm D is clamped across the other end of the loop (II) and supports the valve through a short connecting rod R. A pump supplies the driving fluid through the feeding pipe F and creates a pressure drop P_0 across the orifice at the valve end of the loop. The volume velocity Q_0 through the loop then depends essentially on the area of the circular gap between the valve seat and the valve. It is apparent from the valve assembly shown in Fig. 7.37 that the area of the gap will change

[51] Sound transmission through walls is discussed by E. Meyer, P. H. Parkin, H. Oberst, and H. D. Purkis, *Acustica, Akust. Beih.*, 1 (1951), 17. See also *Handbook of Acoustic Noise Control*, by Bolt, Beranek and Newman, Inc. (1952), Cambridge, Mass.

[52] An interesting study of water-hammer action in hydroelectric machinery is given by Sumiji Fujii, *Sci. Machines* (Tokyo), 1 (1949), No. 1.

[53] This discussion is based upon material supplied from a Ph.D. Thesis entitled *Self-Excited Hydrodynamic Oscillators*, by John V. Bouyoucos, Acoustics Research Laboratory, Harvard University, Cambridge, Massachusetts. See also *Tech. Mem. 36* (July 1954) of that laboratory.

as a result of pressure fluctuations at II acting on the elastic diaphragm
D.

Thus, a positive pressure increment in region II leads to an incremental increase of the gap area, whereas a negative pressure increment reduces the gap area by a small amount. Hence, the flow through the orifice at I is modulated by the pressure fluctuations at II. Let us now assume that because of a transient pressure reduction at II the gap area undergoes an incremental closure. The resulting deceleration of the flow through the orifice brings about a transient increase

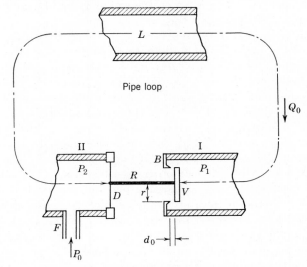

Fig. 7.37. Schematic diagram of hydrodynamic valve oscillator. After J. V. Bouyoucos, Acoustics Research Laboratory, Harvard University.

in the pressure drop across the orifice, and the total pressure at I becomes $P = P_0 + \Delta P$. The increment ΔP constitutes a transient pressure pulse which will propagate with sound velocity into the pipe until it is carried around the loop to region II. The pressure pulse arrives at II after a time interval ΔT, and it raises the pressure acting on the diaphragm D to $P = P_0 + \Delta P$. At the same time, the volume velocity of the liquid flow entering the pipe at F is reduced to $Q = Q_0 - \Delta Q$.

At this instant a similar sequence of incremental changes of flow velocity and pressure is initiated by the valve action at the orifice, although of opposite sign since a positive ΔP at II produces a negative ΔP at I. It is easily seen that after another interval ΔT the whole cycle starts over again. Once started by a transient pressure fluctuation at the diaphragm this oscillatory phenomenon will either build up or decay, depending on the losses in the loop and the magnitude of the feedback between diaphragm and valve.

In this simplified discussion of the hydrodynamic oscillator we have tacitly assumed that only the forces exerted on the diaphragm would determine the displacement of the valve. This can be accomplished only if the valve is designed in such a way as to present negligible active area to the pressure existing in region I. In this case, the feedback is controlled in magnitude by the acoustic impedance Z_v of the diaphragm loaded by the mass of the valve assembly, and in phase by the length L of the loop.

If Z_v represents a stiffness reactance much larger than the acoustic impedance $Z_p = \rho_0 c / S$ of the liquid in the pipe (S = pipe cross section), the diaphragm acts as a hard termination and the optimum length of the loop becomes $L = c \Delta T$. The pipe is then acting as a half-wave transmission line ($L = \lambda/2$), and a standing wave of a resonance frequency $f_0 = \frac{1}{2}\Delta T$ develops. On the other hand, if the stiffness of the diaphragm resonates with the mass of the valve, a soft termination is produced ($Z_v \ll Z_p$) and the pipe length must be chosen to be one quarter wave at this particular frequency. In the general case one finds $\lambda/4 < L < \lambda/2$, depending on the value of Z_v, which acts in much the same way as the backing plate in sandwich transducers (see Section 4.12). In hydrodynamic oscillators designed according to Fig. 7.37, the sound-pressure amplitude P_1 at the valve end may be related to the pressure amplitude P_2 at the diaphragm if suitable assumptions are made for the modulation of hydrodynamic flow by the valve motion.[54] The resulting pressure ratio is

$$\frac{P_1}{P_2} = \frac{\rho_0 S}{j\omega d_0} \frac{Q_0{}^2}{Z_v S_v{}^2} \tag{7.31}$$

in which d_0 is the clearing of the annular valve gap associated with the undisturbed flow Q_0, and $S_v = 2\pi r d_0$ is the area of the gap between valve and valve seat (see Fig. 7.37). We note that eq. 7.31 represents an amplification factor which is analogous to the ratio of related incremental changes of plate voltage and grid voltage for constant plate current in an electronic triode tube.

The system illustrated in Fig. 7.37 is particularly suited whenever a liquid is to be subjected to high periodic pressures. There are other applications in which the forces acting on the diaphragm D are to be transmitted to an external medium. In this case, the design

[54] J. V. Boyoucos, *loc. cit.* (see footnote 53).

shown in Fig. 7.38 has some advantages.   Here the valve V is seated
at one end of a quarter-wave pipe section L, which is terminated at
the other end by a low impedance Z_0, such as that offered by a vessel
of large cross-sectional area.   The valve is held in place by a clamped
diaphragm D or cantilever outside the pipe section.   The fundamental
resonance frequency of the diaphragm must be higher than the frequency to which the water-hammer pipe is tuned; i.e., the impedance
Z_V of the diaphragm-valve assembly must be a pure stiffness.

Safe frequency range for stable operation   The practical
frequency range of hydrodynamic transducers of this type for power
generation is limited to low frequencies ($f \simeq 3$ kcps).   One reason

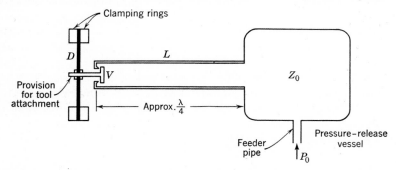

Fig. 7.38.   Hydrodynamic valve oscillator for use with tools attached to diaphragm.   Courtesy of Ultrasonic Corporation, Cambridge, Mass.

is that the power capacity depends on the flow volume which is determined by the pipe cross section whereas the frequency depends on
the length of the pipe.   If the ratio of pipe diameter to pipe length
approaches unity, the stability of the system is reduced due to the
effect of cross-modes.   It is also difficult to provide diaphragms with
a high natural frequency whose stiffness allows for valve displacements
of sufficient amplitude without exceeding the dynamic fatigue stress
limit.   This is apparent from the equations for the fundamental
mode of a clamped circular plate

$$f_0 = 2\pi \frac{t}{D^2} \left(\frac{Y_0}{3\rho(1 - \sigma^2)} \right)^{1/2} \tag{7.32}$$

and for the maximum permissible bending stress

$$T_{\max} = \mu \frac{Y_0 t}{D^2} \xi_{\max} \tag{7.33}$$

in which t is the plate thickness, D the plate diameter, $\xi_{\max}$ the amplitude at the center of the plate, and μ a constant depending on the central mass loading of the diaphragm by the valve. Comparing these two equations we note that the maximum frequency at which a required valve displacement ξ can be obtained safely is limited by the dynamic fatigue stress limit:

$$f_0 \cdot \xi_{max} = \text{constant} \times T_{max} \qquad (7.34)$$

For example, T_{max} in steel is of the order of 40×10^3 psi and a displacement of the order of 0.002 in. is required for stable operation at high amplitude levels. For practical diaphragm configurations the constant in eq. 7.34 has been found to be of the order of 10^{-4} and hence the maximum attainable frequency is about 2 kcps.

The sound-pressure amplitudes in the pipe exceed the cavitation threshold at frequencies below 2 kcps. Hence water-hammer devices of the type described in this section can be used for cavitation treatment if the processing liquid itself is used to drive the unit. It is also possible to use a water hammer for shaking or drilling applications if a suitable member or tool is attached to the vibratory diaphragm.[55]

7.10   Special Mechanical Transducers for Low Frequencies

Our discussion of devices and techniques for sonic processing would be incomplete without a reference to those special methods of generating and utilizing sonic vibrations which do not come under the usual transducer classification. Some of them employ motor-driven eccentric masses or reciprocating pistons operated at frequencies below 60 cps. These methods are based on well established principles of vibration engineering and will not be discussed in this book. Others depend on vortex formation in high-temperature gas streams[56] or on shock-wave formation by electric discharge[57] or by combustion.[58] This field of "thermoacoustics" is still in the research stage, and the information available to date is not sufficient for engineering uses.

[55] Since transducers of this kind are still in the development stage no published reports on their processing efficiency are available to date.

[56] P. L. Rijke, *Poggendorf's Ann. Phys. Chem.*, *107* (1859), 339. K. O. Lehmann, *Ann. Phys.*, *29* (1937), 527. J. J. Coop, *J. Acoust. Soc. Am. 20* (1948), 321. E. M. Kerwin master's thesis 1953, M.I.T. Acoustics Laboratory, Cambridge, Mass. J. L. Neuringer and G. E. Hudson, *J. Acoust. Soc. Amer. 24* (1952), 667.

[57] Shock-wave formation by electric discharge has been described by W. P. Mason, U.S. Pat. 2,403,990, July 16, 1946; W. Schaaffs and F. Trendelenburg, *Z. Naturforschung., 3a* (1948), 656.

[58] A combustion-operated sonic pulse jet has been developed by A. G. Bodine at the Soundrive Corp. in Los Angeles, Calif.

We shall, however, discuss two mechanical methods for the generation of large forces at low frequencies which seem to have some practical importance: sonic well drilling and sonic fibrillation of paper pulp.

Longitudinal vibrator for sonic drilling[59]   It has been found that earthen formations are easily penetrated by applying the fatigue action of periodic elastic impacts.   This is done by generating a longitudinal sound wave of large amplitude in a resonant heavy solid pipe. The pipe is coupled directly to the bottom of the bore hole, and its vibration produces high elastic strains in the rock being drilled.

Experience has shown that the heavy solid pipe should be fairly short, such as only 1 or 2 half wavelengths long.   In a typical application the pipe consists of screwed-together sections totaling about 45 m (150 ft), with the drilling bit on the lower end and the wave generator on the upper end.   The entire 150-ft assembly is a separate and complete sonic unit which, in some instances, will operate as far as 2 miles down within the earth as it drills the oil well.   Drilling rates several times greater than the drilling rate of conventional rotary or percussive drilling methods have been reported.

In all modern forms of oil-well drilling equipment a so-called "drill mud" is pumped down through the drilling pipe to nozzles embodied in the bit for the purpose of washing the cuttings out of the hole.   In sonic drilling the kinetic energy of this mud supplies the power to the wave generator which drives the resonant pipe.   The drill mud thus serves two functions: it drives the wave generator and it washes away the chips that are fractured out by elastic fatigue.

The velocity of sound in a steel pipe is approximately 5.5×10^3 m/sec $(17 \times 10^3$ fps); thus the half-wave resonant frequency of a 45-m pipe is approximately 60 cps.   The center of the bar stands still, and the two ends (generator and bit) oscillate with a total stroke (double amplitude) of approximately $\frac{1}{2}$ in.   This causes a dynamic stress maximum at the center of approximately 12,000 psi, which is well below the fatigue stress limit of good steel.   However, since the pipe may be of the order of 50 in^2 in cross section, this corresponds to about 500,000 lb per cycle, sixty times per second.   In driving a resonant rod of this kind a transducer must be used which is capable of transforming energy from the flowing mud stream, which is a low-impedance source to the rock, which is a high impedance load.   This is accomplished by passing the mud stream through a high-velocity turbine which generates large periodic forces by rotating an eccentric

[59] The discussion in this section is based on information supplied by A. G. Bodine of Soundrive Corp., Los Angeles, Calif.

weight. This impedance adjustment between the power source and the load is the most important feature of the sonic drill.

Figure 7.39 shows the generator assembly which consists of twelve bolted-together units. A view of a single disassembled turbine unit is given in Fig. 7.40. Each unit consists of two longitudinal halves which are welded together. In the center we see the rotor whose mass is unbalanced by an eccentric lead plug. The stator of the turbine is shown at the left. The driving fluid enters at the top and reaches the rotor through radial slots in the stator housing. The driving

Fig. 7.39.   Sonic drill generator assembly.   Courtesy of Soundrive Corporation, Los Angeles, California.

fluid then leaves through a slot at the bottom and enters the next unit. The complete rotor combination turns on sealed roller bearings which are supported by the heavy cantilever pin in the other half of the housing which is shown at the right of Fig. 7.40. Twelve such rotor units are bolted together such that each unit is turned 180° with respect to the neighboring unit. This arrangement makes the alternate rotors turn in opposite directions, which cancels out lateral vibrations. An important feature of this transducer is that without direct interconnection the twelve rotors in the complete generator assembly will run in synchronism once they are coupled to the resonant pipe. One must realize that the pipe resonance is still quite sharp during drilling: the Q without load is about 200; when drilling the Q decreases to about 50.

Transmission lines for sonic power   Let us now derive the acoustic properties of a heavy resonant pipe which is embedded in a viscous mud.   We shall apply the transmission-line theory developed in Chapter 2 to the special case of a cylindrical hollow pipe line of steel carrying longitudinal waves.   Consider a line with uniform linear density ν (g/cm), immersed in a fluid of density ρ_f (g/cm^3), and

Fig. 7.40.   Turbine unit for sonic drill.   Courtesy of Soundrive Corporation, Los Angeles, California.

coefficient of viscosity η_f.   Longitudinal waves in the line produce a viscous drag force per unit length F_f in the fluid which is given by:[60]

$$F_f = 2\pi D \left(\frac{\rho_f \eta_f \omega}{2} \right)^{\frac{1}{2}} (1 + j) \frac{\partial y}{\partial t} \tag{7.35}$$

in which $y = y_0 e^{j\omega t}$ is the (longitudinal) particle displacement in the line, and D is the mean diameter of a pipe in contact with fluid inside as well as outside.   The particle displacement amplitude y_0 is in general a function of x, the distance along the pipe.

Let the alternating acoustic force be $F = F_0 e^{j\omega t}$ newtons.   This is equal to the alternating longitudinal pressure times the solid cross-

[60] W. P. Mason, *Piezoelectric Crystals and their Application to Ultrasonics*, p. 340, Van Nostrand, New York, 1950.   See also Section 8.4 of this book.

sectional area of the pipe S_P. At high amplitudes there may be appreciable damping by internal friction in the pipe material (see Section 8.8). These effects require a modification of Hooke's law such as to include a coefficient of hysteresis η_s:

$$F = -S_p Y_0 (1 + j\eta_s) \frac{\partial y}{\partial x} \tag{7.36}$$

In addition to this complex relation between stress and strain, we need the basic relation for dynamic equilibrium between the inertial force and the opposing elastic and viscous forces per unit length. From eq. 7.35 and 7.36 and the equilibrium condition expressed in eq. 2.7 we find:

$$\nu \frac{\partial^2 y}{\partial t^2} = -\frac{\partial F}{\partial x} - F_f$$

$$= S_L Y (1 + j\eta_s) \frac{\partial^2 y}{\partial x^2} - 2\pi D \left(\frac{\rho_f \eta_f \omega}{2}\right)^{1/2} (1 + j) \frac{\partial y}{\partial t} \tag{7.37}$$

Assuming simple harmonic motion this equation takes the form:

$$\frac{\partial^2 y}{\partial x^2} + \frac{\omega^2}{c^2} y = 0 \tag{7.38}$$

in which

$$c^2 = \frac{Y_0}{\rho} \left[\frac{1 + j\eta_s}{1 + \dfrac{2\pi D}{\nu} \left(\dfrac{\rho_f \eta_f}{2\omega}\right)^{1/2} (1 - j)} \right] \tag{7.39}$$

and $\rho_p = \nu/S_p$ is the density of the pipe material.

Without hysteresis in the pipe ($\eta_s = 0$), and without damping by the surrounding fluid ($\eta_f = 0$), the pipe velocity reduces to the familiar from $c_l = (Y_0/\rho)^{1/2}$, for a thin bar (see Section 2.7). A solution of eq. 7.38 is:

$$y = \mathbf{y}_+ e^{j(\omega t - kx)} + \mathbf{y}_- e^{j(\omega t - kx)}$$

in which k is the wave propagation constant:

$$k = \frac{\omega}{c} = \frac{\omega}{\sqrt{Y_0/\rho}} \left(\frac{1 + \dfrac{2\pi D}{\nu} \sqrt{\dfrac{\rho_f \eta_f}{2\omega}} (1 - j)}{1 + j\eta_s} \right)^{1/2} \tag{7.40}$$

This equation can be simplified if the frictional losses in the pipe and the viscous damping by the surrounding fluid are small. This condition is met with pipes made of steel and damped by ordinary drilling mud, so that we may assume:

$$\eta_s \ll 1 \qquad \text{and} \qquad \frac{2\pi D}{\nu}\sqrt{\frac{\rho_f \eta_f}{2\omega}} \equiv \chi_f \ll 1 \qquad (7.41)$$

We can now rationalize eq. 7.39 to obtain:

$$k \simeq \frac{\omega}{c_l} - j\frac{\omega}{c_l}\left[\frac{\eta_s + \chi_f}{2}\right] = \frac{\omega}{c_l} - jm \qquad (7.42)$$

in which χ_f is the effective coefficient of viscosity owing to the surrounding fluid, and m is the amplitude attenuation coefficient. The solution for the damped waves then becomes:

$$y = \mathbf{y}_+ e^{j\omega(t-x/c_l)}e^{-mx} + \mathbf{y}_- e^{j\omega(t+x/c_l)}e^{+mx} \qquad (7.43)$$

These waves traveling in opposite directions combine to give a damped standing wave with the amplitude distribution (see Section 2.10):

$$y = \mathbf{y}_g\left[\cosh^2(\alpha_L - mx) - \sin^2\left(\beta_L + \frac{2\pi}{\lambda}(L - x)\right)\right]^{\frac{1}{2}} \qquad (7.44)$$

in which $\mathbf{y}_g$ is determined by the generator, L is the length of the pipe, $\lambda = c_l/f$ is the wave length in the pipe, and α_L and β_L are determined by boundary conditions at the end of the pipe ($x = L$).

According to eq. 2.39 the wave impedance looking down the pipe at any point x is

$$Z_x = \nu c_l \tanh\left\{\alpha_L - mx + j\left[\beta_L + \frac{2\pi}{\lambda}(L - x)\right]\right\} \qquad (7.45)$$

$$= F/u$$

and $u = U_g e^{j\omega t} = j\omega \mathbf{y}_g e^{j\omega t}$ is the particle velocity in the pipe. The total power passing through the pipe at a point x is:

$$P_x = \overline{(Fu)}_x = \tfrac{1}{2}U_g^2 R_x = F_g^2/2R_x \qquad (7.46)$$

in which R_x is the real part of Z_x. For small-line damping, and a pipe which delivers a reasonable fraction of its power to a load on the termination, the input impedance is approximately νc_l, and the input power then is:

$$P_g = \tfrac{1}{2}U_g^2 \nu c_l = F_g^2/2\nu c_l = (F_g/S_p)^2 S_p/2\rho_p c_l \qquad (7.47)$$

The force per unit area F_g/S_L, or the stress, is the quantity that usually limits the amount of power that the line can handle. The limiting quantity is the *dynamic fatigue stress limit*, which is always less than the ultimate tensile strength of the material, and which also depends on the static stress in the oscillating line. Unstressed steel will typically handle alternating amplitudes of 15,000 to 30,000 psi (1 to 2×10^7 kg/m^2).

If we assume the smaller figure, and take a typical value of ρc_l for steel, we find that this type of power line will handle about 100 hp/ sq in. of steel section (about 10 kw/cm^2). We also find from the above calculation that the peak particle velocity is about 8 fps (2.5 m/sec) for 110 hp; and the amplitude (half of total excursion) would be about $\frac{1}{4}$ in. (0.6 cm) at a frequency of about 50 cps. Magnitudes such as these have been reported in experimental oil-well drilling with sonic equipment.

Torsional vibrator for shear processing Most materials are much less resistive to shear forces than to compressional forces. This property is utilized in many conventional techniques, such as cutting, grinding, drilling. In some applications a reciprocating action, which involves particle motions of alternating direction and acceleration is superior to a uniform rotation. High-amplitude shear vibrations are particularly useful for the processing of viscous fluids as in paper-pulp fibrillation,[61] in homogenization of biological suspensions, and in micronization of slurries.

There are three ways by which alternating shear forces can be applied to a liquid.[62] (1) Pairs of surfaces are placed opposite each other, and one surface of each pair vibrates in a direction parallel to the surfaces. The material to be treated is passed through the narrow gaps between the stationary and the vibrating surface. (2) Several surfaces vibrate in unison in the direction parallel to the surfaces, and the material is passed between the surfaces. Here a shear force results from the inertia of the material which leads to relative motion between the material and the vibrating surfaces. (3) Similar to 1, but the surfaces are provided with openings or have the shape of blades. In this case the fluid to be treated is passed through these openings or through the gaps between blades.

---

[61] In paper-pulp processing the alternating shear tends to flex the fibers. Single fibers are thereby softened and rendered pliable, while fiber bundles tend to separate into their constituent fibers. Sonic processing affects all the fibers in a slurry uniformly and produces the high degree of homogeneity which is desirable in paper making. (See A. Frey-Wysslingnand K. Muhlethaler, *Textile Research J.*, *17* (1947), 32.

[62] G. S. Seavey and C. B. Horseley, U.S. Pat. 2,584,053, January 29, 1952, and G. S. Seavey, U.S. Pat. 2,625,379 and 2,625,380, January 13, 1953.

To drive the vibrating surfaces or blades a torsional resonator of the type shown in Fig. 7.41 is required. It consists of a torsional rod T of radius R_t which is terminated by two masses M_1 and M_2 of radius R_m at its ends. The rod is supported at the center by a bearing B. An alternating torque is applied to one end of the rod T through

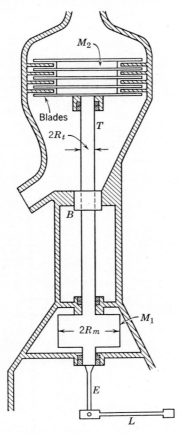

Fig. 7.41. Schematic diagram of torsional transducer for the generator of shear forces. After C. B. Horseley.

a relatively compliant bar E. This bar E, in turn, is driven from a lever L which is actuated by a motor-driven cam.

Let us consider the condition for resonance of a system consisting of one mass M and its associated torsional spring which is embodied in half the rod T. For such a lumped system the equilibrium condition is found from eq. 2.3 by substituting:

for the mass: the moment of inertia I_m (kg·m^2)
for the displacement: the angular displacement α_a (radians)
for the stiffness: the torsional stiffness θ (kg·m^2/sec^2)

which leads to the equilibrium of torques for the free system:

$$I_m \frac{d^2\alpha_a}{dt^2} + \theta\alpha_a = 0 \tag{7.48}$$

For the system depicted in Fig. 7.41 the quantities I_m and θ are defined as:

$$I_m = \int_0^{R_m} r^2 \, dm = \tfrac{1}{2}R_m{}^2 M$$

and
$$\theta = \frac{Y_s}{l}\frac{\pi}{4}R_t{}^4 = \frac{Y_s S}{l}\kappa^2 \quad\Bigg\} \tag{7.49}$$

in which R_m is the radius of the cylindrical end mass M, $Y_s = Y_0/2(1+\sigma)$ is the shear modulus of the rod, l is the rod length S is the rod cross section, and $\kappa = R_t/2$ is the radius of gyration. Solving eq. 7.48 and substituting eqs. 7.49 we obtain for the frequency of torsional resonance:

$$\omega = \left(\frac{\theta}{I_m}\right)^{1/2} = \frac{R_t{}^2}{R_m}\left(\frac{\pi}{2l}\frac{Y_s}{M}\right)^{1/2} \tag{7.50}$$

The shear force is transmitted to the treatment fluid by a multiplicity of flat blades attached to the periphery of one of the drum-shaped masses as shown in Fig. 7.41. The mass of the blades increases the effective moment of inertia I_m above the value given in eq. 7.49. Also, a damping term of the form $R_v \, (d\alpha/dt)$ must be included in eq. 7.48. The damping resistance R_v is proportional to the viscous forces acting on the blades B:

$$R_v \simeq \varphi\left(\frac{\omega\eta\rho}{2}\right)^{1/2}$$

in which η and ρ are the viscosity and density, respectively, of the fluid to be treated and $\varphi = \varphi(S_b, R_b, d)$ is a function of the total effective area S_b of the blades, the blade radius R_b, and the spacing d between the blades in adjacent planes.

The main purpose of the exciter bar E is to provide a low impedance to the driving motor during the periods of starting and stopping of the device. At resonance, the torsional amplitudes of the end masses M_1 and M_2 approach the amplitude of the driving lever L. Once resonance is attained the driving means need only supply the power which is consumed by the fluid load and by the hysteresis and bearing losses.

Figure 7.42 shows a commercial shear vibrator for paper-pulp fibrillation capable of handling 5-kw power at an efficiency of about 80 per cent.   At the right we see the control unit which stabilizes the vibrational amplitude $A = \alpha_a R_b$ to a constant value irrespective of loading

Fig. 7.42.   Unit for sonic shear processing of paper pulp.   Courtesy of Sonic Research Corporation, Boston, Mass.

and frequency drift.   This is achieved by means of a feedback loop between a magnetic pick-up coupled to the torsional vibrator and the drive motor.   The transducer itself shown at left consists of a 3600-rpm drive motor which is geared up to turn a cam at 12,000 rpm (200 cps), a gear housing, and a torsional resonator.   The torsional shaft of the resonator has a length of about 1 m (3 ft) and carries a circular blade array of about 0.45-m (15-in.) diameter.   The processing capacity is of the order of 20 gal/min (1 to 2 ltr/sec).   The resonator Q under load is about 30.

It has been found that mean velocities $U = \omega A/\sqrt{2}$ of the oscillating blade motion up to 5 m/sec (1000 ft/min) can be achieved. The resulting shear forces are capable of refining slurries such as paper pulp to a very high degree. This velocity can be attained with a mean radial displacement amplitude of about 1.1 cm at a frequency of 200, cps corresponding to a peak angular deflection α_a of about 2°. With a spacing d between each plane of vibrating blades and the adjacent plane of stationary blades of about 0.003 cm, the mean shear force per unit blade area and for a treatment material of 0.1 poise viscosity is:

$$T_s = \frac{F_s}{S_b} = \eta \frac{U}{d} \simeq 1.7 \times 10^4 \quad (\text{dynes/cm}^2)$$

$$\simeq 1.7 \times 10^3 \; (\text{newtons/m}^2)$$

We can now make an estimate of the work done by the shear transducer in treating a viscous slurry. Assuming a blade area (double surface) of $S_b = 13$ cm^2 (2 in^2) of each blade and a total number of blades in each plane of $N = 100$ we obtain a power of

$$W = NS_b(T_sU)_{\text{rms}} \simeq 1.1 \text{ kw per plane.}[63]$$

Torsional vibrators of this type have possible applications for sonic sifting of fine granular material. The high alternating accelerations prevent the material from clogging the gaps between the blades, and this makes it possible to use mesh sizes as small as 5×10^{-3} cm (0.002 in.). Encouraging results have been obtained by this method on materials such as drilling mud and paper pulp.

The conversion of mechanical rotational energy into vibrational energy can be achieved by various other means. The frequency range of such mechanical devices is limited by the maximum attainable motor speeds and gearing ratios. It can be extended up into the range of several kilocycles if the multiplication principle of the siren is applied. For example, a circular disc with a large number of radial grooves can be rolled over an equal number of steel balls or rollers placed around a circle on a steel plate. This plate, in turn, is forced with high pressure against the rotating disc. Although this arrangement does not have resonant features vibrational amplitudes of sizable magnitude can be generated with proper design.[64]

[63] Values of this magnitude were obtained with a pilot unit designed by Sonic Research Corporation, Boston, Mass. Higher powers up to 30 kw have been obtained at conversion efficiencies of about 80 per cent by units operated with several decks of blades.

[64] G. S. Seavey and C. B. Horseley, U.S. Pat. 2,607,568, 2,558,089, and 2,620,766.

CHAPTER 8

Principles of Sonic Testing and Analysis

8.1 The Rationale of Sonic Measurements

In the present chapter we shall present the principles underlying the analytical applications of sonics, as outlined in Section 1.3. We shall use the basic concepts that have been introduced in previous chapters, but we shall apply them in various specialized ways, depending upon the particular analytical application that is desired. Furthermore, analytical sonics generally requires specialized test equipment and experimental techniques. The apparatus and measurement methods vary so widely from case to case that they may seem at first sight to be little related to each of the embodiments of sonic principles. A detailed description of these many specialized methods lies outside the scope of this book. Instead, we shall attempt to give an organized rationale for the possible uses of sound in testing and analysis.

All measurements relate to one of three fundamental physical quantities: time, length, or energy loss. These three quantities are involved whether we are locating flaws in solids, analyzing the impurity content in a gas, studying the structure of a high polymer, or determining the geometrical dimensions of an object. With a clear understanding of the basic physical relationships one is in a position not only to utilize the many special techniques that have been developed to date,[1] but also to extend in many new directions the wide capabilities of sonic analysis.

Fundamental quantities The two quantities which are fundamental to all measurements are the sound velocity c and the attenu-

---

[1] A general account of many analytical techniques is given in *Acoustic Measurements*, Leo L. Beranek, John Wiley & Sons, New York, 1949. Detailed description of ultrasonic flaw detection techniques are found in *Ultrasonics*, Benson Carlin, McGraw-Hill, New York, 1949. Ultrasonic viscosimetry is discussed in *Piezoelectric Crystals and Their Application to Ultrasonics*, W. P. Mason: Van Nostrand, New York, 1950.

ation coefficient α. They describe the propagation of plane waves in an attenuating medium in the form[2]

$$A_x = A_0 e^{j\omega(t-x/c)} e^{-\alpha x} \tag{8.1}$$

Both quantities can be combined into a single complex propagation constant $k^* = (\omega/c) - j\alpha = |k^*| e^{-j\varphi}$, in which

$$|k^*| = \left(\frac{\omega^2}{c^2} + \alpha^2\right)^{\frac{1}{2}}$$

and

$$\tan\varphi = \frac{\alpha c}{\omega} = \frac{\alpha\lambda}{2\pi} \tag{8.2}[3]$$

We may now rewrite eq. 8.1:

$$A_x = A_0 e^{j(\omega t - k^* x)}$$

in which A_0 may be the amplitude of sound pressure, particle velocity, or density.

Another presentation uses the concept of a complex velocity $c^* = \omega/k^*$. Usually α may be assumed to be small compared with ω/c, which yields

$$c^* = c \Big/ \left(\left(1 - j\frac{\alpha c}{\omega}\right) \simeq c\left(1 + j\frac{\alpha c}{\omega}\right)\right) \tag{8.3}$$

A complex velocity, in turn, allows one to define a complex stiffness modulus $Y^* = \rho_0 c^{*2}$. For example, in a thin rod (diameter $d \ll \lambda$) the modulus for longitudinal waves is

$$Y^* \simeq Y_0\left(1 + j2\frac{\alpha c}{\omega}\right) \tag{8.4}$$

in which Y_0 is Young's modulus.

Physically, each parameter or degree of freedom of a system subjected to sonic analysis is fully described by three separate measurements. They are measurements of time, of length, and of a signal ratio, as indicated in Table 8.1.

Time measurements To this category belong the determination of frequency $f = 1/T_0$, of bandwidth $B = \Delta f$ (see eq. 2.18), and of time delay Δt. The necessary instrumentation is mainly electronic. For

---

[2] Equation 8.1 follows from eq. 2.8 and 2.19. The damping factor $e^{-\alpha x}$ for spatial decay is obtained from the temporal damping factor $e^{-\kappa t}$ in eq. 2.8 by setting $t = x/c$; hence $\kappa/c = \alpha$.

[3] Physical mechanisms leading to a phase lag between sound pressure and density are discussed in the appendix.

Table 8.1   Basic Measurements Involved in Sonic Analysis

Time		Space		Signal Ratio	
Resonance frequency	$\omega_0 = \dfrac{2\pi}{T_0}$	Sample thickness	b	Bandwidth	$B = \dfrac{\omega_0}{Q}$
(a) Lumped system	$\omega_0{}^2 = \dfrac{K}{M}$	Cross-sectional area S		Decay time	$1/\kappa$
(b) Distributed system	$\omega_n{}^2 = \dfrac{n^2\pi^2}{l^2} c^2$	Path length	l	Half-value layer	$HL = \dfrac{ln2}{2\alpha}$
Phase difference	$\Delta\varphi = 2\pi \dfrac{b}{\lambda}$	Wavelength	λ	Standing-wave ratio SWR	
Time delay	$\Delta t = \dfrac{l}{c}$	Volume	V	Phase angle of impedance ψ	

high measuring accuracy, the generating equipment must provide high stability of the sound amplitude and clean definition of wave form or pulse shape. At the receiving end, special receivers (both wide and narrow band) and calibrated sweep circuits and gating circuits are used.[4] Standard electronic techniques can yield time measurements with an error of the order of 0.1 μsec (10^{-7} sec). Which of the two quantities, f or Δt, can be determined more accurately depends on the frequency range of interest and on the type of electronic equipment which is commercially available.

Length measurements   Here we are concerned with a direct determination of the path length l in the medium or the thickness b of a sample, of the wavelength λ and, in some optical methods, of the distance D between the sound wave and its image. Length is usually measured by direct mechanical means such as micrometers, with accuracies up to 1 micron (10^{-4} cm). In cases where the sound velocity c is known, time and length measurements are interrelated; the depth d of a flaw in steel is described by a time delay $\Delta t = d/c$; the thickness of a steel plate is determined by its resonance frequency $f_0 = c/2b$; or the time delay in a delay line may be expressed by its length $l = c\,\Delta t$.

Measurements of energy dissipation   The energy losses can be determined by combining a time or length measurement with a reading of signal amplitude. The four basic techniques which can be used for damping measurements are summarized in Table 8.2.

In a standing-wave system, for example, one may determine the resonance frequency and bandwidth, or the time required for a decay of the sound amplitude to half its value. For progressive waves, the distance in which the intensity drops to half its value can be measured.

---

[4] An excellent discussion of the principles, techniques, and circuits applicable to electronic time measurements is given in Vol. 20 of the Massachusetts Institute of Technology Radiation Laboratory Series, McGraw-Hill Co., New York, 1949.

Table 8.2. Basic Techniques for Damping Measurements. The symbols used in this table are defined in Table 8.3.

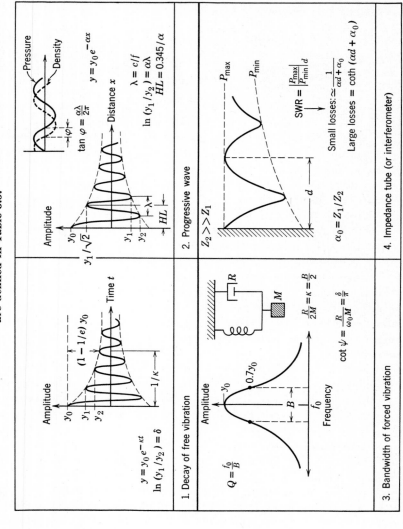

1. Decay of free vibration

$$y = y_0 e^{-\kappa t}$$

$$\ln (y_1 / y_2) = \delta$$

2. Progressive wave

$$\tan \varphi = \frac{\alpha \lambda}{2\pi}$$

$$y = y_0 e^{-\alpha x}$$

$$\lambda = c/f$$

$$\ln (y_1 / y_2) = \alpha \lambda$$

$$HL = 0.345/\alpha$$

$$Z_2 \gg Z_1$$

$$\alpha_0 = Z_1/Z_2$$

$$\text{SWR} = \left| \frac{P_{max}}{P_{min}} \right|_d$$

Small losses: $\simeq \dfrac{1}{\alpha d + \alpha_0}$

Large losses $= \coth (\alpha d + \alpha_0)$

3. Bandwidth of forced vibration

$$Q = \frac{f_0}{B}$$

$$\frac{R}{2M} = \kappa = \frac{B}{2}$$

$$\cot \psi = \frac{R}{\omega_0 M} = \frac{\delta}{\pi}$$

4. Impedance tube (or interferometer)

In some techniques, the impedance of a transducer which is loaded by the medium under investigation is measured electrically, and its variations are used to calculate the phase angle of the complex load impedance and hence the damping property of the medium.

Table 8.3. Relationships among Quantities Related to Damping

Derived Quantities	Symbol	B	κ	δ	SWR	α
			(Measured Quantities)			
Quality factor*	Q	ω_0/B	$\omega_0/2\kappa$	π/δ	$\pi\text{SWR}/2$	$\pi/\alpha\lambda$
Temporal damping constant	κ	$B/2$	—	$f_0\delta$	$2f_0/\text{SWR}$	$c\alpha$
Logarithmic damping decrement	δ	$\pi B/\omega_0$	κ/f_0	——	$2/\text{SWR}$	$\alpha\lambda$
Standing-wave ratio in distributed systems†	SWR	$2\omega_0/B\pi$	$2f_0/\kappa$	$2/\delta$	——	$2/\alpha\lambda$
Phase angle of mechanical impedance in lumped systems‡	$\cot\psi$	B/ω_0	$2\kappa/\omega_0$	δ/π	$2/\text{SWR}\pi$	$\alpha\lambda/\pi$
Phase angle between pressure and velocity in progressive wave	$\tan\varphi$	$B/2\omega_0$	κ/ω_0	$\delta/2\pi$	$1/\text{SWR}\pi$	$\alpha\lambda/2\pi$
Spatial attenuation constant for progressive waves§	α	$B/2c$	κ/c	δ/λ	$2/\text{SWR}\lambda$	——

* The quality factor is here defined for a lumped system as $Q = Q_L = \omega_0 M/R_m$ according to eq. 2.17. It is related to the ratio $Q_D = \omega_0/2\,\Delta\omega$ ($\Delta\omega =$ frequency shift for which amplitude drops to $1/\sqrt{2}$ of its maximum value) of a distributed system (transmission line) by $Q_L/Q_D = (\sqrt{2} - 1)^{\frac{1}{2}} = 0.645$, provided that $Q \geq 5$.

† For $\alpha_0 < 0.3$ and small losses, eq. 2.40 reduces to SWR $\simeq 1/(\alpha_0 + \alpha L) \simeq 1/\alpha L$. The error in this assumption is smaller than 10 per cent.

‡ The quantity $\cot\psi$ is defined as the ratio of the imaginary part to the real part of the complex impedance of a resonator.

§ The distance in which the intensity drops by a factor 2 is defined as half-value layer: $HL = ln2/2\alpha = 0.345/\alpha$.

The sonic measurement may yield an impedance change, a damping decrement, a bandwidth or a spatial attenuation constant, but all these quantities express the same physical phenomenon: the energy lost per cycle. Some useful relationships between the measurable quantities related to damping are given in Table 8.3. The choice of the quantity that is most suitable measured depends on the kind of the medium and the frequency range, inasmuch as they both determine which analytical technique is most suitable. The approximate definitions for Q and SWR used in this table are valid for small losses ($Q > 5$, or $\tan\varphi \leq 0.1$) with an error of less than 2 per cent.

In geometrical analysis by sound, such as flaw detection, thickness gauging, or determination of cavity volume, the problem is usually simplified inasmuch as no accurate knowledge of absorption is necessary. This quantity enters only as a limiting factor, for example, with regard to depth of penetration. Further, in most devices of this kind the evaluation is based on a comparison with a standard of known dimensions and quality. For example, in flaw detection, an indication of the presence and approximate location of the flaw is usually sufficient. Only in special cases is an attempt made to express the observed deviations from normal in accurate numbers.[5]

Correlation of sonic measurements with physical properties
We have stated that the propagation of sound waves is described by a velocity c and an attenuation α or by any one of the complex quantities k^*, c^*, or Y^*. Each of these quantities is a macroscopic manifestation of one or more basic properties of matter. The reaction of the medium to the periodic condensations, deformation or stresses produced by a sound wave is characteristic of the physical state of the medium. The common distinction between gaseous, liquid, and solid state is based on the three fundamental forms of packing and structure in which the building blocks of matter can be arranged. In the study of the underlying forces of interaction, sonic methods assume a position similar to those of optical, electrical, chemical, and thermodynamic methods. In combination with these other methods, sonic measurements may assist one to achieve an objective of all physical research: to relate a maximum of different responses to a minimum of causes.

We may ask which basic physical properties of matter are significantly related to sonically measurable quantities. For gases and liquids this question is discussed from a microscopic, molecular point of view in the appendix to this book. To apply the same point of view to solids is beyond the scope of this book, since this would require a considerable amount of background in solid-state physics.[6] Pertinent information on ultrasonic propagation in solids, as related to non-destructive testing, is given in Section 8.8. Some important aspects of the response to elastic strains of matter in gaseous, liquid, or solid form are summarized in Table 8.4. We note the increasing complexity of such interaction mechanisms as the closeness of packing

---

[5] Benson Carlin *Ultrasonics*, McGraw-Hill, New York, 1949.

[6] *Introduction to Solid State Physics* by C. Kittel, John Wiley & Sons, New York, 1953. One notable relationship between lattice forces and compressibility is expressed by the socalled *Grüneisen rule;* see C. Zwikker, *Physical Properties of Solid Materials*, Interscience Publishers, New York, 1954, Chapter *VI*, § 5.

Table 8.4   The response of matter to elastic strains.

Physical Property	Gases	Liquids	Solids
Main determining factor for compressibility	$\gamma = \dfrac{C_p}{C_v}$ and M	Packing factor s of molecules c = constant $\times s$ (constant $\simeq 5000$ m/sec)	Lattice forces (Grüneisen's rule)
Elastic bulk modulus	$\gamma P_0 = \rho_0 c^2$ $P_0 \rho_0$ = const. $\times v_m{}^2$	$\gamma/\beta_{is} = \rho_0 c^2$	$\lambda' + 2\mu = \rho_0 c^2$ $= Y_0 \dfrac{1 - \sigma}{(1 + \sigma)(1 - 2\sigma)}$ Isotropic case: $\lambda' + 2\mu = c_{11}$
Elastic shear modulus	None	Present in liquids of high s and then derived from viscosity η	$\mu = Y_0/2(1 + \sigma)$ Isotropic case: $\mu = (c_{12} - c_{11})/2$
Elastic anisotropy	None	In some birefringent + polar liquids	In single crystals
Number of elastic constants c_{hk}	1	1 (in some polar liquids and, in very viscous liquids, 2)	Isotropic 2 Cubic 3 Hexagonal and trigonal 5 Tetragonal 6 Rhombic 9
Geometrical boundary effects on velocity	Negligible, except for ducts of capillary cross section	In tubes; dispersion due to cross modes	In rods, plates, bars: dispersion due to crossmodes; special wave types
Electrical or magnetic effects	Interaction with gas discharges	Electrostriction in some polar liquids	Ferroelectricity Piezoelectricity Magnetostriction
Optical effects $\dfrac{dn}{n}$ = const. $\times \dfrac{d\rho}{\rho}$	Main significance in shock-wave studies	Schlieren + diffraction methods, mainly at higher frequencies (>1 mcps)	Photoelastic effects with polarized light
X-ray effects	None	Shock waves only μ_x/ρ = const. $\times A$	Shock waves; also scattering from Debye heat waves
Main cause of losses	Thermal collisions	Viscosity and structure	Hysteresis in plastics and rubbers; scattering at grain boundaries and heat conduction in metals
Effect of phase transition	Extrema for c and α at critical point	$c_{gas}/c_{liquid} \simeq 1 - s$	For metals: $c_{melt} \simeq c_l$ high α at melting point

Definition of Symbols

c = bulk velocity
γ = specific heat ratio
ρ_0 = density
β_{is} = isothermal compressibility
$s = \dfrac{4}{3}\pi R_m{}^3 \dfrac{N}{V}$ packing factor
V = molar volume
R_m = molecular radius

N = Avogadro's number
α = absorption coefficient
$M = \rho_0 V$ molecular weight
v_m = mean molecular velocity in a gas
n = index of refraction
C_p, C_v = specific heats
Y_0 = Young's modulus
λ' = elastic Lamé constant

μ = shear modulus
σ = Poissons' ratio
c_{hk} = elastic constant
$c_l = (Y_0/\rho)^{1/2}$ longitudinal velocity (thin rod)
μ_x = mass absorption coefficient for X-rays
A = atomic number
P_0 = hydrostatic pressure

and the structural order increase in the progression from gases to solids.

Classification of sonic techniques The experimental procedures by which the sound velocity and the sound attenuation coefficient are determined through measurements of time, length, and a damping factor may be classified as follows:

   a. Standing-wave techniques.
   b. Continuous progressive-wave techniques.
   c. Reverberation and decay techniques.
   d. Pulse techniques (transmission or reflection).

We shall review the underlying principles of these techniques in the following paragraphs. Some typical examples will illustrate the usefulness of sonic methods for material testing and process control.

In a large number of analytical applications the information derived from one single measurement of this type is insufficient, since the physical response of most media varies characteristically with temperature, pressure, or frequency. In most gases a decrease in pressure is equivalent to an increase in frequency; the significant parameter is the ratio f/p or the equivalent ratio L_m/λ of the mean free path to the wavelength (see Section 6.3), which determines the collision probability per cycle.[7] In some solids, on the other hand, an increase in frequency is equivalent to a decrease in temperature.[8]

Thus, for many substances, a complete analysis requires the determination of the dependence of the complex propagation constant on one or several of the parameters frequency, pressure, or temperature. For certain substances which are characterized by a relatively sharp transition of physical state it is sufficient to determine the position of the attenuation maximum as a function of temperature or time or other relevant variable. This is the case, for example, in the control of the state of polymerization of thermosetting plastics.[9] A similar situation exists in the processing of viscous fluids, such as oils, syrups, paints, and many colloidal suspensions, whose physical state is characterized by density and shear viscosity. Here a continuous impedance measurement at a fixed frequency and temperature will indicate

---

[7] *Ultrasonic Physics*, by E. G. Richardson, Elsevier, Amsterdam, New York, 1952, p. 128.

[8] A behavior of this kind is observed in rubber-like materials: A. W. Nolle, *J. Polymer Sci.*, *5* (1950), 1, p. 3.

[9] G. A. Sofer and E. A. Hauser, *J. Polymer Sci.*, *8* (1952), 611. This report reveals that an ultrasonic pulse technique (2.4 mcps) permits a rapid determination of the degree of cure of resins such as methyl methacrylate, Laminac, and Resinox.

or control the condition of the fluid at any time of the processing cycle.[10]

8.2   Resonance Techniques

Formal expressions for standing waves were introduced in Section 2.9 (see eq. 2.39 and 2.40 in terms of acoustic transmission-line theory. We have already used these expressions in the analysis of resonant crystals and sandwich transducers. Thus we are aware that the specific acoustic impedance $\rho_0 c[\phi]$ which is measured at the input of a finite column of a medium (gaseous, liquid, or solid) depends on the acoustic termination of the column and varies periodically with the length of the column. These relationships are fundamental to all standing-wave techniques, although there are many possible methods of analyzing the variations of specific acoustic impedance.

Most easily observed are resonance effects, which may take place in two alternative forms: either as half-wave resonance, if the impedance Z_t of the termination or reflecting surface is transformed to the input of the column in the ratio 1:1, i.e., $Z_i = Z_t$; or as quarter-wave resonance, where Z_t is transformed into an input impedance equal to

$$Z_i = \rho_0 c[\phi]_{l=\lambda/4} \simeq (\rho_0 c)^2/Z_t$$

Both types of resonance were studied in connection with transducers in Chapter 4, and they are equally useful in such techniques as sonic interferometry, plate transmission, or the determination of resonant bandwidth.

Simple resonance techniques have their main application at low frequencies, using either lumped systems in which the sample to be tested acts as a lossy spring, or distributed systems such as a resonant bar or strip made out of the sample material.

Resonant lumped systems   One classic example of a resonant lumped system is the so-called Helmholtz resonator.[11]   As shown in Fig. 8.1a, it consists of a gas-filled cavity of volume V and a constriction of cross section S and effective length l_e.[12]   The cavity

[10] J. A. Woodward, *J. Acoust. Soc. Amer.*, *25* (1953), 147.   W. Roth and S. R. Rich, *J. Appl. Phys.*, *24* (1953), 940.   The principle of operation of such impedometers is discussed in Section 8.6.

[11] L. E. Kinsler and A. R. Frey, *Fundamentals of Acoustics* Chapter 8, John Wiley & Sons, New York, 1950.   See also P. M. Morse, *Vibration and Sound* 2nd edition, p. 235, McGraw-Hill, New York, 1948.

[12] Since some air beyond the ends of the constriction moves along with the air in the constriction, an effective length $l_e > l$ must be used in calculating the resonator impedance.   It turns out that $l_e \simeq l + 0.8S^{1/2}$.

volume acts as a spring of a compliance $C = V\beta_a = V/\rho_0 c^2$, and the gas in the constriction represents a mass which is analogous to an inductance $L = \rho_0 l_e/S$, where ρ_0 is the density and c the sound velocity of the gas in the cavity.[13] The acoustic impedance of the Helmholtz resonator is then

$$Z = R + j\left(\omega L - \frac{1}{\omega C}\right) \tag{8.5}$$

in which the damping due to sound radiation from the orifice is represented by a resistance $R \simeq \rho_0 \omega^2/2\pi c$. For small damping the react-

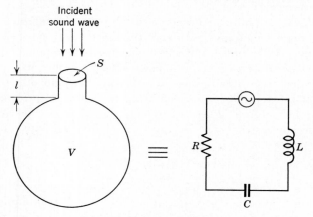

Fig. 8.1a. Helmholtz resonator and its equivalent circuit.

ances in eq. 8.5 cancel at a resonance frequency

$$\omega_0 = c\left(\frac{S}{l_e V}\right)^{1/2} \tag{8.6}$$

and the quality factor of the resonator becomes

$$Q = \frac{\omega L}{R} \simeq 2\pi \frac{c}{\omega_0} \frac{l_e}{S} \tag{8.7}$$

It is important to note that this expression holds only for small ratios l_e/S where viscous losses in the constriction can be neglected. It turns out that eq. 8.7 is valid only for $Q \lesssim 10$. At higher values of Q the damping term R in eq. 8.5 must be modified to include viscous losses.

[13] The quantities ωL and $1/\omega C$ are "acoustic" impedances. Note that according to Section 2.9 acoustic impedance Z_A and mechanical impedance Z_M are related as $Z_A = Z_M/(\text{area})^2$.

The orifice impedance then becomes non-linear, and the maximum attainable Q is limited to values less than about 50.[14]

Sonic cavitometry It is apparent from eq. 8.6 and Fig. 8.1*a* that cavity resonance provides a convenient way of measuring the volume V of a cavity which is coupled to a constriction of known dimensions. In this method (see Fig. 8.1*b*) a constant velocity source G (high internal impedance) is coupled to the constriction O and the pressure amplitudes in the cavity V are detected by a probe microphone M. By means of a closed feedback loop L the system will then resonate at the frequency of cavity resonance.

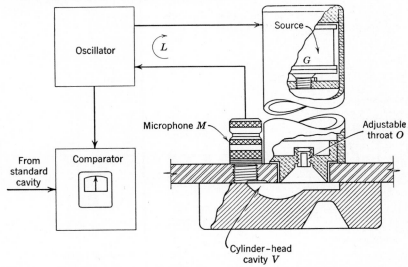

Fig. 8.1*b*.   System for sonic cavitometry.   Courtesy of Poole Manufacturing Co., Houston, Texas.

In practice, the frequency of a standard cavity is compared with the frequency of the test cavity which eliminates the influence of fluctuations of the ambient temperature or humidity on the compressibility of the gas.   Deviations of the test volume from the standard volume appear as a frequency difference or a phase shift which can be measured electronically and used to operate a reject mechanism or warning signal. Sonic cavitometry in the frequency range from 50 to 500 cps thus makes possible the automatic production control of critical volumes, such as in automobile cylinder heads, certain types of containers, or bore holes.[15]

[14] U. Ingard, *J. Acoust. Soc. Amer.*, *25* (1953), 1037.
[15] F. M. Poole, *Product Eng.*, January 1949, p. 93.

The rocking-beam oscillator   Another example of a lumped system operating between 0.1 and 30 cps is the so-called rocking-beam oscillator illustrated in Fig. 8.2.[16]   This device has been employed to determine the complex modulus $Y^* = K^*l/S$ of rubber samples of length l and cross-sectional area S.   The sample provides the restoring force $F = K^*y$ for an oscillating beam of known effective mass M_b.[17] The resonance frequency $\omega_b = (K^*/M_b)^{1/2}$ of the system can be adjusted by changing the position of the weights shown in Fig. 8.2. The quantities measured are ω_b and the bandwidth B or quality factor

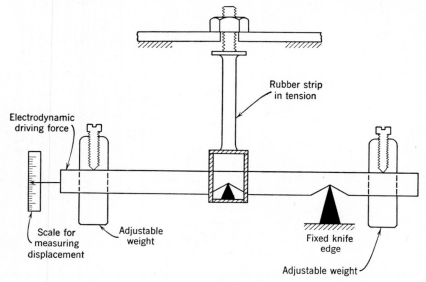

Fig. 8.2.   Rocking-beam oscillator (A. W. Nolle).

$Q = \omega_b/B$ which the system exhibits if it is excited electrodynamically. For small losses ($Q \geq 5$) the complex modulus is given with an error of less than 2 per cent by

$$Y^* \simeq \omega_b{}^2 \frac{l}{S} M_b \left[1 - j \frac{1}{Q} \right] \qquad (8.8)$$

[16] A. W. Nolle, *J. Appl. Phys.*, *19* (1948), 753.

[17] The effective mass of the rocking-beam oscillator is found by substituting a spring for the rubber sample, and using a relationship:

$$M_b = M_0(\omega_0/\omega)^2$$

in which ω_0 is the natural frequency of the spring in combination with a known mass M_0, and ω is the natural frequency of the same spring connected to the rocking beam.

The phase angle ψ of the mechanical impedance is obtained (see Table 8.2) by:

$$\cot \psi = \left| \frac{Y^*_{IM}}{Y^*_{RE}} \right| \simeq \frac{1}{Q} \qquad (8.9)$$

These relationships characterize the viscoelastic properties of rubber-like materials for a given temperature and a specific static prestressing.

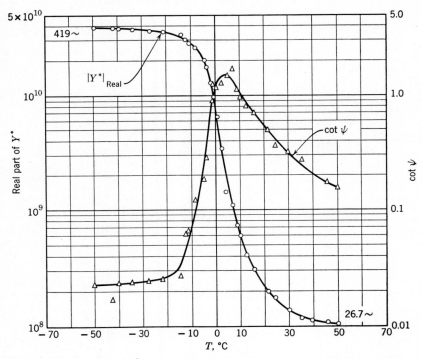

Fig. 8.3. Variation of elastic modulus and loss factor with temperature in a typical rubber (A. W. Nolle).

It is therefore important to provide means for accurate control of these parameters, irrespective of the type of sonic measuring technique used. As a typical example of the effects of temperature, Fig. 8.3 shows data obtained on a Buna-N carbon-loaded synthetic rubber in the frequency range from 30 cps to 400 cps. We note that the loss factor $\cot \psi$ shows a pronounced peak near 5°C. This peak will shift to higher temperatures as the frequency is increased, and its position in an ω, T diagram is characteristic of the relaxational behavior of a rubber. (See Appendix).

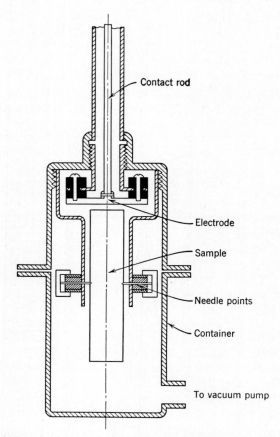

Fig. 8.4.   Electrostatic excitation of resonant metal bar (P. G. Bordoni).

Resonant-bar methods   At higher frequencies, systems with distributed mass and stiffness are used.   The loss factor is related to $\Delta\omega$, the frequency shift required for a drop of the vibration amplitude to $1/\sqrt{2}$ of its resonant value by:

$$\cot\psi \simeq 1.55\,\frac{2\,\Delta\omega}{\omega_0} \qquad (8.10)[18]$$

A typical arrangement of this type which is suitable for measurements on solids in the frequency range between 10 and 50 cps is illustrated in Fig. 8.4.[19]   A half-wave resonant bar is supported at the

[18] G. G. Parfitt, *Brit. J. Appl. Phys.*, *2* (1951), 327.

[19] D. Bancroft and R. B. Jacobs, *Rev. Sci. Instr.*, *9* (1938), 279.   P. G. Bordoni, *J. Acoust. Soc. Amer.*, *26* (1954), 495.

nodal plane by needle points. It is excited by electrostatic forces (see Table 4.8) acting between a stationary electrode and one end of the bar. The changes of the capacity of the electrode gap due to the bar vibration are used to modulate the frequency of an RF oscillator ($\omega_{bar} \ll \omega_{osc} \simeq 10^6$ cps). The output voltage of an FM disciminator which is connected to this RF circuit is proportional to the amplitude of vibration. The rod is housed in a closed, temperature-controlled chamber which is evacuated to avoid damping by the surrounding medium.[20]

The resonant-rod technique may be modified in various ways. A typical system for the analysis of small samples of viscoelastic materials or of adhesive bonds is depicted in Fig. 8.5.[21] One may compare the damping of a continuous half-wave bar with a split bar of the same material whose two quarter-wave sections are joined together by the adhesive to be tested, as shown in Fig. 8.5a. Alternatively, one may load a standard half-wave bar at one end by a test sample which is backed by a quarter-wave section, as illustrated in Fig. 8.5b. The first technique is especially suited for the testing of rigid adhesives since the sample is located at a stress maximum.[22] In the second case the sample is held under static compression between the very high impedance presented by the air-backed quarter-wave rod and the low impedance presented by the face of the half-wave driving bar. This technique is therefore most suitable for highly compliant adhesives or rubber-like materials. The half-wave bar may be driven electrostatically (see Fig. 8.4) or magnetically.[23] Both techniques shown in Fig. 8.5 use an electrostatic pick-up to measure the relative amplitude of vibration of the rod assembly. The effect of the added compliance of the sample on the mechanical impedance of the rod can be analyzed by means of the equivalent circuits given in Fig. 8.5. We note that in case a the compliance C_1 of the sample acts as a shunt to the compliance C_0, whereas in case b it is connected in series. It follows from these circuits that, with suitable approximations, the real part of the complex elastic modulus of the sample is given by

[20] The various causes of damping due to the surrounding medium have been discussed by H. O. Kneser, *Z. angew. Phys.*, *3* (1951), 113.

[21] A. W. Nolle and P. J. Westervelt, *J. Appl. Phys.*, *21* (1950), 304.

[22] A. G. H. Dietz, H. N. Bockstruck, and G. Epstein, *Special Tech. Pub.* 138, *Am. Soc. Testing Materials* (1952), 40.

[23] Magnetic excitation may be achieved by means of the eddy currents induced at one end of a metal bar, as described by R. H. Randall, F. C. Rose, and C. Zener, *Phys. Rev.*, *56* (1939), 343, or by means of a driving coil attached to the bar, as shown by K. W. Hillier, *Proc. Phys. Soc. (London), B, 64* (1951), 998. Magnetostrictive excitation has been discussed by A. W. Nolle, *loc. cit.* (see footnote 16).

Case (a): $\left| Y^*{}_{\mathrm{RE}} \right| \simeq \dfrac{\rho l b \omega_0{}^2}{\pi^2} \dfrac{\omega_c}{\omega_0 - \omega_c}$ (8.11a)

Case (b): $\left| Y^*{}_{\mathrm{RE}} \right| \simeq \rho l b \omega_c (\omega_0 - \omega_c)$ (8.11b)

in which ρ is the density of the bar material. For the phase angle of the impedance of the sample we obtain

$$\cot \psi = \frac{\left| Y^*{}_{\mathrm{IM}} \right|}{\left| Y^*{}_{\mathrm{RE}} \right|} \simeq \pm \frac{1}{2} \frac{\Delta \omega_c - \Delta \omega_0}{\omega_0 - \omega_c} \qquad (8.12)$$

in which the positive sign applies to case a and the negative sign to case b. The meaning of the various quantities occurring in eqs. 8.11 and 8.12 is apparent from Fig. 8.5. The error involved in these

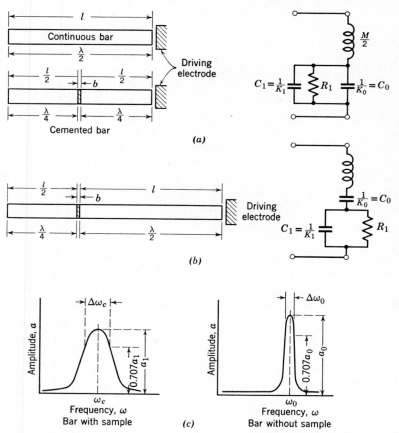

Fig. 8.5.   Dynamic testing of adhesive bonds (A. G. H. Dietz).

approximate expressions is less than 5 per cent if $\Delta\omega_c/\omega < 0.1$ and $(\omega_c - \omega_0)/\omega_0 < 0.05$. For lower values of Q the analysis becomes more complicated, since the elastic modulus and loss factor are not necessarily constant within the bandwidth of the resonator.[24]

Another variation of the resonant-bar method uses torsional vibrations. One such system which is driven by electrodynamic forces is illustrated in Fig. 8.6.[25] A three-quarter-turn loop driving coil is attached to the free end of a rigidly supported quarter-wave bar. The interaction between a current flowing through the loop and a

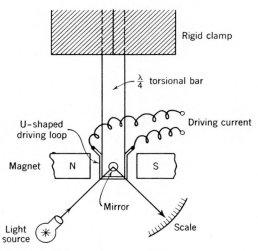

Fig. 8.6. Torsional resonant system for the determination of the complex shear modulus of solids.

strong magnetic field produces a driving torque. The angular strain is determined by a light beam reflected from a small mirror attached to the end of the bar. The dynamics of such a torsional system are discussed in Section 7.10 (see eqs. 7.48 to 7.50). With the use of the equivalent circuit shown in Fig. 8.5a expressions can be derived for the complex shear modulus which are similar to those given in eqs. 8.11a and 8.12.

[24] An excellent summary of the theories related to the dynamic analysis of elastic properties is found in *Stress Waves in Solids*, Chapters 5 and 6, by H. Kolsky, Clarendon Press, Oxford, 1953.

[25] This method implies the use of a non-conductive rod material in which eddy-current effects are absent. See J. J. Benbow, *Jour. Scientific Instr.* (London), *30* (1953), 412.

8.3 Optical Analysis of Standing Waves

So far we have discussed techniques which employ electrical means for the analysis of resonances in suitably shaped samples. For one class of substances, both liquid and solid, which is characterized by transparency to light, optical methods are available for the measurement of elastic constants. These methods are limited to the higher ultrasonic frequencies ($f > 1$ mcps), and they do not generally yield information on losses.[26] For a determination of sound velocity, however, they have some advantage over other methods since they require only small quantities of the test material. Optical techniques

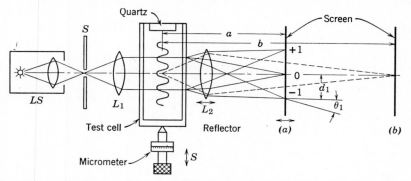

Fig. 8.7. Optical determination of sound velocities in liquids. For screen position (a) the lens L_2 produces an image of the slot S at 0; for screen position (b) the lens L_2 can be adjusted to form an image of the standing wave in the test cell.

are ideally suited for the analysis of the elastic properties of single crystals and glasses.

Light passing through a transparent medium carrying standing waves of sound is diffracted in a manner similar to the way it is diffracted by an optical grating.[27] This effect is caused by the periodic compressions and rarefactions in the sound field; the amount of interaction between light and matter is proportional to the number of atoms or molecules which are present in a given volume element.[28] This phenomenon allows a determination of the periodicity of a stationary sound field in two ways, as illustrated in Fig. 8.7. A slit S is illuminated by a monochromatic light source LS. By means of a set of two lenses L and L_2, an image of the slit is formed in a plane

[26] An optical analysis of losses is possible in progressive waves and is discussed in Section 8.5.

[27] Criteria for ultrasonic light diffraction effects are discussed in L. Bergmann, "Der Ultraschall," and by G. W. Willard, *J. Acoust. Soc. Amer.*, *21* (1949), 101.

[28] See Section A.5, footnote 38.

located at (a). The lenses are so adjusted that the light between them is parallel as it passes through the flat glass walls of a small test cell. A standing sound wave is set up in the cell between the quartz crystal and the reflector, with parallelism between the wave fronts of the sound and the optical axis of the system. In order to produce the desired diffraction effects, the width of the light beam must be larger than the wavelength of the sound. This condition can be easily met at ultrasonic frequencies above 10^6 cps.

Measurements of light diffraction in liquids One modification of the optical method makes use of the diffraction pattern formed on a screen, located at (a) in Fig. 8.7. The angles of diffraction are given by

$$\sin \theta_n = \frac{n\lambda_0}{\lambda} = n\lambda_0 \frac{f}{c} \tag{8.13}$$

in which θ_n is the angle between the direct slit image and the diffracted image of nth order, λ_0 is the wavelength of the light and λ the wavelength of the sound, c is the velocity, and f the frequency, of the sound wave.[29] If a is the normal distance between the axis of the sound beam and the screen at a, and d_n is the distance between the zero-order and the nth-order slit images on the screen, we may write, assuming $a > 10^2 d_n$:

$$c \simeq n\lambda_0 f \frac{a}{d_n} \tag{8.14}[30]$$

The accuracy of this method is illustrated by the following example. At a frequency of 20 mcps, a focal length of L_2 of 2 m and a sound velocity of the order of 10^3 m/sec, the use of green light results in a spacing of the diffraction images of about 2 cm. This distance can be measured with an error of about 0.05 per cent using a narrow slit and a micrometer microscope.

Light-diffraction patterns in solids (photoelasticity) Let us replace the test cell in Fig. 8.7 by a transparent solid cube, e.g., of glass. The cube may be excited with high-frequency vibrations by a thin quartz crystal coupled through an oil film to one of its faces. Multiple reflections and mode coupling at the boundaries (see Section 3.5) produce within the sample a three-dimensional system of standing waves of both the compressional bulk type and the transverse shear

[29] This diffraction effect is commonly called the Debye-Sears effect, since it was first reported by P. Debye and F. W. Sears in *Proc. Nat. Acad. Sci. Wash.*, *18* (1932), 410.

[30] The corrections necessary, if a is not much larger than d_n and if account is taken of the refraction between the liquid in the test cell and the surrounding air, are discussed by W. Schaaffs, *Ergeb. exakt. Naturw.*, *25* (1951), 122.

type.   Let us also replace the slit in Fig. 8.7 by a small pinhole.   The light is then diffracted by the elastic strain lattice to produce regular systems (circles, ellipses, or higher-order contours) on the screen, which closely correspond to the Laue diagrams obtained by X-ray diffraction in crystals.[31]

As an example, the diffraction patterns observed in glass, quartz, and lithium fluoride are shown in Fig. 8.8.   We note that from the specified diameters of the diffraction rings one can compute the various elastic constants.   For isotropic materials like glass one simply obtains two diffraction rings of radius r_t and r_l.   The larger ring is

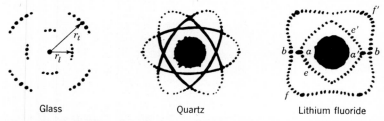

| Glass | Quartz | Lithium fluoride |

Fig. 8.8.   Typical diffraction patterns obtained by optical analysis of vibrating solids (L. Bergmann).   The geometry of the pattern allows the direct determination of the elastic constants.   For example, in LiF which belongs to the cubic system and has three elastic constants (c_{11}, c_{12}, and c_{44}), the following relations hold: $c_{11} = C/(a - a')^2$, $c_{44} = C/(b - b')^2$, $c_{11} - c_{12} = 2C/(f - f)^2$,   and $c_{11} + c_{12} + 2c_{44} = 2C/(e - e')^2$,   in which C is a constant depending on A, λ_0, and f (see text).

produced by the shear waves whose smaller wavelength, according to eq. 8.13, produces a larger angle of diffraction.   The shear modulus is then given by

$$\mu = (A\lambda_0 f/r_t)^2 \rho = c_s{}^2 \rho \qquad (8.15)$$

in which A is the distance between the center of the specimen and the screen, ρ is the density of the specimen, f is the ultrasonic frequency, and c_s is the velocity of the shear waves.   From eq. 8.14 it follows that $r_l/r_t = c_b/c_s$, and with the use of eqs. 2.26 we obtain for Poisson's ratio:

$$\sigma = \frac{2 - (r_l/r_t)^2}{2 - 2(r_l/r_t)^2}$$

$$= \frac{2 - (c_b/c_s)^2}{2 - 2(c_b/c_s)^2} \qquad (8.16)$$

[31] For theoretical details of these phenomena see W. H. Zachariasen, *Theory of X-Ray Diffraction in Crystals*, John Wiley & Sons, New York, 1944; and H. Mueller, *Phys. Rev.* (2), *52* (1937), 223.

In anisotropic solids the analysis is complicated in that the observed patterns depend on the orientation of the light beam to the crystal axes, and on the planes of polarization of the light.[32] For example, if a purely compressional wave is set up in a crystal, e.g., in the x and z directions in quartz (see Section 4.2, eq. 4.11) the intensity of the diffracted light depends on the angle θ between the plane of optical polarization and the wave front of the standing sound wave. Specifically, the ratio between the light intensity $\mathbf{I}_{\parallel}$ obtained for $\theta = 0$ to the intensity $\mathbf{I}_{\perp}$ for $\theta = 90°$ is equal to the square of the ratio of the associated photoelastic stress constants p_{ik}.[33] In the case of X-cut quartz one obtains:[34]

$$\mathbf{I}_{\parallel}/\mathbf{I}_{\perp} = (p_{11}/p_{12})^2 \qquad (8.17)$$

The method of secondary interferences Let us return to Fig. 8.7, in which we move the screen to position (b) at a distance $b > a$, from the test cell. We are now able to adjust a lens L_2, of suitable focal length l_f (approximately $a < l_f < b$) to produce on the screen an image of the ultrasonic wave pattern in the test cell. This is made possible by secondary interference of the light which has been diffracted into the various orders according to eq. 8.13. To show this we may visualize the periodic compressions and rarefactions in the sound wave as a parallel array of cylindrical lenses. The refraction of these lenses will cause the individual rays of the lightbeam to cross over several times after emerging from the sound field. The cross-over region constitutes an interference field of the same periodicity as the primary grating. In a standing wave this leads to an image of a periodicity of $\lambda/2$. If the magnification of the lens L_2 is $\mathbf{m}$, and if s is the spacing between n bright lines of the screen image, the sound velocity is given by

$$c = \frac{f}{\mathbf{m}} \frac{s}{n-1} \qquad (8.18a)$$

In place of a determination of $\mathbf{m}$, one may perform a measurement on a known liquid of sound velocity c_0 leading to a spacing s_0 between n_0 image lines. In this case we obtain:

$$c = c_0(n_0 - 1)s/s_0(n - 1) \qquad (8.18b)$$

In a third measuring technique, the test cell is moved in the direction of the sound beam by a micrometer, and the number n of lines which pass through a scale or cross-hair in an ocular for a given micrometer displacement s is counted. This leads to:

$$c = 2fs/(n - 1) \qquad (8.18c)$$

---

[32] C. L. Schaefer and L. Bergmann, (*Sitzber. Berliner Akad. Wiss. Phys. Math. Kl.*, *14* (1935), 222, and E. Fues and H. Ludloff, *ibid.*, p. 225.

[33] A determination of the constants p_{ik} in various materials is of importance for photoelastic stress analysis and for shock-wave studies. See, for example, H. Mueller, *Z. Krist. (A)*, *99* (1938), 122, and H. Schardin and W. Struth, *Glastech. Ber.*, *16* (1938), 219.

[34] J. K. Galt, *Phys. Rev. (2)*, *73* (1948), 1460.

With the three modifications described of the method of secondary interferences, a relative accuracy of better than 0.001 per cent can be obtained.[35] It should be noted that for high accuracies one must reduce the sound intensity to the minimum value required to produce a clearly perceivable image. The results that have been obtained with these techniques are summarized in Sections A.5 and A.6.[36]

8.4 Interferometric Techniques

We have seen that resonant-bar techniques are used mainly for the evaluation of solid materials, and that optical methods are most suitable for liquids. For gases, on the other hand, the acoustic interferometer has become the standard instrument since it allows determination of both sound velocity and absorption, with high precision. For liquids, both optical and interferometric techniques are applicable with about equal accuracy.

The main range of application of the interferometer is at ultrasonic frequencies ($f > 20$ kcps), while measurements in the audible frequency range are commonly performed with impedance tubes.[37] Both devices are based on the acoustic transmission-line equations 2.39 and 2.40. The difference between them lies in the method of detection of the characteristic properties of the standing wave. In the impedance tube a source of high internal impedance is used to eliminate the reaction of the sound field on the source. A probe measurement of the standing-wave ratio and the location of maxima and minima allows determination of the acoustical properties of the material terminating the tube, or of the gas in the tube. In the interferometer, on the other hand, the reaction of the line impedance on the source under known terminating conditions is determined by electrical measurements of the motional current drawn by the source.

Interferometry in fluids The source commonly consists of an air-backed piezoelectric crystal mounted at one end of a fluid column and an adjustable rigid reflector at the other end, as shown in Fig. 8.9.

[35] C. Bachem and E. Hiedemann, *Z. Phys.*, *94* (1935), 68. E. Schreuer, *Akust. Z.*, *4* (1939), 215.

[36] Two other modifications of the optical method should be mentioned: the Schlieren technique and the divergent light technique. The Schlieren principle will be discussed in Section 8.5 dealing with progressive waves. The divergent light technique is extremely simple, since it does not require lenses. It operates as follows: if divergent light from a line source parallel to the ultrasonic wave fronts falls through the test cell on a screen, one observes a line pattern which can be analyzed by use of eq. 8.18c. See L. Bergmann and H. J. Goehlich, *Phys. Z.*, *38* (1937), 9, and W. Schaaffs, *op. cit.* p. 131, see Footnote 30.

[37] L. L. Beranek, *Acoustic Measurements*, Chapter 7, John Wiley & Sons, New York, 1949.

One may vary either the path length l at constant frequency or the frequency at fixed path length; in both cases the ratio l/λ is changed. According to eq. 2.39 this will reflect as a change of the input impedance of a rigidly terminated $(\alpha_0 = 0, \ \beta = \pi/2)$ transmission line.

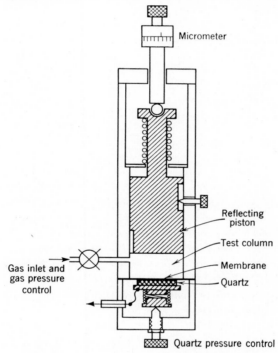

Fig. 8.9. Ultrasonic interferometer for gases.

Using $k^* = (\omega/c) - j\alpha$ (see eq. 8.2) we obtain for the load impedance of the interferometer crystal:

$$Z_L = A \ \tanh\left[\alpha l + j\left(\frac{\omega}{c} l + \frac{\pi}{2}\right)\right]$$

$$= A \ \coth\left[\alpha l + j\frac{\omega}{c} l\right] \simeq \rho_0 c \ \coth \ (jk^*l) \qquad (8.19)$$

in which α is the linear attenuation coefficient of the medium.[38]

[38] If the impedance $\rho_R c_R$ of the reflector cannot be assumed to be infinite compared with the medium of the interferometer column, as, for example, in liquids, eq. 8.19 assumes the form

$$Z_L \simeq \rho_0 c \ \frac{\coth \ (jk^*l) + \rho_0 c/\rho_R c_R}{1 + (\rho_0 c/\rho_R c_R) \coth \ (jk^*l)}$$

The quantity $A = \rho_0 c \Big/ \left(1 - j\,\dfrac{ac}{\omega}\right)$ is a constant for variable-path interferometers, but depends on frequency for fixed-path interferometers. Often $ac/\omega \ll 1$ and A is simply the specific acoustic impedance $\rho_0 c$ of the fluid.

We shall discuss only the theory of fixed-frequency variable-path interferometers which are the type most commonly used in fluids.[39] Consider a crystal transducer driven from a source E_0, R_0 at resonance, and with the static capacity C_0 tuned out by an inductance L_0. The equivalent circuit of Fig. 4.5 then takes the form shown in Fig. 8.10a, in which R_{HR} represents the losses caused by mounting and by radiation from the back of the transducer. The current i into the crystal then is:

$$i = \frac{E_0}{R_0 + (R_{\mathrm{HR}} + Z_L)/4\alpha^2} \tag{8.20}$$

If the path length of the interferometer is varied, Z_L goes through a maximum whenever $\omega l/c = n\pi$. Hence for an integral number of half wavelengths the current reaches a minimum. This allows us to determine the sound velocity by counting the number n of current dips occurring for a given displacement l of the reflector, which yields $c = (2l/n)f$. A typical plot of i versus l is shown in Fig. 8.10b. From such a plot and by using eqs. 8.19 and 8.20 one can determine the sound attenuation by the relation

$$\tanh \alpha l = \left(\frac{(i_m/i_r - 1)(i_m/i_0 - i_m/i_a)}{(i_m/i_0 - 1)(i_m/i_a - 1)}\right)^{1/2} \tag{8.21}$$

in which i_r and i_a are the corresponding values of the upper and lower envelope of the oscillating current curve at the distance x, i.e., i_r is the locus of the resonance and i_a in the locus of the antiresonance of the interferometer column. The quantities i_m and i_0 are the values of i_r and i_a, respectively, extrapolated to $l = 0$.

For large values of αl, the variation i_a with l is small, and both the denominator and the second numerator factor in eq. 8.21 are approxi-

[39]A general theory of the acoustic interferometer on the basis of eqs. 4.51 for motional transducer impedance is given by F. E. Borgnis, Calif. Inst. of Tech., Norman Bridge Laboratory of Physics, *Tech. Rept.* 3, January 25, 1952. See also R. D. Fay and J. White, *J. Acoust. Soc. Amer.*, 20 (1948), 98, and W. P. Mason, *Piezoelectric Crystals and Their Application to Ultrasonics*, Van Nostrand, New York, 1950, pp. 314–320.

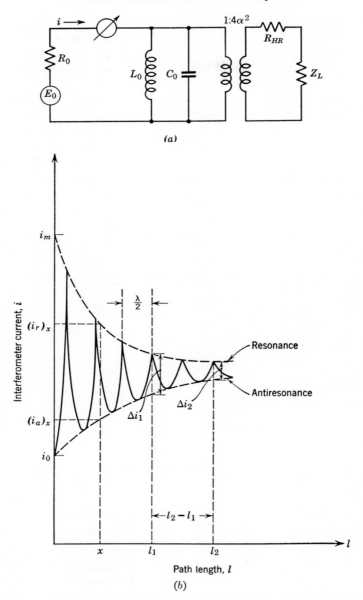

Fig. 8.10. *a,* Equivalent circuit for acoustic interferometry. *b,* Plot of interferometer current versus path length, facilitating the evaluation of *c* and α.

mately constant. One may then determine i_r at two distances l_1 and l_2 and take the ratio:

$$\frac{\tanh \alpha l_1}{\tanh \alpha l_2} \simeq \left(\frac{1/i_{r_1} - 1/i_m}{1/i_{r_2} - 1/i_m}\right)^{\frac{1}{2}}$$

which with $i_r \ll i_m$ and for $\alpha l \gg 1$ reduces to the simple approximation:

$$2\alpha \approx \frac{\ln\,(i_{r_1}/i_{r_2})}{l_2 - l_1} \tag{8.22}$$

The electronic circuitry used to measure the reaction of the interferometer impedance on the source must meet two main requirements:[40] (a) high-frequency stability for the accurate determination

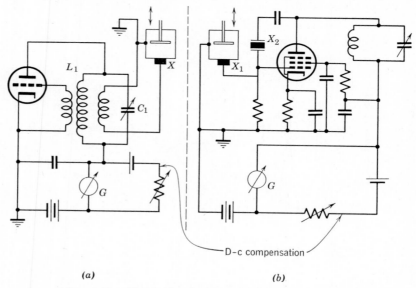

(a)   (b)

Fig. 8.11.   Simple circuits for acoustic interferometer.

of velocity, (b) high sensitivity to changes of the motional current, for the evaluation of absorption. Two simple circuits which provide sufficient accuracy for many purposes are presented in Fig. 8.11. In Fig. 8.11a the interferometer crystal X is coupled inductively to a tuned-plate oscillator circuit L_1C_1. The changes of the motional

[40] Details on the design of such circuits are given for gas interferometers by A. Van Itterbeck and W. Van Doninck, *Proc. Phys. Soc.* (*London*), *62* (1949), 62, and for liquid interferometers by D. R. McMillan, Jr., and R. T. Lagemann, *J. Acoust. Soc. Amer.*, *19* (1947), 956.

part of the plate current are detected in the galvanometer G by means of d-c compensation. A circuit of this type is suitable for interferometric measurements in liquids where the Q factor of the crystal is low compared with the Q of the parallel L_1C_1 combination. If both liquids and gases are to be examined, a circuit of the type shown in Fig. 8.11b is preferable. Here a second crystal X_2 of high Q is inserted between grid and plate to insure frequency stability.[41]

Ultrasonic thickness gauges In solid materials there is generally no way to vary the path length, but an analysis of standing-wave conditions is possible by finding the fundamental or harmonic resonances of the fixed path. This method is used in a number of commercial instruments to determine the thickness of metal plates or the presence of flaws, such as inclusions in bar stock, lamination in strip steel, or lack of bond in bearing materials on steel back.[42] For the theory underlying these resonant devices the reader is referred to Section 4.12 on transducer sandwiches. The combination of test piece and crystal acts as a coupled system which is characterized by one or several motional impedance loops of the type shown in Fig. 4.14. If the wave number kb in a test piece of thickness b is $n\pi$ ($n = 1, 2, 3, \cdots$) near the frequency of fundamental crystal resonance, a change in frequency by $\Delta f = mc/2b$, ($m = 1, 2, 3 \cdots$) will result in m additional impedance loops. According to the discussion of motional impedance in Section 4.7 each harmonic resonance of the test piece produces a variation in crystal reactance of the form shown in Fig. 4.11.

A frequency-modulated constant-current source may be used to drive the crystal according to the arrangement illustrated in Fig. 8.12. Both modulation of the oscillator and sweep of the detecting CR-scope are actuated by the same motor-driven capacitor. Whenever the frequency coincides with one of the resonances, the vertical deflecting voltage on the scope goes through a dip and peak as in Fig. 4.11, which occurs at horizontal deflections proportional to $nc/2b$. For $n = 1$ and a material of known sound velocity c, the horizontal scale may be directly calibrated in thickness b. For higher values of n one may use the same scale, since

$$f_n = c/2b_n \qquad f_{n+m} = c/2b_{n+m} \qquad \text{and} \qquad \Delta f = mc/2b$$

[41] The circuit of Fig. 8.11b combines in simple form the basic features of the Pierce-type and the Hubbard-type interferometer. See F. W. Pierce, *Proc. Am. Acad. Arts Sci.*, *60* (1925), 271, and J. C. Hubbard, *Phys. Rev.*, *38* (1931), 1011.

[42] U.S. Pat. 2,431,233 and 2,431,234 issued to General Motors Corporation. Instruments of this type are manufactured by Branson Instruments, Inc. at Stamford, Conn. ("Audigage"); by Magnaflux Corporation, Chicago, Ill. ("Sonizon"), and by Sperry Products, Inc., Danbury, Conn. ("Reflectogage").

in which $b_n = b/n$ and $b_{n+m} = b/(n + m)$ are the apparent thicknesses read on the scale.   Combining these equations we obtain

$$\Delta f = f_{n+m} - f_n = \frac{c}{2}\left(\frac{1}{b_{n+m}} - \frac{1}{b_n}\right) \tag{8.23}$$

which yields for the actual thickness

$$b = m\left(\frac{b_{n+m} - b_n}{b_{n+m}b_n}\right) \tag{8.24}$$

We note that no knowledge of the actual harmonic number n is required by this technique, m being the number of spaces between a

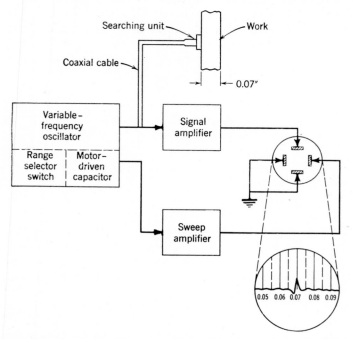

Fig. 8.12.   Schematic diagram of ultrasonic thickness gauge.   ("Sonizon," by Sperry Products, Inc.)

set of harmonic peaks which appear on the scope.   In some commercial instruments, several testing ranges (in steel from about 0.025 in. to 0.3 in.) are provided in combination with associated crystal units.   For larger thicknesses up to 4 in., the harmonic technique discussed above is used.   For curved test pieces, such as pipes or bearing sleeves, curved crystals are available.   The accuracy of this method is of the order of 1 per cent, provided that higher harmonics are used and that the initial calibration is accurate.[43]

Velocity measurements by the coincidence principle An analysis of the elastic constants of isotropic solids may be carried out

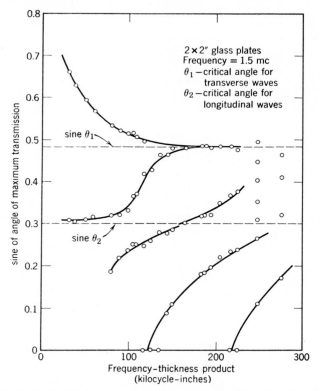

Fig. 8.13.   Angles of maximum transmission through plates versus $f \times b$, according to R. D. Fay.   The branch above sin θ_1 represents the fundamental flexural mode of the plate (see Fig. 3.16).   The S-shaped branch between sin θ_2 and sin θ_1 results from the transition from bar velocity (θ_2) to shear velocity (θ_1).   The remaining branches represent higher modes.

by measuring the angles θ of transmission through a plane parallel plate which is submerged in a coupling liquid.   We saw in Section 3.5 that the coincidence principle leads to selective transmission

---

[43] Near fundamental resonance the three-layer combination metal, oil film and quartz may display special impedance characteristics such as described in Section 4.12.   This phenomenon may lead to considerable error in calibration; see E. G. Cook, Paper G7, presented at 46th meeting of the Acoustical Society of America at Cleveland, Ohio, in October 1953.

maxima through such a plate, owing to space resonance. This occurs whenever the trace velocity of the incident wave is equal to one of the dispersive free velocities in the plate. One may thus determine $\sin \theta = c_{\text{liq}}/c_{\text{plate}}$ as a function of the product of frequency times thickness for the plates under study. The resulting curves obtained with a pulse-transmission technique for a glass plate are shown in Fig. 8.13. We recognize the presence of several modes of propagation for any given value of the product of f and b.[44] The transmission angle θ_2 is

Table 8.5   Elastic Constants of Some Isotropic Solids (typical values)

Velocities (m/sec)	Steel	Copper	Aluminum	Glass	Natural Rubber
Thin bar c_l	5190	3670	5090	5300	46
Thin plate c_p	5420	3900	5410	5460	53
Bulk c_B	5940	4560	6320	5800	1040
Shear c_s	3220	2250	3100	3350	27
Rayleigh wave c_R	2980	2120	2970	3080	26
Density $\rho(\text{kg/m}^3)$	7.8×10^3	8.9×10^3	2.7×10^3	2.5×10^3	0.93×10^3
Elastic constants* (newtons/m^2)					
λ'	11.2×10^{10}	9.6×10^{10}	5.6×10^{10}		
μ	8.1×10^{10}	4.5×10^{10}	2.6×10^{10}		
Y_0	2.1×10^{10}	12×10^{10}	7×10^{10}		
$K_c = \lambda' + \frac{2}{3}\mu$	16.7×10^{10}	12.5×10^{10}	7.3×10^{10}		
Poisson's ratio σ	0.29	0.34	0.34	0.25	0.5

* See footnote 44a. The elastic proerties of polycrystalline metals are strongly affected by the kind of pretreatment, such as annealing or coldworking. See W. Koester and K. Rosenthal, *Z. f. Metallkunde 30* (1938), 345.

associated with the bar velocity which for $fb \to 0$ approaches the value $c_l = (Y_0/\rho)^{1/2}$. The cut-off frequencies at $\sin \theta = 0$ of certain higher modes correspond to half-wave resonances at the bulk velocity

$$c_B = 2\frac{f_{(\theta=0)}b}{n} = c_l \left[\frac{1 - \sigma}{(1 + \sigma)(1 - 2\sigma)} \right]^{1/2}$$

As fb goes to infinity, all the higher modes approach, asymptotically, the velocity of Rayleigh waves, which is slightly lower than that of shear waves (see Section 2.7). It is thus possible to determine c_l, c_B, and σ from angular transmission measurements based on the phenomenon of "space resonance."

Values for the sound velocities, and for the derived elastic constants,

[44] F. Firestone, *J. Nondestructive Testing*, Fall Number, 1948, p. 12. N. Holden, *Nat. Bur. Standard Tech. J., 30* (1951), 956. R. D. Fay and O. Fortier, *J. Acoust. Soc. Amer., 23* (1951), 339.

which have been obtained for five common solids by the various resonance methods discussed in this section, are tabulated in Table 8.5 (see also Table 7.2).[44a]

8.5 Continuous-Wave Propagation Techniques

Wave-propagation methods have the advantage over resonance methods in that a continuous range of frequencies can be covered with a single test sample.   But it is not always possible to provide the conditions necessary for purely progressive waves of a particular type.   In liquids, the test column must be terminated by special absorbers to suppress reflected wave components, unless the losses in the liquid and/or the length of the column are large enough to achieve the same purpose.[45]   In solids only the latter condition can be realized and the progressive-wave method is limited to long lossy rods, strips, or filaments whose diameters are small enough ($d \ll \lambda$) to eliminate velocity dispersion effects.[46]

Phase technique in lossy solids   In Fig. 8.14 is shown a block diagram of the experimental set-up used in work of this kind.[47]   The driving unit can be of piezoelectric, magnetostrictive, or electrodynamic type, depending on the frequency range used.   A longitudinal wave travels along a strip of the material under test, which is suspended between the transducer and a sufficiently remote support. A vibration detector of the phonograph type and of suitable frequency response (see Section 4.14) is moved along the strip.   The output voltage of the detector is compared with the driving voltage by either

[44a] Table 8.5 lists values for the elastic constants λ' and μ, commonly called *Lamé* constants.   The constant μ represents the shear modulus, as defined in eq. 2.26c.   In the absence of shear rigidity ($\mu = 0$) such as in a fluid, the constant λ' is equal to the modulus of volume elasticity: $\lambda' = K_c$.   In solids $\mu \neq 0$ and $K_c = \lambda' + \frac{2}{3}\mu$.   Young's modulus is related to the Lamé constants by $Y_0 = 3\mu K_c/(\lambda' + \mu)$, and Poisson's ratio by $\sigma = \lambda'/2(\lambda' + \mu)$.   For soft rubbers $\sigma \simeq 0.5$ and $Y_0 \simeq 3\mu$.   The sound velocity for solid media in bulk defined in eq. 2.26b can be written as

$$c_B = \left(\frac{\lambda' + 2\mu}{\rho}\right)^{\frac{1}{2}} = \left(\frac{K_c + 4\mu/3}{\rho}\right)^{\frac{1}{2}}$$

[45] Absorbers may consist of ρc rubber wedges, brushes, or steel-wool scatterers imbedded in castor oil; see footnote 18 of Chapter 5.   Conditions for progressive wave propagation in lossy media are expressed in Table 6.1.

[46] T. F. Hueter, *Z. angew. Phys.*, **1** (1949), 274.   R. W. Morse, *J. Acoust. Soc. Amer.*, **20** (1948), 585.

[47] J. W. Ballou and S. Silverman, **16** (1944), 113.   K. W. Hillier and H. Kolsky, *Proc. Phys. Soc. (London)* B **62** (1949), 111.

a phase bridge or a cathode-ray oscilloscope.[48]   If the contact of the detector with the strip generates a reflected wave of r times the amplitude of the incident wave, the observed phase shift φ is related to the sound velocity c_l and sound attenuation αL in the strip by

$$\frac{\tan \varphi}{\tan (\omega L/c)} = \frac{1 + re^{-2\alpha L}}{1 - re^{-2\alpha L}} \qquad (8.25a)$$

which for $r \ll 1$ and $\alpha L > 1$ reduces to

$$c = \frac{\omega L}{\varphi} \qquad (\varphi \text{ in radians}) \qquad (8.25b)$$

Usually the distances L_n are found at which $\varphi = n\pi$ and $L_n = n\lambda/2$. For high values of αL and small values of r, the attenuation coefficient

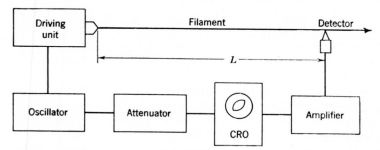

Fig. 8.14.   Analysis of wave propagation in thin filaments and strips (H. Kolsky).

may be simply determined from the attenuator setting required to keep the signal amplitudes balanced as L is increased by a known amount, or it may be found from a logarithmic sound-level recording of receiver amplitude versus distance, by taking the slope of the recorded curve.

A similar technique may be applied to liquids.[49]   It has been used mainly for absorption measurements in conjunction with radiation-pressure-sensitive detectors, such as small reflecting solid spheres or torsional vanes.[50]

In some testing applications the degree of sound transmission from a sound source through an immersed test object to a receiving element

[48] M. Levy, *Elec. Commun.*, *18* (1940), 206.

[49] P. Tamarkin, *J. Acoust. Soc. Amer.*, *21* (1949), 612.

[50] F. E. Fox and G. D. Rock, *J. Acoust. Soc. Amer.*, *12* (1941), 505, have used this technique to measure α in water; P. Rieckmann, *Phys. Z. 40* (1939), has also determined α in mercury by this method.

is measured by means of continuous-wave ultrasound.[51]   This method
has the advantage that the required electronics are simple and that
the coupling between the transducers and the object by means of a
liquid is easily achieved.   However, if a piezoelectric receiver is used
the problem of radiation shielding between transmitter and receiver
may be rather difficult to solve.   Further, if the thickness and
position of the test object vary, there may be difficulties due to standing waves.   They can be suppressed to some extent by frequency-
modulating the transmitter.[51a]

Schlieren optical analysis of progressive waves   The effects of
a high-frequency sound wave on a beam of light are mentioned in
Section 8.4.   Let us again consider Fig. 8.7 with lens L_2 adjusted to
produce a diffraction pattern in plane (a).   For standing waves, we
could show that this adjustment produces an image of the sound field
in plane (b), owing to secondary interferences.   With progressive
waves this effect cannot take place, unless a dark field is provided in
plane (b).   This is achieved by blocking the undiffracted light of
the zero-order slit image in plane (a).   This is called the Schlieren
method, in which only diffracted light is used to produce an image of
the sound field.   Unless stroboscopic illumination is used, the individual wave fronts in the sound wave are not visible.   The light
intensities at each particular point of the image produced by the
sound field are a function of the sound amplitudes at that point, and
of the distance traversed by the light in the sound beam.

   Two modifications of the Schlieren technique are shown in Fig. 8.15.
We note from Fig. 8.15A that for large distances between the test cell
and plane (a) only three lenses are required: the condenser lens L_c, the
collimating lens L_1, and the image-forming lens L_2.   There are two
ways to obtain a Schlieren image: either by blocking the zero-order
light by means of an opaque thin bar or wire, or by rejecting all the
light diffracted into higher orders by means of a slit positioned exactly
at that point in plane (a) at which the zero order of the diffraction
pattern is formed.[52]   In Fig. 8.15B an arrangement is shown which

   [51] E. Meyer and E. Bock, *Akust. Z.*, *4* (1939), 231 (testing of concrete beams
and rails).   J. Goetz, *Akust. Z. 8* (1943), 145, and A. Trost, *Z. Ver deut. Ing. 87*
(1943), 352 (testing of steel plates and plywood panels).   W. E. Morris, U.S. Pat.
2,378,237, 1945, (testing of tires).   R. Esche, *Acustica, Akust. Bei. 2* (1952), 71
(absorption measurements in animal tissues).
   [51a] Some commercial devices operating on this principle and applicable to the
testing of metal sheets and wires are described by R. Pohlman, *Draht* (Fachzeit-
schrift, Coburg, Germany), *4* (1953), 211; and *Mitt. Forschungs-gesellschaft Blech-
verarbeitung*, 1952, *23*.
   [52] If white light is used in conjunction with the slit, the sound-field image appears

employs a spherical reflector R in conjunction with a reflecting ribbon and a screen S. This technique allows large-field image formation, and is particularly suitable for studies of acoustic or thermal disturbances in gases.[53]

Ultrasonic velocity measurements by the Schlieren method Direct measurements of sound velocity in fluids by the Schlieren method are cumbersome since they require the use of rotating mirrors or stroboscopic illumination to

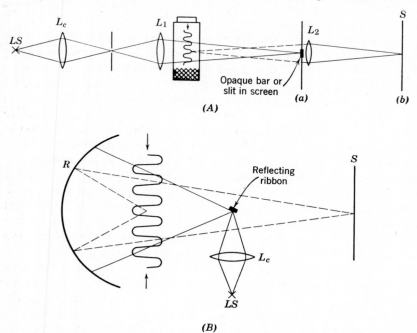

Fig. 8.15. Optical Schlieren techniques. A, Image formation by means of lenses. B, Image formation by means of mirror. The curvature of the mirror has been exaggerated in this drawing; the ribbon reflector is to be located at the center of curvature to provide a good dark field.

produce standing images of the wave fronts.[54] For indirect measurements of the sound velocity in immersed solids relative to that of a known liquid medium, the

---

in various colors. This is a consequence of eq. 8.13a, which contains the wavelength of the light, λ_0. The colors in the sound-field image vary as a function of the sound intensity, which allows one to plot the field pattern by tracing the curves of equal color or "isochromates." See *Grundlagen und Ergebnisse der Ultraschallforschung*, by E. Hiedemann, W. de Gruyter, 1939, Berlin.

[53] H. Schardin; *Ergeb. exakt. Naturw.*, *20* (1942), 303.

[54] L. Bergmann and H. Oertel, *Akust. Z.*, *3* (1938), 332. A. Giacomini *Ricerca Sci.*, *17* (1947), 900.

method has some merits. In this technique the solid to be measured is formed to the shape of a planoconcave lens with a radius of curvature r (see Section 7.4). From a Schlieren picture of the converging sound field produced by the lens in the surrounding liquid, the focal length l_F is determined. According to eq. 7.6 the sound velocity of the solid is found to be

$$c_B = c_{\text{liq}} \left(\frac{l_F}{l_F - r} \right) \tag{8.26}$$

The error in this method is about 2 to 5 per cent, depending on the attenuation of the lens material. Some investigators have used a similar approach with wedges, thick plates, or thick rectangular bars. The sound velocities are found from the angles of refraction of collimated ultrasonic beams which are either

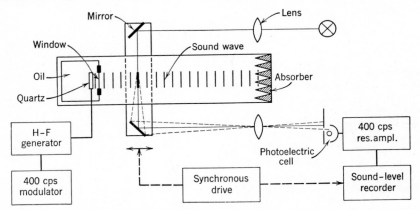

Fig. 8.16. Apparatus for schlieren optical measurement of ultrasonic absorption.

directly transmitted through these objects or which emerge after multiple internal reflections.[55] At certain angles compressional waves incident at the boundaries of the solid test piece are partly converted into shear waves, which in turn lead to compressional radiation at characteristic angles from the solid-liquid boundary (see Section 3.5). By measuring these angles a complete determination of all the elastic constants of isotropic solid samples is possible.

Ultrasonic absorption measurement by the Schlieren method The principle of absorption measurements in liquids by the Schlieren method is illustrated in Fig. 8.16. We note that the optical set-up is similar to the one shown in Fig. 8.15a, except that only the light which is diffracted to the first order is used as a measure of the intensity of the sound field.

This technique requires that the sound amplitude be sufficiently small to insure proportionality between the amount of light I_m diffracted to the mth order and the sound intensity g.[56] The relationship between these two quantities can be found

[55] R. Baer, *Helv. Phys. Acta*, *13* (1940), 61. S. Bhagavantam and J. Bhimasenachar, *Proc. Indian Acad. Sci.*, *20* (1944), 298. G. W. Willard, *J. Acoust. Soc. Amer.*, *23* (1951), 83.

[56] T. H. Sanders, Can. *J. Research A*, *14* (1936), 158. T. F. Hueter and R. Pohlman, *Z. angew. Phys.*, *1* (1949), 405.

from the condition for the phase modulation of a light wave:

$$\mathbf{I}_m = \text{constant} \times J_m{}^2 \left(\frac{2\pi l}{\lambda_0} \Delta n \right) \tag{8.27}$$

in which λ_0 is the wavelength of the light, l is the length of the path traversed by the light in the sound field, Δn is the maximal change of the index of refraction, and J_m is the Bessel function of mth order.[57]   The relationship of Δn to the amplitude of excess density ρ_e is found from the law of molecular refraction

$$\frac{(n^2 - 1)}{(n^2 + 2)\rho_0} = \text{constant} \tag{8.28}$$

Differentiating eq. 8.28 we obtain

$$\Delta n = \frac{(n^2 - 1)(n^2 + 2)}{6n\rho_0} \rho_e \tag{8.29}$$

Combining eqs. 8.27 and 8.29 and using $\rho_e = p_e/c^2$ (see eq. 2.28a), we are finally able to relate the light intensity $\mathbf{I}_1$ in the first order of the diffraction pattern to the excess pressure amplitude p_e in the sound wave, and thus to the sound intensity $\mathit{s} = p_e{}^2/2\rho_0 c$.   For small sound amplitudes the first-order Bessel function approaches the value of its argument, which yields

$$\mathbf{I}_1 \simeq \text{constant} \left[\left(\frac{2\pi l}{\lambda_0} \right) \frac{(n^2 - 1)(n^2 + 2)}{nc} \right]^2 \frac{\mathit{s}}{\rho_0 c} \tag{8.30}$$

This approximation is valid for $\Delta n < 0.1(\lambda_0/l)$.   For example, if red light ($\lambda_0 \sim 6 \times 10^{-5}$ cm) is used, and if the path length of the light in the ultrasonic beam is 3 cm, Δn must be smaller than 1.5×10^{-6}.   For water ($n = 1.33$) this corresponds to a sound-pressure amplitude $p_e \simeq 10^4$ newtons/m^2, and to a sound intensity $\mathit{s} < 3 \times 10^{-3}$ watt/cm^2.   At a frequency of 5 mcps the voltage required to generate this intensity by a quartz crystal is, according to Table 4.5, about 10 volts.

Under these conditions a photographic or photoelectric evaluation of the decrease in intensity along the axis of an ultrasonic beam, which is propagated through an attenuating liquid, allows a determination of the absorption coefficient α.   For example, in the apparatus shown in Fig. 8.16 the modulated output of a photomultiplier is logarithmically recorded on a sound-level recorder in synchronism with the displacement of the test cell.   The slope of the straight line thus obtained represents the attenuation in db/cm.

Ultrasonic image converter

Most of the optical techniques outlined in this section and in Section 8.4 are useful in research but are not likely to assume great importance for routine testing purposes.   There is, however, one optical method which has been used successfully in some special applications for non-

[57] C. V. Raman and N. S. Nagandra Nath, *Proc. Indian Acad. Sci.*, A, *2* (1935), 406, 413, and *3* (1936), 75, 119, 495.

destructive testing. This method uses ultrasonic lenses[58] to form an image of the radiation scattered by flaws within the test piece. The problem of converting the ultrasonic image into a visible picture can be solved by suspending a large number of small disc-shaped aluminum particles in a flat thin-walled cell on which the image is focused.[59] A schematic illustration of the ultrasonic image converter is given in Fig. 8.17.[60] If the diameter of the aluminum particles is much smaller than the wave length in the suspending liquid (e.g., toluene) and if their diameter-to-thickness ratio is large ($d \sim 20\mu$, $t \sim 1.5\mu$) the hydrodynamic forces associated with a sound field tend to orient these particles such that their disc-normal becomes parallel

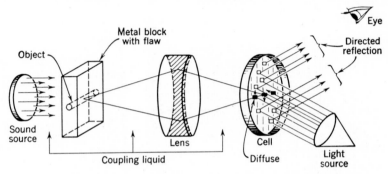

Fig. 8.17.   Ultrasonic image converter (R. Pohlman).

with the sound-wave normal (see Section 6.6). As indicated in Fig. 8.17 the particles in the image converter cell reflect light depending on their degree of orientation. On the average there is a preferred orientation at which the d-c forces and the random forces due to Brownian motion are in equilibrium.

The minimum intensity required to produce an increase in brightness of about 50 per cent over the background brightness level of such a converter cell is of the order of 10^{-4} (watts/cm^2); and the dynamic range of the cell is about 20 db. A comparison of the possibilities

[58] Steel lenses surrounded by mercury have been found suitable (see Table 7.3). The use of mercury as a coupling liquid reduces reflection losses with iron or steel samples. See also R. B. de Lano, Jr., U.S. Pat. 2,525,873, October 17, 1950.

[59] An ultrasonic image converter using an electronic scanning tube similar to the television iconoscope has been described by S. Sokoloff, *Uspekhi Fiz. Nauk* (U.S.S.R.), January 1950, p. 3; see also G. B. Devey, *Radio Television News*, Radio Electronic Dept. *49* (February 1953), 967, and R. H. Rines, U.S. Pat. 2,528,725, November 7, 1950.

[60] R. Pohlman, *Z. angew. Phys.*, *1* (1948), 181. The instrument described by this author has been used for inspection of shell cases during World War II.

and limitations of this technique with other flaw detection methods is given in Table 8.8.[60a]

8.6 Electric Impedance Methods

Progressive CW techniques may be of two kinds. One measures directly the propagation constants of a medium through which a sound wave is transmitted a certain distance; it uses separate transmitting and receiving elements, some of which have been described in the preceding part of this chapter. The other technique makes use of the reaction of the loading medium on the source impedance, as do

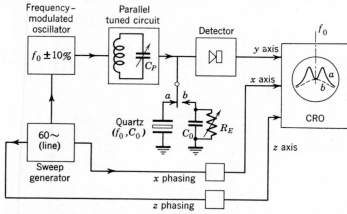

Fig. 8.18.   Electrical determination of load impedance (J. Paetzold).

the interferometric methods discussed in Section 8.4. With progressive waves, however, the evaluation is not based simply on the periodicity of one electrical quantity, but requires an absolute determination of the changes in the resonance and damping of the transducer.

We shall first consider a simple system that has been used for a relative determination of the specific acoustic impedance $\rho_0 c$ of lossy media; it illustrates the principle of such measurements for the case of compressional waves. We must bear in mind, however, that the main application of the impedance method is not with compressional waves, whose propagation is more conveniently and accurately analyzed with transmission methods, but rather with shear waves in viscous media.

The system represented schematically in Fig. 8.18 uses a frequency-modulated source of high internal impedance. A constant-current

[60a] A simplified commercial version of this image converter is described in a technical bulletin issued by the Lehfeldt Company, Heppenheim, Germany.

signal is applied to a parallel tuned circuit whose total capacitance consists of the static capacitance C_0 of the transducer crystal and of a variable parallel capacitance C_p. The voltage across the crystal is rectified and applied to the y axis of a cathode-ray tube. The horizontal sweep of the cathode-ray tube is synchronized with the modulation frequency of the oscillator. If the crystal probe is clamped rigidly, the voltage resonance curve of a simple parallel tuned circuit would appear on the scope. Without clamping, the mechanical series branch (see Fig. 4.5) of the crystal produces a voltage dip at the center frequency f_0, as shown by the CRT trace (a) on Fig. 8.18. The magnitude of this dip depends on the radiation damping $\rho_0 c$ of the loading medium. This quantity can be determined by substituting a resistance R_E for the transducer. If this resistance is made equal to $\rho_0 cS/4\alpha^2$ (see eq. 4.35b), the trace (b) on the CRT, representing a damped parallel circuit, will be tangent to the center depression of trace (a) at f_0. It is convenient to calibrate the device with a load of known impedance, such as water, in which case we obtain

$$\rho_0 c = \rho_w c_w \frac{R_E}{R_w} \tag{8.31}$$

where the subscript w refers to the water load.[61] In general, the losses in the medium under examination lead to a complex load impedance (see eq. 8.3). For high losses the imaginary part may become appreciable so that a reactance $-\rho_0 c^2 S\alpha/j\omega$ is added to the mechanical series branch of the transducer. This raises the frequency of mechanical resonance and leads to asymmetry of the double humped CRT trace (a). Symmetry can be reestablished, however, by reducing C_p by an amount ΔC, which is thus a measure of the phase angle of the attenuated sound wave.

Sonic analysis based on impedance measurements has become a valuable tool for the determination of viscoelastic properties of rubberlike polymers, colloidal systems, and other non-Newtonian substances.[62] Such measurements must be carried out over extended ranges of frequency and/or temperature in order to gain an insight into the underlying viscoelastic relaxation mechanisms (see Section A.3). Thus variable-frequency transducers are desirable, although in some

[61] J. Paetzold, W. Guettner, and H. Bastir, *Strahlentherapie, 86* (1952), 298.

[62] *Mechanical Behavior of High Polymers*, by T. Alfrey, Interscience Publishers, New York, 1948. T. L. Smith, J. D. Ferry, and F. M. Schemp, *J. Appl. Phys.*, *20* (1949), 144. J. D. Ferry, E. R. Fitzgerald, L. D. Grandine, and M. L. Williams, *Ind. Eng. Chem.*, *44* (1952), 44. W. Roth and S. R. Rich, *J. Appl. Phys.*, *24* (1953), 940.

cases a variation of temperature at a fixed frequency will take the substance under study through a particular relaxation region. In the audible frequency range electrodynamic transducers of the moving-coil type (see Section 5.1) are a suitable means of subjecting materials to dynamic shear stresses over a frequency range from 10 to 10^4 cps. In the ultra-audible range, crystals vibrating in the shear mode or in the torsional mode have been used at selected frequencies up to 10^2 mcps.

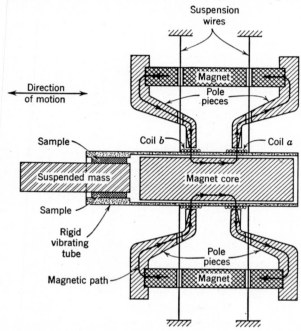

Fig. 8.19.   Electrodynamic shear impedometer (Fitzgerald apparatus).

In some applications, e.g., in the control of mixing and curing, continuous-reading magnetostrictive devices operating at one frequency between about 20 to 100 kcps are used.

Basically, all these devices operate on principles similar to that of the device illustrated in Fig. 8.18. Since in many applications the quantity of greatest interest is the complex shear modulus, a discussion of some special features of shear-wave impedometry is indicated.

Electrodynamic shear impedometer[63]   The operating principle of this device is illustrated in Fig. 8.19. A rigid tube is suspended by eight fine wires so that it is free to move axially in a radial magnetic field of uniform and constant flux density B. The tube carries a

[63] E. R. Fitzgerald and J. D. Ferry, *J. Colloid Sci.*, 8 (1953), 1.

driving coil a and a pick-up coil b, which consist of wire of length l_a and l_b, respectively. Each of the coils is located in one of the two circular gaps between the magnet core and the pole pieces. Let us first consider the motional impedance of the unloaded tube. According to eqs. 5.4 and 5.11, the mechanical impedance Z_{MO} arising from the mass of the tube and coils is obtained from the ratio of force F exerted by coil a to velocity U imparted to coil b:

$$Z_{MO} = \frac{F}{U} = -Z_{EM}^2 \frac{i_a}{V_b}$$

$$= -B^2 l_a l_b Y_{ab} \qquad (8.32a)$$

in which i_a is the driving current, V_b is the pick-up voltage, Z_{EM} is the mutual impedance of the transducer (see Section 5.1), and $Y_{ab} = i_a/V_b$ is the electric transfer admittance.

Let us now insert a sample of viscoelastic material between the vibrating tube and a stationary surface, such as to provide a shear-type load to the tube. One way of doing this is illustrated in Fig. 8.19 in which a large mass suspended by wires serves as an opposing surface. The total mechanical load impedance of the tube is then $Z_M = Z_{MO} + Z_{MS}$, where Z_{MS} is the mechanical impedance of the sample of surface area S and thickness h.

$$Z_{MS} = \frac{G^*S}{j\omega h} = \frac{S}{\omega h}(\omega\eta - j\mu) \qquad (8.32b)$$

in which G^* is the complex shear rigidity, μ is the elastic shear modulus, and η is the dynamic viscosity.

In order to obtain the magnitudes and phase angles of the mechanical impedances Z_{MO} and Z_{MS} measurements of the motional impedance Z_a of the driving coil a with and without the sample are made. A bridge circuit of the type shown in Fig. 8.20 is used.[64] For a particular setting of R_3 and C_4 the bridge is balanced by adjusting R_1 and C_1. At balance we obtain for the motional impedance:

$$Z_a = \frac{Z_3 Z_1}{Z_4} = \frac{j\omega C_4 R_3 R_1}{1 + j\omega C_1 R_1}$$

$$= \frac{\omega^2 C_1 C_4 R_3 R_1^2}{1 + \omega^2 C_1^2 R_1^2} + j\frac{\omega C_4 R_3 R_1}{1 + \omega^2 C_1^2 R_1^2} \qquad (8.33)$$

[64] In practice, the circuit shown in Fig. 8.20 must be modified in order to eliminate magnetic coupling between the two coils. This may be achieved by an additional shielding coil. For further details see E. R. Fitzgerald and J. D. Ferry, *op. cit.* (see footnote 63). A commercial impedometer of this type is made by the Atlantic Research Corporation, Alexandria, Va.

The total mechanical impedance Z_M is then found to be

$$Z_M = \frac{B_a l_a{}^2 (1 + ar)}{Z_{a0} - Z_a} \qquad (8.34)$$

in which $a = B_b l_b / B_a l_a$, r is the ratio I_2/I_1 of the currents through the two coils, which for small coil impedances is approximately $r \simeq R_3/R_A$, and Z_{a0} is the clamped electric impedance of coil a. From eqs. 8.33 and 8.34 the sample impedance $Z_{MS} = Z_M - Z_{MO}$ can be obtained if Z_a is measured with and without load. If this technique is applied to viscoelastic media a similar dependence of the shear modulus μ and the loss tangent $\eta\omega/\mu$ on frequency is found as the

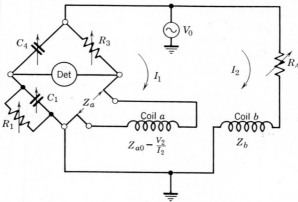

Fig. 8.20.   Bridge circuit for impedometer.

one depicted in Fig. 8.3 for compressional strains.[65] This may be interpreted as an increase of the frictional coupling between adjacent elements of the polymer chains as the frequency is raised, or as the temperature is lowered. As a result, the chain segments themselves become more and more deformed and the dynamic response of the material changes from viscous to elastic. A behavior of this kind is called relaxation and may be likened to the behavior of an electric parallel RC circuit, as is shown in Section A.3. In many substances, however, the observed frequency response makes it necessary to assume a distribution of relaxation mechanisms, which control both the mechanical and the dielectric behavior of the polymer.[66]

[65] E. R. Fitzgerald, L. D. Grandine, Jr., and J. D. Ferry, *J. Appl. Phys.*, *24* (1953), 650; L. D. Grandine, Jr., and J. D. Ferry, *J. Appl. Phys.*, *24* (1953), 679.

[66] A. V. Tobolsky and R. D. Andrews, *J. Chem. Phys.*, *13* (1945), 3. J. D. Ferry and E. R. Fitzgerald, *J. Colloid Sci.*, *8* (1953), 224. K. W. Scott and R. S. Stein, *J. Chem. Phys.*, *21* (1953), 224. P. E. Rouse, Jr., *J. Chem. Phys.*, *21* (1953), 1272. R. B. Blizard, *J. Appl. Phys.*, *22* (51), 730.

Theory of ultrasonic shear-wave impedometry in liquids   In liquids viscous relaxation effects come into play mainly at the higher ultrasonic frequencies where piezoelectric, and in some cases magneto-strictive, transducers have to be employed.   For the generation of a viscous shear wave the motion of the transducer must be parallel to its surface.   The quantity of interest is the load impedance offered to a transducer operated in this fashion.   Let us first consider a purely viscous wave, which is characterized by the following equation of motion:[67]

$$\rho \frac{\partial u_y}{\partial t} = -\eta \frac{\partial^2 u_y}{\partial z^2} \tag{8.35}$$

in which $u_y = U_y e^{j(\omega t - kz)}$ is the velocity in the y direction parallel to the transducer face, and z is the direction normal to the transducer face.   The viscous force (see eq. 6.4b) acting on the transducer ($z = 0$) then is $F_{y0} = -S\eta(\partial u_y/\partial z)_0$, and the specific acoustic load impedance becomes

$$Z_0 = \frac{F_{y0}}{u_{y0}S} = j\eta k \tag{8.36a}$$

in which $jk = (j\omega\rho/\eta)^{1/2}$.   Using the conversion $\sqrt{j} = \sqrt{\tfrac{1}{2}}(1 + j)$, eq. 8.36a can be written in the form

$$Z_0 = (\pi f \rho \eta)^{1/2}(1 + j)$$

$$= R_m + jX_m \tag{8.36b}$$

We note that in this case the phase angle of the impedance is 45°, since $X_m/R_m = 1$.   We may thus represent the viscous load by an equivalent transmission line consisting of series impedance elements $Z_1 = j\omega\rho\, dz$ and shunt impedance elements $Z_2 = \eta/dz$, as shown in Fig. 8.21a.   The line input impedance is then given by $Z_0 = (Z_1 Z_2)^{1/2}$ which corresponds to eq. 8.36b.

Let us now extend this analysis to include the effects of relaxation, which bring shear elasticity into play if the frequency is high enough This is accomplished by shunting the viscous elements in Fig. 8.21a with a shear compliance $C_s = 1/\mu$ as shown in Fig. 8.21b.   The shunt impedance Z_2 then becomes

$$Z_2 = \frac{1}{(j\omega C_s + 1/\eta)\, dz}$$

[67] W. P. Mason, W. O. Baker, H. J. McSkimmin, and J. H. Heiss, *Phys. Rev.*, 75 (1949), 936.

and the line input impedance takes the form

$$Z_0 = (Z_1 Z_2)^{\frac{1}{2}} = \left[\frac{\omega^2 \rho \eta^2 C_s + j\rho\eta\omega}{\omega^2 C_s^2 \eta^2 + 1} \right]^{\frac{1}{2}} \qquad (8.37)$$

Introducing the parameters $g = \omega^2 \eta^2 C_s$ and $h = gC_s + 1$ and using

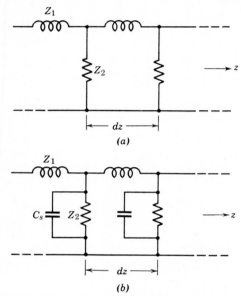

(a)

(b)

Fig. 8.21. Transmission-line analogy, (a) for a purely viscous medium; (b) for a
medium with both viscosity and shear rigidity.

the relationship $Z_0 = \sqrt{R_m^2 + X_m^2}\, e^{j\varphi}$ we obtain the following
expressions for R_m^2 and X_m^2:

$$\left. \begin{aligned} R_m^2 &= \frac{\rho}{2h} \left(\sqrt{g^2 + \omega^2 \eta^2} + g \right) \\[2mm] X_m^2 &= \frac{\rho}{2h} \left(\sqrt{g^2 + \omega^2 \eta^2} - g \right) \end{aligned} \right\} \qquad (8.38)$$

These expressions can be simplified if one introduces the relaxation
frequency ω_r, defined as that frequency at which the phase angle β
of the shunt impedance Z_2 becomes 45°; i.e., $\tan \beta = 1$ for $\omega_r = \mu/\eta$.
This leads to

$$g = \mu(\omega/\omega_r)^2 \qquad \text{and} \qquad h = (\omega/\omega_r)^2 + 1 \qquad (8.39)[68]$$

[68] This notation may be applied equally to the treatments of W. P. Mason, *Piezoelectric Crystals and their Application to Ultrasonics*, D. Van Nostrand Co., New

Combining eqs. 8.38 and 8.39 we obtain

$$R_m = \left[\frac{\omega}{\omega_r}\frac{\rho\mu}{2h}\left(\sqrt{h} + \frac{\omega}{\omega_r}\right)\right]^{1/2}$$

$$X_m = \left[\frac{\omega}{\omega_r}\frac{\rho\mu}{2h}\left(\sqrt{h} - \frac{\omega}{\omega_r}\right)\right]^{1/2} \qquad (8.40)$$

$$\tan\varphi = \frac{X_m}{R_m} = \left[\frac{\sqrt{\omega^2 + \omega_r{}^2} - \omega}{\sqrt{\omega^2 + \omega_r{}^2} + \omega}\right]^{1/2}$$

Since $Z_0 = \rho c^*$, we find for the complex sound velocity of the viscous shear wave

$$c^* = \left[\frac{\omega}{\omega_r}\frac{\mu}{\rho\sqrt{h}}\right]^{1/2}(\cos\varphi + j\sin\varphi)$$

$$= \left[\frac{2\omega\eta}{\rho}\frac{1}{(\sqrt{h} + \omega/\omega_r)}\right]^{1/2}(1 + j\tan\varphi) \qquad (8.41)$$

We note that at low frequencies, where $\omega \ll \omega_r$, the real and imaginary parts of Z_0 become equal and the phase factor is unity, in accordance with eq. 8.36b. Physically this represents a purely viscous damping action of the medium on the transducer. The associated viscous wave has a phase velocity $c_v = (2\omega\eta/\rho)^{1/2}$. However, it is highly attenuated and has a skin depth $\delta = (2\eta/\omega\rho)^{1/2}$, i.e., its amplitude has decayed to 0.37 of its original value at a distance $\delta = \lambda/2\pi$ from the transducer face. For example, at 20°C a 100-kcps viscous wave has a skin depth of $\delta = 46.3$ microns in glycerin, and of $\delta = 1.6$ microns in water.

As the frequency is increased the effects of relaxation become increasingly felt as C_s in the equivalent circuit of Fig. 8.21b begins to shunt out η.

At high frequencies ($\omega \gg \omega_r$) the real part of Z_0, which represents the radiation load resistance, approaches asymptotically the value $R_m = \sqrt{\rho\mu} = \rho c_s$. The imaginary part, on the other hand, which represents the absorption per wave length $\alpha\lambda$ in the medium, goes through a maximum near ω_r and approaches zero as the frequency increases further. Figure 8.22 illustrates this dependence of R_m and X_m on frequency. Note that the decrease of the absorption per wavelength above the relaxation region corresponds to a constant value of the absorption per unit length equal to $\alpha = (\rho\mu)/2\eta$.

York, 1950 and W. Roth (loc. cit., see Footnote 62). See also eqs. A.16 to A.21 in Section A.3 of this book.

Liquids which exhibit a viscoelastic relaxation of this type are called "non-Newtonian" since they do not follow the simple relationships of eqs. 6.4b and 8.36b, which lead to $R_m = X_m$ at all frequencies. Most petroleum products, oils, varnishes, and syrups, exhibit Newtonian behavior, while colloids, emulsions, polymer suspensions, and most biological materials are non-Newtonian.

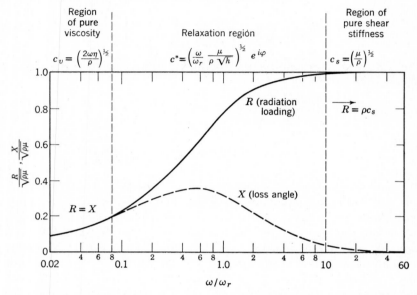

Fig. 8.22.   Frequency dependence of load resistance and reactance for liquids displaying viscous shear relaxation.

The deviations from "Newtonian" behavior can be of different kinds, depending on the flow characteristics of the liquid through a capillary tube.   They are illustrated by Fig. 8.23, in which the flow velocity v is plotted as a function of the pressure difference Δp across the tube.   Only in Newtonian liquids is v linearly related to Δp, as shown by curve N.   Some materials, called "dilatants," exhibit an increase of viscosity with pressure, as exemplified by curve D.   The opposite effect takes place in "thixotropic" materials, which are represented by curve T. Still another class of substances, illustrated by curve (P), shows "plastic" behavior. Here a critical value Δp_y of the pressure, the so-called yield point, must be exceeded before any flow occurs.   Typical examples of these different mechanisms are as follows: castor oil is a Newtonian liquid, starch in solution is a dilatant, colloidal gels are thixotropic, and ductile metals under high stress display plasticity.

Shear-wave techniques for analysis of viscous liquids   As shown earlier in this section, the impedance Z_0 offered the transducer by the loading medium reflects to the electric input terminals in form of a change ΔR_e in electric resistance, and of a decrease Δf of the resonance frequency of the crystal. These two quantities are accessible to absolute measurement by an electric bridge and a suitable receiver. Or, for relative evaluation of the $\eta\rho$ product in the purely viscous region ($\omega \ll \omega_r$), the time decay of an intermittently excited transducer can be related to the magnitude of Z_0, since it follows from eqs. 8.40 that $[R_m{}^2 + X_m{}^2)^{\frac{1}{2}} = \text{constant} \times \sqrt{\eta\rho}$. In general one may write

$$\Delta R_e = K_1 R_m \qquad \text{and} \qquad \Delta f = K_2 X_m \tag{8.42}$$

in which ΔR_e and Δf are the measured differences between the transducer response under a load and in a vacuum, while K_1 and K_2 are

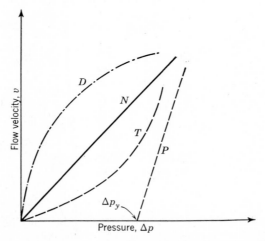

Fig. 8.23.   Flow characteristics of different kinds of fluids.   (N), Newtonian fluids; (D), dilatants; (T), thixotropes; (P), plastics.

constants of the apparatus depending on the crystal geometry and the mounting. Usually these constants are evaluated indirectly by carefully measuring ΔR_e and Δf for a Newtonian liquid of accurately known density ρ and viscosity η. At a given frequency and temperature, R_m and X_m can be computed for this liquid from eqs. 8.40,[69] and hence K_1 and K_2 can be found from eq. 8.42.

Three different experimental techniques are available for the measurement of the reaction of viscous liquids to ultrasonic shear forces:

[69] Suitable liquids are benzene or cyclohexane.   For details of this calibration procedure see W. O. Baker, W. P. Mason, and J. H. Heiss, *J. Polymer Sci.*, *8* (1952), 129.

a. The magnetostrictive blade technique, operating in the frequency range from 20 to 100 kcps.

b. The torsional crystal technique, operating in the frequency range from 20 to 200 kcps.

c. The shear-wave reflection technique, operating in the frequency range from 1 to 100 mcps.

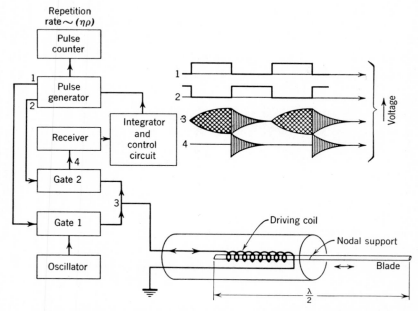

Fig. 8.24.   Functional diagram of apparatus for viscosimetry, using longitudinally vibrating magnetostrictive blade (after W. Roth).   The voltage-time curves on the upper right illustrate the operation of the device: gate 1 connects the oscillator to the probe whose vibrations build up, as shown by the cross-hatched portion of curve 3.   The excitation is then turned off and gate 2 connects the probe to the receiver, which passes a voltage proportional to the decaying vibrations, as shown by curve 4.   By integrating this voltage V_4 a control signal is derived which triggers the pulse generator such as to keep $\int V_4\, dt$ over unit time constant.   The resulting pulse repetition rate is a measure of $\eta \times \rho$.

The principles of operation of these three techniques are illustrated in Fig. 8.24 to 8.26.   In the magnetostrictive probe (Fig. 8.24) the shear action is obtained at the lateral faces of a longitudinally vibrating flat blade.   Since the area of these faces is of the order of 10^3 times larger than the cross-sectional area of the blade, the compressional loading at the end of the blade can be neglected compared with the shear loading at the face.   The magnitude $|Z_0| = \text{const} \times (\eta\rho)^{\frac{1}{2}}$

of the load impedance can be evaluated from the rate at which the blade vibration decays after the driving current is turned off.[70]

In the torsional quartz probe shown in Fig. 8.25 the motion is likewise all tangential to the transducer surface. The quartz rod is cut with its length parallel to the crystallographic x axis, and pairs of electrode strips of evaporated gold are provided at angles 45° to the y axis. Four wires are soldered to these electrodes in the nodal plane, thus serving both as leads and as supports. Evaluation of the loading effect is made on the basis of eqs. 8.42 and allows separation of the two unknown quantities η and μ, by means of eqs. 8.40. A quartz

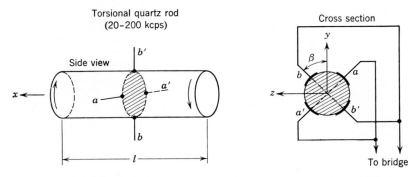

Fig. 8.25.   Resonant torsional quartz probe for the analysis of viscoelastic relaxation (W. P. Mason). The frequency of fundamental torsional resonance of a quartz rod cut in this fashion is $f_r = (c_{66}/\rho)^{1/2}/2l$, where $c_{66} = (c_{11} - c_{12})/2$ and
$$c_{11} = 8.75 \times 10^{10} \text{ newton/m}^2, \; c_{12} = 7.6 \times 10^9 \text{ newton/cm}^2.$$

probe is suitable for measurements in liquids having a viscosity below 10 poises; while for higher viscosities more accurate results are obtained with torsional ADP crystals.[71] A variation of this method uses a torsional crystal which is cemented to the end of a long (30 to 50 cm) glass or metal rod. Short trains of torsional waves are sent periodic-

---

[70] A commercial instrument operating on this principle is the "Ultraviscoson," which has found many applications in industrial process control. It measures the product $\eta\rho$ in centipoises $\times$ gram/cm^3 over a range from 1 to 10^4. The minimum amount of liquid required for a test is about 4 cm.^{3} The quantity $\eta\rho$ is evaluated electronically by finding the pulse repetition rate required to keep the area under the time-decay curve constant per unit time. However, this method is not capable of separating the effects of shear viscosity from those of shear rigidity.

[71] For more details see W. P. Mason, op. cit. (See footnote 68), p. 342; a discussion of the precision attainable with the torsional crystal method is given by P. E. Rouse, E. D. Bailey, and J. A. Minkin, Laboratories of the Franklin Inst., Rept. 2048 (1950).

ally down the rod, and the attenuation and phase change of the reflected waves are analyzed by a bridge circuit.[72]

Finally, at the higher ultrasonic frequencies ($f > 3$ mcps) the shear-wave reflection method illustrated in Fig. 8.26 is used. A shear wave is generated and received by a set of Y-cut or AT-cut quartz crystals cemented to the two opposite end faces of a fused silica rod. The end faces of the rod are inclined such that the waves are transmitted from one crystal to the other by means of reflection on the upper flat surface of the rod, at an angle θ. To insure that no longitudinal components

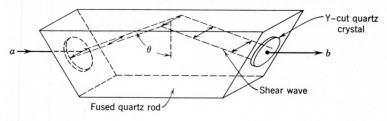

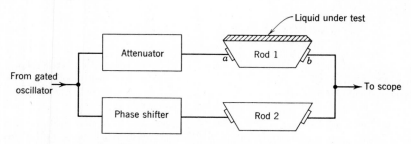

Fig. 8.26.   Shear wave reflection technique (McSkimmin).

are generated at the reflecting boundary the shear motion must be polarized parallel to the reflecting surface. When the liquid under test is placed on this surface, a change in both the amplitude and the phase of the reflected wave is produced. These changes can be measured by balancing the signals transmitted through two identical rods, one being loaded (1), and one unloaded (2). The load impedance Z_0 offered by the liquid then is found to be

$$Z_0 = Z_q \cos \theta \left[\frac{1 - r^2 + 2jr \sin \varphi}{1 + r^2 + 2r \cos \varphi} \right] \tag{8.43}$$

[72] W. P. Mason and H. J. McSkimmin, *Bell System Tech. J.*, *31* (1952), 122. The device described by these authors can measure dynamic viscosities from 10 to 10^3 poises with an accuracy of the order of 10 per cent.

in which Z_q is the shear-wave impedance in the rod material, r is the amplitude ratio of the attenuated to the unattenuated signal, and φ is the phase shift between channels 1 and 2.[73]

The techniques described above have proved extremely valuable in determining the mechanical properties of discrete polymer molecules. By plotting the measured shear stiffness μ versus frequency one can

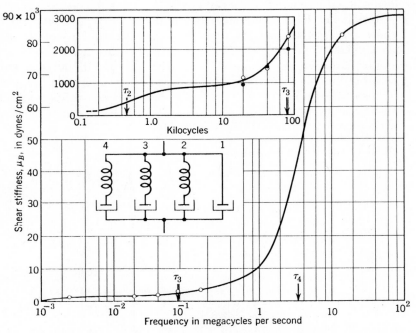

Fig. 8.27. Shear relaxation in dilute polymer solution (W. P. Mason). Curves of this kind may be analyzed by mechanical models, as shown by the combination of springs and dashpots. Each of the series elements 2, 3, and 4 relaxes at a particular frequency $\omega_r = 1/\tau$ which is determined by the ratio (spring stiffness)/(damping resistance) $= \mu/\eta$.

recognize the presence of specific relaxation processes. As an example, Fig. 8.27 presents a plot of shear stiffness μ versus frequency f for a 1 per cent solution of polyisobutylene in cyclohexane at room temperature. Here three relaxation frequencies $1/\tau_2$, $1/\tau_3$, and $1/\tau_4$ are present as indicated by the three inflection points of the μ, f curve. Results of this type may be analyzed by means of mechanical models consisting of suitable combinations of so-called "Maxwell elements," i.e., series combinations of springs and dashpots. It has thus been

[73] H. T. O'Neil, *Phys. Rev.*, *75* (1949), 928.

possible to calculate intrachain stiffnesses and cross linkages of polymer molecules.[74]

8.7   Decay and Reverberation Techniques

In Section 8.2 we considered those resonance techniques in which the response of a vibrating system to a constant force or constant velocity is analyzed. The energy lost in a resonant system can also be determined by a measurement of the decay of its free vibrations, as shown in Table 8.2. In the present section we shall discuss briefly some special techniques which are suitable for absorption measurements in liquids in the frequency range between 5 and 500 kcps, and in solids at audible frequencies. The quantity of interest in decay or reverberation studies is the temporal damping constant κ which, according to Table 8.3, is directly related to the absorption coefficient α or the loss factor $\tan \varphi$ of the sound wave.

High Q spherical resonator

Relative absorption measurements in the frequency range from 5 to 50 kcps have been made by a study of the decay of a spherical glass

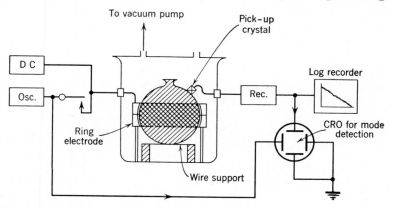

Fig. 8.28.   Apparatus for the measurement of the decay of spherical vibrations (G. Kurtze and K. Tamm).

resonator filled with the liquid under test.[75] The experimental arrangement for this type of work is illustrated in Fig. 8.28. A typical resonator is made of Pyrex glass and has a diameter $2R$ of about 1 ft (about 30 cm) and a wall thickness d of about 40 to 100 mils

[74] W. Kuhn and H. Kuhn, *J. Colloid. Sci.*, *3* (1948), 11.

[75] R. W. Leonard, Univ. Calif. Los Angeles Physics Dept., *Project NRO* 14-302, *Tech. Rept.* 1, June 1950. G. Kurtze and K. Tamm, *Acustica*, *3* (1953), 33.

(1–2.5 mm). The fundamental resonance of a water-filled glass sphere of these dimensions, which holds about 12 l (3 gal) of liquid, is about 4 kcps. For thin vessels ($d \ll R$), the approximate resonance frequencies (overtones) for the spherical modes can be found from $\omega_n \simeq n\pi c/R$, which is a zero-order approximation for the spherically symmetrical modes of a free-boundary liquid sphere.[76]

It is important to reduce external damping by suspending the vessel on thin wires and by operating the resonator in a vacuum. The larger the radius R of the resonator, the less is the influence of the losses in the wall material compared with the ones in the liquid volume, since the ratio of surface area to volume decreases with $1/R$. With proper precautions the Q of a large water-filled resonator will thus be of the order of 10^5, at a frequency of about 10^4 cps. This allows an accurate determination of the effect of adding varying amounts of impurities to a known solvent, which often increases the absorption appreciably without large chances of sound velocity. Some examples, such as electrolytic solutions and water-alcohol mixtures are discussed in Section A.6.

The excitation may be electrostatic by means of an external annular electrode which is spaced closely to a corresponding ring-shaped section of the vessel which is coated with conductive paint. For the detection of the radial vibrations, an ADP crystal stack (see Section 4.14) is cemented to the glass sphere. Its output is amplified and recorded on the logarithmic scale of a sound-level recorder.

An absolute measurement of absorption by this method is quite difficult because of the residual damping offered by the glass and the supporting wires. Usually the losses are determined relative to a known standard liquid, for example, distilled water. It is important, however, that the two liquids to be compared have nearly equal sound velocity c. In this case the temporal damping constants κ of the standard (κ_s) and the test liquid (κ_t) may be determined for the same spherical mode of vibration of the resonator. The coefficient of sound absorption is then found to be

$$\alpha_t = \frac{(\kappa_t - \kappa_s)}{c} \qquad (8.44)$$

Reverberation method At frequencies above 100 kcps the overtone spectrum of a resonator of the type described above becomes

---

[76] A rigorous treatment of spherical vibrations requires the use of spherical Bessel functions and, for asymmetrical modes, of Legendre functions. See, for example, P. M. Morse, *Vibration and Sound*, 2nd edition, McGraw-Hill, New York, 1948, p. 316.

very dense and it is difficult to distinguish between the desired symmetrical modes and indirectly excited asymmetrical modes.   It is then easier to determine a mean decay factor κ from the reverberation time of a system which is excited at the same time to many statistically distributed normal modes.   Although the interferences among these modes lead to fluctuations of the decaying sound-pressure amplitudes, an approximately linear logarithmic decay curve is obtained, if the number of modes of vibration in the tank is high enough;[77] i.e., if a large number of normal modes of vibration are set up in different directions within a test tank a diffuse sound field is approximated.   For this purpose a liquid-filled tank of unsymmetrical shape is excited by a frequency band (e.g., 10 to 20 kcps bandwidth) which may be obtained by pulsing (see Section 8.8), or by frequency modulation.

If the resulting modes are nearly uniformly affected by the boundary losses, an approximately exponential decay of the sound energy contained in the system occurs when the driving source is turned off.[78] The corresponding plot of the decaying received signal, which is fed into a logarithmic sound-level recorder, is linear and has a slope of κ nepers/sec or 8.686 κ db/sec.   The reverberation time T_R, defined as the time required for the average of the fluctuating sound pressure to decrease by 60 db below its steady-state value, is then given by

$$T_R = 6.91/\kappa \qquad (8.45)$$

In general there are two causes for the loss of energy: absorption in the medium within the tank, and wall losses.   The second part can be evaluated if a set of measurements is obtained with tanks of different sizes.   One may then plot the damping factor κ versus the reciprocal of the tank dimensions, and determine the y axis intercept of the resulting curve.   This intercept, $\kappa_0 = \alpha c$, represents the volume losses of an infinitely large vessel.   If a standard liquid of known properties is available, one may also use eq. 8.44 for a relative evaluation of α.

The apparatus used for reverberation work in liquids is similar to the one depicted in Fig. 8.28, except for the use of a frequency band. The desired asymmetry of the tank can be simply achieved by tilting a cylindrical container at a slight angle.   Excitation and detection

[77] Reverberation measurements are widely used in room acoustics.   For a general review of reverberation techniques see L. L. Beranek, *Acoustic Measurements*, John Wiley & Sons, New York, 1949, p. 794.

[78] V. J. Knudsen, *J. Acoust. Soc. Amer.*, *3* (1931), 126.   C. E. Mulders, *Nature*, *164* (1949), 347.   E. Skudrzyk, *Österr. Ing. Arch.* (Vienna), *4* (1940), 408.

of the vibrations is accomplished by ADP crystals cemented externally to the tank walls.

Decay measurements in solids   Low-frequency ($f < 50$ kcps) decay measurements of vibrating solids are carried out, with slight modifications, by the techniques discussed in Section 8.2.   The rate of decay of the vibration energy from the steady-state level can be observed by electrostatic, electrodynamic, or optical means, and longitudinal, torsional, or flexural vibrations can be analyzed.   At higher frequencies pulse techniques, as discussed in Section 8.9, are preferable.

8.8   Internal Damping in Metals

In this section we digress from the discussion of analytical methods in order to present a brief account of the origin of losses in metals and glasses.   The energy losses of a sound wave which is propagated through a solid may be attributed to four different mechanisms: heat conduction, viscous friction, elastic hysteresis, and scattering.   It is very difficult to conclude from the data obtained by simple experiments which of these mechanisms plays the major part in a given material.   Different mechanisms appear to be important at different regions of the frequency scale.   Also, the various types of losses obey different laws with regard to their frequency dependence.   Finally, the observed attenuation depends greatly on the type and structure of the material and may change with the kind of pretreatment to which a material has been subjected.

The losses in high-polymer materials such as plastics and rubbers are mainly of viscous nature.   Here one encounters the phenomena of viscoelastic relaxation mentioned in Section 8.6.   Within a relaxation region, which may extend over a wide frequency range, the loss per cycle is constant ($\alpha/\omega = $ constant).   Below and above the relaxation region α increases in proportion to ω^2 and $\omega^{1/2}$, respectively, as is shown in Section A.3.

Thermal waves   In metals, on the other hand, all four loss mechanisms come into play.   Let us first consider that part of the dissipation which is due to heat conduction.   The deformations occurring in the sound wave are no longer adiabatic if the time of each vibrational half cycle is sufficiently large that the heat developed in one crystallite or grain can equalize with its neighbors.   We saw in Section 6.3 that heat is equivalent to molecular motion, and we must add that in a crystal this motion can be visualized as vibrations or *heat waves* traveling with a velocity $c_h = \sqrt{2\omega\kappa_h}$, κ_h being the coefficient of thermal diffusion.[79] If the frequency of the sound vibrations transmitted through a polycrystalline material is such that a quarter wavelength of the heat wave λ_h is equal to the mean size D of the grains, a maximum of heat exchange between grains occurs. This condition can be expressed by the relationship

$$\lambda_h/4 = c_h/4f = (\pi \kappa_h/4f)^{1/2} = D \tag{8.46}$$

or, solving for frequency:

$$\omega_h = 2\pi f = \pi^2 \kappa_h/2D^2 \simeq 0.8 k_h/C_v D^2 \tag{8.47}$$

It can be shown that the resulting sound absorption takes the form

$$\alpha_h \sim \frac{\beta_h T}{2\pi C_v} \frac{\omega^2/\omega_h}{1 + (\omega/\omega_h)^2} \tag{8.48}$$

in which β_h is the linear thermal expansion coefficient of the metal and C_v is the specific heat at constant volume.[80]

We note that eq. 8.48 indicates a relaxational behavior with a maximum of $\alpha\lambda$ (or a minimum of $Q = \pi/\alpha\lambda$) at $\omega = \omega_h$. For single crystals D is very large and this thermal relaxation effect occurs at frequencies of the order of 1 cps. If the grain size is small, ω_h may lie in the ultrasonic frequency range; for example, with $D \simeq 10^{-3}$ cm and $\kappa_h \simeq 1$ cm^2/sec the relaxation frequency ω_h is of the order of 10^2 kcps.[81]

Viscous effects at grain boundaries Viscous friction between the grains accounts for part of the losses in polycrystalline materials. This mechanism is related to such static phenomena as creep and plasticity which have been traced to slipping of the grain boundaries.[82]

[79] The coefficient κ_h is defined by $4\pi\kappa_h = k_h/C_v = c_h\lambda_h$, in which k_h is the heat conductivity and C_v the specific heat (see Table 6.2). The dimension of κ_h is m^2/sec.

[80] C. Zener, *Elasticity and Anelasticity of Metals*, Chicago University Press, 1948. In the interaction between the ultrasonic waves and Debye heat waves the energy contained in both types of wave is assumed to be quantized and one speaks of quantum exchanges between "phonons." See also L. Landau, *Phys. Z. U.S.-S.R.*, *11* (1937), 71, and *Phys. Rev.*, *6* (1941), 358.

[81] Taking copper as a typical metal, we find for the thermal conductivity at room temperature about $k_h \simeq 1$ cal/(cm·sec·degree), for the specific heat $C_v \simeq 5$ cal/mole·degree). The atomic weight is $A = 63$ and the density $\rho = 8.9$. Hence

$$4\pi\kappa_h = \frac{k_h}{C_v} \frac{A}{\rho} \simeq (1/5)(63/8.9) \simeq 1.4 \text{ cm}^2/\text{sec}$$

[82] E. Orowan, "Creep in Metallic and Non-Metallic Materials," *Proc. First Nat. Congr. Appl. Mech.*, 1951, p. 453.

Losses of this type also display relaxation. The frequency $\omega_v = 1/\tau$ at which the absorption maximum occurs depends on temperature T and follows a law of the type $\omega_v = \omega_0 e^{-H/k_B T}$, in which H is the activation energy required for the dislocation of an atom at the grain boundary and k_B is Boltzman's constant.[83] To observe this absorption maximum at a frequency of about 1 mcps the temperature must be near the melting point.

Temperature dependence of absorption   The temperature dependence of the above-mentioned loss mechanism is most suitably described in terms of the so-called characteristic Debye temperature Θ. This quantity is an important parameter in the Debye theory of specific heat which treats the thermal energy of a solid as a superposition of a large number of very high-frequency ($f \simeq 10^{11}$ to 10^{13} cps) sound waves traveling back and forth in all directions.[84] The Debye temperature is defined by

$$\Theta = \frac{hc}{2\pi k_B} (6\pi^2 N)^{\frac{1}{3}} \qquad (8.49)$$

in which h is Planck's constant, c is the velocity of the thermal lattice vibrations, and N is the number of atoms per unit volume in the metal.[85]   Values of Θ in degrees Kelvin for some representative metals are given in Table 8.6.

As the temperature is lowered from the melting point at constant frequency, say about 10^2 kcps, one first encounters a maximum of $\alpha\lambda$, due to viscous grain-boundary sliding, which falls in the region $2\Theta < T < 3\Theta$. Near the Debye temperature the losses are due mainly to heat conduction, and in the region $T \gtrsim \Theta/2$ one may expect another maximum of $\alpha\lambda$ owing to slip between planes of the crystal lattice if vacant sites (dislocations) are present in the lattice.   An example of this phenomenon is shown in Fig. 8.29 in which $1/Q = \alpha\lambda/\pi$ is plotted versus absolute temperature for chemically pure copper. The high losses found in the unannealed polycrystalline material are greatly reduced by 10 hours of annealing at 150°C.   The single crystal

[83] P. G. Bordoni, *Nuovo Cimento*, 7 (Series 9, 1950) Supplement No. 2, p. 144. Experimental evidence of the viscous behavior of grain boundaries in metals has also been given by Ting-Sui-Ke, *Phys. Rev.*, 71 (1947), 533.

[84] An introduction to the theories of lattice vibrations is given in *Introduction to Solid State Physics*, by C. Kittel, Chapters 4 and 5, John Wiley & Sons, New York, 1953.   See also C. Kittel, *J. Acoust. Soc. Amer.*, 21 (1949), 308.

[85] Estimates of the value of c at frequencies near 10^6/mcps can be made by the study of X-ray scattering: G. N. Ramachandran and W. A. Wooster, *Acta Cryst.*, 4 (1951), 335 and 431; H. Cole and B. E. Warren, *J. Appl. Phys.*, 23 (1952), 335.

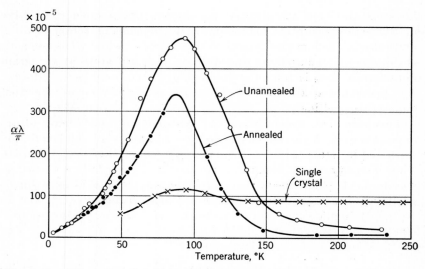

Fig. 8.29.   Effect of grain size on the losses for copper ($\omega \sim 5 \times 10^4$ cps) (P. Bordoni).

displays only a very slight maximum. Studies of this kind yield valuable information on the metallurgical properties of metals.[86]

We note from Table 8.6 that at room temperature most metals, with the exception of lead, fall in the range $\theta/2 < T < 2\theta$ where

Table 8.6   Debye Temperature and Melting Point of Various Metals

Metal	Symbol	θ^* (°K)	T/θ at Room Temperature[†]	T/θ at Melting Point
Silver	Ag	215	1.4	5.7
Aluminum	Al	398	0.75	2.35
Copper	Cu	315	0.95	4.3
Iron	Fe	420	0.71	4.3
Magnesium	Mg	290	1.03	3.2
Nickel	Ni	370	0.8	4.8
Lead	Pb	88	3.4	6.8
Platinum	Pt	225	1.3	9
Tungsten	W	310	0.97	11.8
Zinc	Zn	235	1.28	2.9

* Degrees Kelvin (°K) = degrees Centigrade (°C) + 273.
† Room temperature is taken to be 300°K, or 27°C.

thermal effects prevail. Experimental investigations in the ultrasonic frequency range from 1 to 10^2 mcps have shown that polycrystal-

[86] For example, differences in the state of germanium semiconductors can be analyzed by ultrasonic attenuation measurements: R. Truell and J. Bronzo, *Phys. Rev.*, *90* (1953), 152.

line metals at room temperature display essentially a linear increase of attenuation versus frequency.   It appears that this linearity is the result of a combination of the three above-mentioned loss mechanisms which is consistent with the finding that the magnitude of $\alpha\lambda$ depends on the grain size.

In general, the damping is strongly increased by cold work and permanent strain, whereas annealing produces a substantial reduction of the losses.   Further, the energy lost in the transmission of an ultrasonic wave depends on the degree of isotropy in the solid; the losses are particularly small in aluminum, magnesium and tungsten whose elastic constants differ only slightly in the different crystal directions.   The lowest losses are encountered in single crystals and amorphous materials like fused quartz.   The smaller the grain size D of a polycrystalline material, the higher are the losses.   For frequencies at which $D/\lambda > 0.3$ the following empirical relationship fits the measured data for many materials:

$$\alpha = \mathbf{K}\frac{\omega}{D} + \Sigma(D) \qquad (8.50)$$

in which $\mathbf{K}$ and $\Sigma(D)$ are constants which depend on the degree of anisotropy in the material.[87]   In Table 8.7 some metals of the cubic system are listed together with their degree of anisotropy, as expressed

Table 8.7   **Anisotropy and Absorption of Some Cubic Metals**

Metal	Symbol	$\dfrac{2(s_{11} - s_{12})}{s_{44}}$	Relative Degree of Attenuation
Silver	Ag	2.85	Medium
Aluminum	Al	1.24	Low
Copper	Cu	3.2	High
Iron	Fe	2.38	Medium
Lead	Pb	3.85	Very high
Tungsten	W	1	Very low

by the ratio $2(s_{11} - s_{12})/s_{44}$ of their elastic compliance constants s, and their relative absorption behavior.[88]

Scattering   The exact combination of effects which leads to the behavior expressed by eq. 8.50 is not as yet fully understood.   The experimental data indicate that sound energy is reflected or scattered

[87] A more refined version of eq. 8.50 has been given by R. K. Roney, Ph.D. thesis, Calif. Inst. of Tech., 1950.   He interprets the first term of eq. 8.50 as due to hysteresis and the second term as due to scattering.

[88] W. Roth, *Quart. Progress Rept.*, R.L.E.—Massachusetts Institute of Technology, October 15, 1947.   In the frequency range where eq. 8.49 is valid, the Q of the material is constant.   For example, for aluminum $Q \simeq 10^4$, for magnesium $Q \simeq 6 \times 10^3$, for clear fused quartz $Q \simeq 4 \times 10^4$.

from the elastic discontinuities at the grain boundaries. Classic theory predicts that the energy which is scattered from a particle smaller than wavelength $(D \ll \lambda)$, is proportional to the fourth power of the frequency (see eq. 3.29a). However, at the lower frequencies where $D/\lambda \ll 1$, the above-mentioned viscous and thermal loss mechanisms seem to overrule the effects of scattering. In turn, at the higher frequencies $(D/\lambda > 0.3)$ the data presented in Fig. 8.30 show

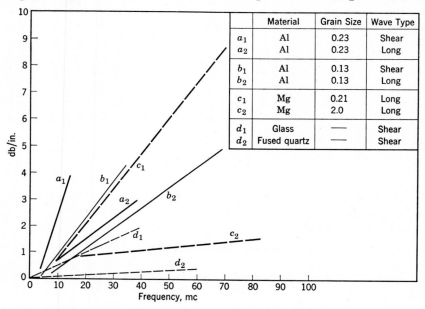

Fig. 8.30.   Measured attenuation versus frequency for some materials and grain sizes (Mason and McSkimmin).

that the attenuation in many solids, whether polycrystalline-anisotropic, or amorphous-isotropic, can be expressed in terms of a linear relationship as in eq. 8.50.[89]

Elastic Hysteresis   A behavior of this type in which the value of $Q = \pi/\alpha\lambda$ is independent of frequency can be treated phenomenologically as an elastic hysteresis.   One then obtains a relationship between elastic stress T_{ij} and elastic strain S_{ij} of the form

$$T_{ij} = [(c_{ik})_a + j\psi_{ik}]S_{ij} \tag{8.51}$$

in which c_{ik} and ψ_{ik} are the real and imaginary part of the complex stiffness constant (see eq. 8.4) and the subscript a indicates adiabatic conditions.   We note

[89] See, for example, the data presented by W. P. Mason and H. J. McSkimmin, *J. Acoust. Soc. Amer.*, *19* (1947), 464, and by R. L. Wegel and H. Walther, *Physics*, *6* (1935), 141.

that the imaginary part ψ_{ik} is assumed to be independent of frequency for this group of solids, while it must be considered to increase with frequency in viscoelastic materials, as is shown in Section A.3.[90]

Equation 8.51 leads to a constant value of $Q = (c_{ik})_a/\psi_{ik}$ and suggests a nonviscous loss mechanism in which the dissipation of energy is proportional to the strain, rather than to the time rate of change of the strain. Such processes are known to occur in crystals, but a quantitative correlation between crystal properties and high-frequency vibrational losses still awaits further theoretical and experimental work.[91]

8.9   Complex Wave Forms and Transient Pulses

The analyses in this book have been restricted essentially to steady-state vibrations of simple harmonic form. The transducer design equations have been expressed in terms of a single frequency at which the sound is generated or received, and we have discussed transmission characteristics and wave phenomena by considering what happens at one particular frequency. We shall now indicate how all these results can be extended, at least within certain limits, to encompass waves and vibrations of much more general form, including pulsed wave trains, square waves, and individual transients such as are obtained in shock excitation.

Several types of continuous waves are illustrated in Fig. 8.31, plotted in amplitude as a function of time. A truly "pure tone" is a simple harmonic wave of infinite duration (Fig. 8.31a), and its spectrum is a single line at the frequency $f_1 = 1/T_1$. A complex harmonic tone (Fig. 8.31b) has a single spectral line at its fundamental $f_1 = 1/T_1$, and in addition a finite number of higher harmonics at integral multiples of the fundamental. The particular amplitudes and frequencies of the harmonics determine the "tone quality" of a sound that is heard by the ear. Square waves (Fig. 8.31c), and any other forms with discontinuous changes in slope, have a fundamental and an infinite number of harmonics, each of which is, however, a single line in the spectrum. Random noise (Fig. 8.31d), unlike the above three forms, has a spectrum that is continuous within some range of frequencies.

In Fig. 8.32, on the other hand, four wave forms of *finite* duration are shown. This characteristic inherently requires their spectra to be of continuous-band character. A spectrum with true lines, i.e., with components of "zero width" at particular frequencies, is possible

[90] W. P. Mason, *Piezoelectric Crystals and Their Application to Ultrasonics*, D. Van Nostrand, New York, 1950, p. 482. A stress-strain relationship for viscous fluids which is analogous to eq. 8.51 but contains a frequency dependent imaginary part $\omega\xi$ is derived in Section A.3, leading to eq. A.11.

[91] R. L. Roderick and J. Truell, *J. Appl. Phys.*, *23* (1952), 267.

only with a wave that repeats itself forever. In practice, the number of cycles of repetition need be only "large," such as a few hundred, for the lines to become so narrow that their finite breadth cannot be measured. From this point of view, a continuous spectrum noise

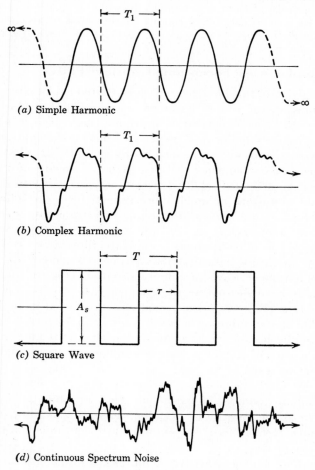

(a) Simple Harmonic

(b) Complex Harmonic

(c) Square Wave

(d) Continuous Spectrum Noise

Fig. 8.31. Typical shapes of continuous waves.

(Fig. 8.31d), even though it may be of infinite duration, cannot have a line spectrum because no one part of the wave form repeats itself exactly; noise is a continually changing series of wave forms of finite duration.

Spectral frequency function Let us examine these spectral characteristics more closely with reference to Fig. 8.33. The ordinate gives the relative amplitude S/A of any spectral component wave, (which may be a wave of voltage, current, sound pressure, vibration displacement, etc.) at a relative frequency $f\tau$ as shown along the abscissa. The normalizing quantities A and τ are related to the pulse length and width as indicated in Fig. 8.31 and 8.32.

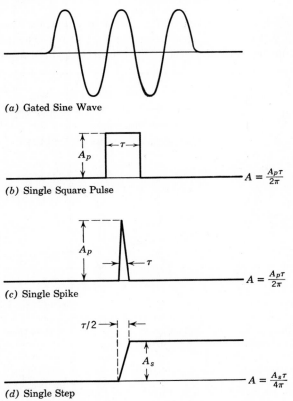

(a) Gated Sine Wave

(b) Single Square Pulse $A = \frac{A_p \tau}{2\pi}$

(c) Single Spike $A = \frac{A_p \tau}{2\pi}$

(d) Single Step $A = \frac{A_s \tau}{4\pi}$

Fig. 8.32. Typical wave forms of finite duration. The quantity A shown at the right-hand side of the graph is the normalized amplitude to be used in Fig. 8.33.

The solid vertical lines at $f\tau = 0.5,\ 1.5,\ 2.5,\ \cdots$ give the spectrum of the symmetrical square wave shown in Fig. 8.31c, where A_s and T are marked. For a 50 per cent duty cycle ($T = 2\tau$), the fundamental frequency is equal to the repetition rate $f_1 = 1/T$ with an amplitude

$$S_1 = \frac{4}{\pi} A_s \frac{\tau}{T} = 0.64 A_s.$$ The higher components are odd harmonics

of the repetition rate at $f_m = mf_1$, $m = 3, 5, 7$, whose amplitudes diminish as $1/m$.

In general, for all values of the duty cycle τ/T the complete wave form is given by

$$F(t) = \frac{2A_s}{\pi} \sum_{n=1}^{n=\infty} \frac{1}{n} \sin\left(n\pi\tau/T\right) \qquad (n = 1, 2, 3, 4, \cdots) \qquad (8.52)$$

where $n = f/f_r$ is the spectral frequency divided by the repetition rate $f_r = 1/T$, A_s is the pulse amplitude, and τ is the pulse width. We note from eq. 8.52 that for $\tau/T < 0.5$ the spectrum contains also

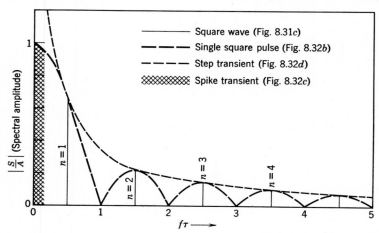

Fig. 8.33. Spectral frequency functions for three kinds of transients, and for continuous square waves. Only the latter produce a line spectrum, as shown by the vertical lines $n = (m + 1)/2$, $m = 1, 3, 5, \cdots$. For narrow spikes ($\tau \gtrsim 10^{-7}$ sec.), the shaded region at left, which contains a continuous frequency spectrum up to several megacycles, indicates the minimum bandwidth required for reproducing this type of transient with fair accuracy.

even harmonics and that the number of harmonics that lie between $f = 0$ and the first minimum of the frequency function (at $f = 1/\tau$) is then given by T/τ.

The first three components of the line spectrum for a 50 per cent duty cycle ($\tau/T = 0.5$) are drawn in Fig. 8.34, and their summation is seen to be an approximation to the shape of a square wave. As more components are added the corners become sharper and the top flatter.

If a true square wave is generated electrically and fed to a transducer or other system that can pass only the first three components, the output wave will look much like the sum shown in Fig. 8.34. In general, the upper frequency limit f_u of a system determines the "sharpness" of the wave forms it can pass; the rise time of the sides of the pulse is roughly $\tau_r \simeq 1/4f_u$. A sharply tuned system, such as a resonant transducer, will respond only to components lying within its bandwidth, regardless of other frequencies that may be present in the input.[92]

We have already mentioned that the finite duration of the wave train leads to a broadening of the spectral lines. If a square wave persists for several cycles and then stops, its spectrum will be a series of bands of finite width, each centered on one of the line components. The limiting case is a single square pulse (Fig. 8.32b), and its spectrum,

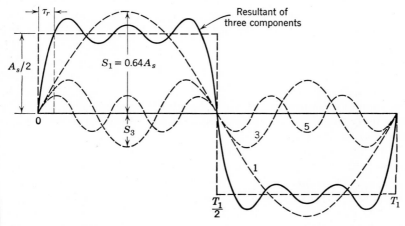

Fig. 8.34.   Superposition of first three harmonic components in a square wave.

as shown in Fig. 8.33, is a series of bands centered at $f\tau = \frac{1}{2}, \frac{3}{2}, \frac{5}{2}, \frac{7}{2}, \cdots$, dropping to (theoretically) zero value only at discrete points $f\tau = 1, 2, 3 \cdots$.   The equation for this spectrum is:

$$S/A = \sin\,(\pi f\tau)/\pi f\tau \tag{8.53}$$

in which $A = A_p T/2\pi$ and τ is the pulse width.

In eqs. 8.52 and 8.53 the sine function is negative at $f\tau = \frac{3}{2}, \frac{7}{2}, 1\frac{1}{2}, \cdots$ and the corresponding spectral line components S are also negative.   The physical meaning of the sign alteration is clear from Fig. 8.34: at the center of the square pulse (or of each half-cycle of the square wave) the third harmonic component is down when the first and fifth harmonic components are up.   Only by this successive

[92] If, for example, the transducer pass band is $4 < f\tau < 5$, the square-wave spectrum shown in Fig. 8.33 yields only a single frequency response at $f\tau = 4.5$; i.e., the transducer will "ring" at this frequency.

alteration in signs can all the components average out to give the flat top. Phase relations of this kind usually are of little practical concern, for we are mainly interested in the power carried by the wave or its components. Thus, in Fig. 8.33 we show only the absolute magnitude $|S/A|$, the square of which is proportional to power.

If the width of the single square pulse is made very small, as in a spike transient (Fig. 8.32c), $f\tau$ becomes small up to very high values of f, and eq. 8.53 approaches a constant value of unity. This means that practically the whole wide-frequency band required to reproduce the spike is contained within the shaded region of Fig. 8.33. On the other hand, the spectrum of a single step function (Fig. 8.32d) can be shown to vary as $1/f$. In order to plot the spectrum against $f\tau$ in Fig. 8.33 we ascribe a value $\tau/2$ to the rise time of the step. The effective "amplitude" is then $A = A_s\tau/4\pi$, and the spectral function is $S/A = 1/\pi f\tau$. In both cases, the spike transient and the step transient, the width of the required spectrum is determined by the rise time or steepness τ. Thus a transducer or receiver must have an essentially flat response up to a frequency $1/\tau$ in order to reproduce a transient of this kind.

The square pulse and the spike have finite values of energy at zero frequency, unlike harmonic and other periodic waves of infinite duration. This means that a "direct-current" component is involved. In the step transient the d-c amplitude approaches infinity. For example, the onset of a single explosion, in which gases expand suddenly outward at high pressure, approximates a step wave. However, in the tail of the resulting shock wave the gas flows back to the reduced pressure region, and this causes the total d-c component to be finite. Besides, infinite steepness of the wave front cannot be realized because of dissipation in the medium.[93]

Bandwidth requirements   In the foregoing discussion we have demonstrated the inherent spectral characteristics of some complex wave forms. In analytical applications of sonics we are mainly concerned with wave trains of a specific carrier frequency f_0 which are pulsed at some repetition rate f_r. Each pulse then consists of a number of sinusoidal oscillations which, at the leading edge of the pulse and at the end of the pulse, take a finite number of oscillations in order to rise and to decay, respectively. For accurate pulse propa-

---

[93] We saw in section 6.5 that the non-linearity of the medium produces wave-shape distortion, if airborne sound is generated at intensity levels above 150 db, such as in siren applications. The resulting wave assumes the shape of a sawtooth whose steepness remains finite, since the higher harmonics are more strongly attenuated in the medium.

gation measurements the length of the pulse is required to be much smaller than the path length of transmission, or of the distance between two echo-producing objects that are to be resolved.

Let this distance be of the order of 1 cm and let two oscillations be required both for build-up and for decay of the pulse. For steel $[c = 5.8 \times 10^3$ (m/sec)] the frequency of a 4-cycle wave train of 1-cm length then becomes about 2.5 mcps. Applications such as the localization of flaws in solids by means of sound waves thus requires the use of ultrasonic frequencies in the megacycle range. For propagation measurements in extended media or for underwater signaling, on the other hand, much longer pulses and hence lower frequencies are permissible. As the frequency is lowered, beam-width considerations (see Sections 3.3 and 5.9) impose the main limitation to pulse techniques.

The frequency spectrum of repetitive wave forms of short duration as used in ultrasonic pulse techniques is contained in a band centered around the carrier frequency f_0. Just as a sinusoidally modulated carrier wave has two side bands $f_0 \pm f_m$, a pulse-modulated carrier wave has two side bands of a spectral distribution as given by eq. 8.52. For square pulses and a duty cycle of 50 per cent the frequencies on the side bands are given by $f_0 \pm n f_r$, where f_r is the repetition frequency of the pulses. Both the electronic circuits and the electromechanical transducers of a pulse system must be capable of passing a major part of the frequency spectrum to retain the original pulse shape.[94] In many cases it is sufficient to provide a bandwidth $B = 2\,\Delta f$ wide enough to pass the tenth harmonic of $f \simeq 1/\tau$, where τ is the pulse width. For example if $\tau = 10$ μsec at $f_0 = 5$ mcps, the necessary bandwidth becomes $B = 2$ mcps. If a resonant transducer is used, its Q should be about 2.5. We saw in Section 4.6 that special damping must be provided in order to reduce the Q of crystal transducers to such low values.

The 10-μsec pulse of the example mentioned above corresponds to a length of the wave train in steel of about 6 cm. For the detection of flaws near the surface of a work piece this is much too long, and even shorter pulses, of the order of 1 μsec are desirable. Unless the frequency of the carrier is raised considerably, which often is ruled out by the losses encountered in the medium at such high frequencies, the performance of resonant transducers is severely limited. Operation in the flat region of the response curve below resonance, however, inherently leads to reduced sensitivity while the transducer still tends

[94] For very short pulses a highly attenuating medium may act in itself as a low pass filter, which leads to a rounding of the edges of the pulse owing to reduction of the high-frequency components.

to "ring" in its own mechanical resonances after the excitation is turned off.

Some practical aspects of ultrasonic pulse techniques are discussed in Section 8.10. Other examples of the use of transient excitation for generating powerful sonic signals are the explosive shock waves used in geophysical and oceanographic exploration,[95] successive impacts of a hammer on a metal plate,[96] and electric spark discharges in a gas.[97] Detailed analysis of transient phenomena are thoroughly covered in other books,[98] but the elementary discussion given above will provide a useful starting point on questions of spectral character and bandwidth requirements.

8.10   Ultrasonic Pulse Techniques

We shall limit the final section of this chapter to a discussion of those pulse methods which are widely used in industry for the non-destructive testing of materials. The basic principles involved in the generation and detection of pulse-modulated ultrasonic signals are much the same as in radar systems. For details on the required electronic circuitry the reader is thus referred to standard textbooks.[99] On the other hand, ultrasonic pulse-propagation studies on a model scale in bounded media of specific shape and structure can be helpful in evaluating a variety of elastic wave phenomena, such as the reflection and mode conversion of seismic waves, the refraction of sound waves in the ocean and—except for non-linear effects—the propagation of shock waves in all kinds of media.[100]

[95] Instrumentation for geophysical exploration is discussed by D. H. Clewell et. al., *Rev. Sci. Instr.*, 24 (1953), 243. Shock-wave phenomena under water are treated by M. F. M. Osborne and J. L. Carter, *J. Appl. Phys.*, *17* (1946), 871; M. F. M. Osborne and A. H. Taylor, *Phys. Rev.*, *70* (1946), 322.

[96] Methods for impact studies are described by H. Gerdien and W. Schaaffs, *Frequency* (Berlin), *2* (1948), 49.

[97] X-ray studies of shock waves are reported by W. Schaaffs and F. Trendelenburg, *Z. Naturforsch.*, *3a* (1948), 656; R. Schall and G. Thomer, *Z. angew. Phys.*, *3* (1951), 41. See also O. von Schmidt, *Z. tech. Phys.*, *19* (1938), 554.

[98] G. Doetsch, *Theorie und Anwendung der Laplace Transformation*, 1937, Springer Verlag, Berlin; M. F. Gardner and J. L. Barnes, *Transients in Linear Systems*, 1942, John Wiley & Sons, New York; I. N. Sneddon, *Fourier Transforms*, McGraw-Hill, New York, 1951.

[99] Massachusetts Institute of Technology, *Radiation Laboratory Series*, Vol. 1 and 20, McGraw-Hill, New York 1949. O. S. Puckle, *Time Bases*, Wiley, New York, 1943. Ellmore and Sands, *Electronics*, McGraw-Hill, New York, 1949.

[100] It is beyond the scope of this book to deal in any detail with the special properties of shock waves. This subject is fully discussed in R. Courant and K. O. Friedrichs, *Supersonic Flow and Shock Waves*, Interscience Publishers, New York, 1950, and G. I. Taylor and J. W. Maccoll, *The Mechanics of Compressible Fluids*,

Most ultrasonic pulse methods, whether used for the testing of material properties or for the localization of reflecting objects (flaws in solids, obstacles under water) rely on a presentation of the received signals on a time scale. This principle, already alluded to in Section 8.1, has several advantages over CW methods; the average power is low while the peak power is high enough to operate at a favorable signal to noise ratio; it is possible to discriminate in the time domain against unwanted reflections or wave types, and against direct electromagnetic radiation; the flexibility of pulse systems is considerable, since both liquids and solids can be analyzed and parts can be tested without disassembly.[101]

The generation and reception of the pulses can be achieved in two ways: by the transmission method, which uses two transducers separated by a suitable distance in the test medium; or by the reflection method, which uses only one transducer for both sending and receiving. The reflection method requires certain precautions against overloading of the receiver by the transmitted primary pulse. However, it has the great advantage of requiring accessibility to only one side of a test piece and of being sensitive to very small amounts of radiation scattered back from inhomogeneities in the medium. Thus the reflection method is employed mainly for localization purposes in media of known velocity, whereas the transmission method is preferably used in the determination of sound velocity c and sound absorption α in liquids or immersed solids. The significance of measurements of c and α for a study of molecular properties is the subject of the appendix in this book.[102]

Pulse-reflection methods A typical pulse-reflection system is depicted in Fig. 8.35. Square pulses of short duration τ, say 1 to 10 μsec, and occurring at regular intervals T, say 100 to 1000 times per second, are used to modulate the RF signal which drives the transducer crystal. Pulse modulation can be effected in several ways. In systems of the kind shown in Fig. 8.35 either the oscillator

Springer Verlag, Berlin, 1935. Fractures produced by stress pulses in solids are treated in H. Kolsky, *Stress Waves in Solids*, Clarendon Press, Oxford, 1953.

[101] Typical examples are the testing of pipes, boilers, railroad tracks, locomotive axles, turbine shafts. Detailed reports on these and other applications can be found in *Nondestructive Testing*, journal published by the Society for Nondestructive Testing, 1109 Hinman Ave., Evanston, Ill.

[102] Special techniques for such measurements have been discussed by P. Biquard and G. Ahier, *Cahiers Phys.*, 15 (1943), 21; J. R. Pellam and J. K. Galt, *J. Chem. Phys.*, 14 (1946), 608; S. C. Mowry *J. Acoust. Soc. Amer.*, 20 (1948), 432; G. Bradfield, *Nuovo Cimento*, Suppl. to 7 (1950), 162; E. L. Carstensen, Kam Li, and H. P. Schwan, *J. Acoust. Soc. Amer.*, 25 (1953), 286.

or the power stage of a multistage transmitter may be gated by pulses derived from a multivibrator. Other systems use self-pulsed (self-quenched) oscillators, or shock excitation, as discussed below.

The crystal emits a short ultrasonic wave train of length $c\tau$ which travels into the test medium to be partly or wholly reflected. The amount of reflected energy which is returned to the crystal depends on the size, shape, and orientation of the reflecting interface (i.e., its scattering function; see Section 3.7), on the impedance values at the interface, and on the product αx of the attenuation α in the medium and the path length x. The sonic echo is converted to an

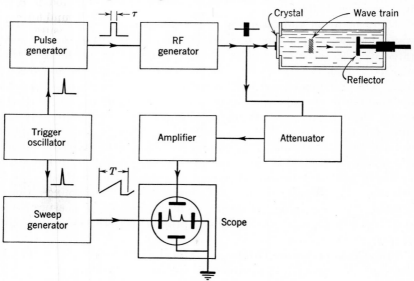

Fig. 8.35.   Schematic diagram of a pulse-reflection system.

electrical RF pulse in the crystal, which is then amplified and displayed on a cathode-ray tube. The time base of the cathode-ray tube is provided by a periodic saw-tooth deflection voltage which is synchronized with the original trigger pulses. As the distance between crystal and reflector is changed one may either determine the changes in position and amplitude of the echoes on the scope, or one may keep the position and the amplitude of the received echo constant by inserting known amounts of sweep delay and attenuation, respectively. Of the two methods, the former is mainly used for flaw detection and quality control in industrial parts, whereas the latter is superior in applications where the elastic propagation constants c and α are to be evaluated with high accuracy.

Pulse-phase methods   The accuracy of determining the position of a delayed pulse echo is limited by the finite width of the leading edge of the pulse.   For high-precision analysis of small solid specimens the technique can be refined by means of a phase analysis of the pulses propagated through the test material.   A schematic diagram of this method which is similar to the one exemplified in Fig. 8.26 is

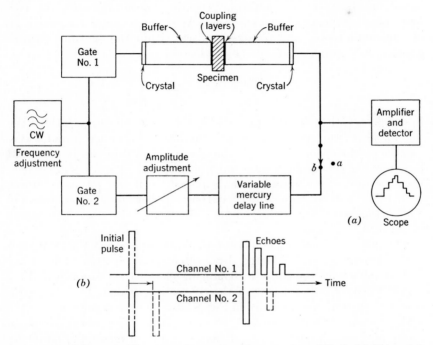

Fig. 8.36.   Schematic diagram of a pulse phase system (H. J. McSkimmin). With switch position *a* the step-ladder pattern (*a*) is observed on the scope if the frequency is adjusted according to eq. 8.54.   With switch position *b* pulse cancellation can be achieved, as shown by the lower diagram (*b*).

shown in Fig. 8.36.   The oscillations from a continuous RF generator are gated by d-c pulses.   One gate feeds pulses to the crystal transducer attached to one end of a transmission path, which consists of two silica rods separated by the specimen.   The other gate feeds pulses of identical shape into a variable mercury delay line.[103]   The performance of both gating circuits must be such that the pulse position in time is variable.   Both channels, the one consisting of the

---

[103] H. J. McSkimmin, *J. Acoust. Soc. Amer.*, *22* (1950), 413.   Mercury delay lines are described by the same author in U.S. Pat. 2,505,364, April 25, 1950.

silica rods and the one consisting of a mercury column, are terminated by a receiving crystal whose output is fed to a wide band converter-amplifier with diode.

The system depicted in Fig. 8.36 can be used in two ways. One, designated by the switch position (a), uses only channel (1) for a determination of sound velocity c in the specimen. This method is based on the fact that multiple reflections occur between the two faces of a specimen of thickness b. At one particular frequency ω_n of the oscillator all the reflected pulses within the specimen are in phase, which corresponds to the condition

$$\frac{2b\omega_n}{c} + 2\varphi_n = 2\pi n \qquad (8.54)$$

in which φ_n is the phase change produced by the impedance ratio at the boundaries of the specimen and n is the integral number of half wavelengths in the specimen. This "in-phase" condition can be detected by widening the applied pulse until overlapping of subsequent reflections occurs. The frequency is adjusted until the pulses reinforce each other and a "step-ladder" pattern appears on the oscilloscope. The sound velocity c of the sample can then be determined by means of eq. 8.54, if φ_n is known.[104]

The other variant of the phase technique depicted in Fig. 8.36 uses both channels, as designated by switch position (b). The delay and amplitude of the pulse in balancing channel (2) are adjusted for complete cancellation of one of the echoes in channel (1). This procedure is shown schematically in Fig. 8.36b. The accuracy obtainable with the cancellation method is about 1°, which corresponds to errors of 1 part in 10^4, provided that the system meets the following requirements.

The length l of the buffer rods must be sufficient that reflections from the rod ends are delayed beyond the time taken by the desired number n of multiple reflections within the specimen of thickness t:

$$\frac{2l}{c_{\text{rod}}} > n \frac{2t}{c_{\text{specimen}}}$$

Further, the time T between pulses must be long enough to prevent the echoes produced by one pulse from overlapping the echoes from the succeeding pulse. Finally, the diameter of the buffer rods should be about 30 wavelengths or greater to minimize subsidiary echoes

[104] The determination of φ_n is described by H. J. McSkimmin, *loc. cit.* (see footnote 103).

resulting from waves impinging on the lateral boundaries of the rods. The influence of the boundaries on divergent wave components may be further suppressed by roughening and coating the rod surfaces with absorptive material and by employing crystals of a diameter which is somewhat smaller than the rod diameter.

The methods described above may be varied in a number of ways. For example, the determination of the depth of an echo-generating interface can be effected quite simply by a circuit in which each received echo triggers the next transmitted pulse. In a system of

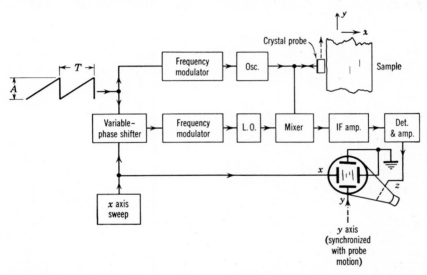

Fig. 8.37. Schematic diagram of a frequency-modulated system (D. C. Erdman). The variable phase shifter acts, in conjunction with a sharp IF filter, as a delay gate which is swept through the depth coordinate of the sample in synchronism with the x-axis CRO-sweep.

this kind the pulse repetition rate is a direct measure of the depth, provided that there is but one reflecting interface, as in some maritime fathometer applications.

Frequency-modulated systems Another modification of the pulse-reflection method uses frequency-modulated pulses. In this case the depth of the reflecting object is not identified by the time delay between transmitted and received pulses, but by the frequency difference between the received FM pulse and a frequency-modulated local oscillator.

A system of this type is illustrated in Fig. 8.37. Since pulsing is not a basic requirement in a FM system, the figure demonstrates the essential features of this method in terms of continuous oscillations whose frequency varies in a sawtooth fashion.[105] There are two channels which are both frequency modulated by the same sawtooth voltage. One channel drives the crystal probe; the other provides a reference signal whose frequency modulation can be delayed relative to the first channel. The outputs of both channels are connected to a mixer stage which is followed by a sharply tuned IF filter. The waves reflected from a flaw within a test piece produce a difference frequency which is accepted only by the IF filter, if the modulating saw tooth for the reference signal is delayed by an amount proportional to the depth of the flaw.

We note from Fig. 8.37 that the position of the delay gate controls the horizontal deflection on the scope, whereas the occurrence of a difference frequency which passes the filter leads to a bright marking on the face of an intensity-modulated long-persistence tube. A cross-sectional view is obtained if the vertical deflection on the scope is synchronized with the scanning motion of the transducer across the surface of the test piece.[106] The scanning of a crystal probe over a work piece is often facilitated by immersion of the piece in a water bath, in which the transducer moves back and forth at some distance from the piece.

Presentation techniques   The type of scope presentation illustrated above is known as "*B*-scan." It yields a two-dimensional picture of a cross-sectional plane through the test piece and is used for flaw detection in metal plates and pipes,[107] for medical diagnosis of abnormal tissue changes,[108] and for mapping of the sea bottom. Two typical recordings obtained by similar principles, but in widely different applications, are shown in Fig. 8.38 in order to illustrate the possibilities of *B*-type presentation. Figure 8.38*a* is a pulse-echo recording on electrosensitive paper obtained with a commercial magnetostrictive fathometer. It shows a large school of herrings located midway between the sea bottom and the surface of the ocean. Figure 8.38*b* is an oscillographic recording of a ⅝-in. aluminum plate containing

[105] A frequency-modulated wave of constant amplitude has a frequency spectrum similar to Fig. 8.33, but the sine-function is replaced by a Bessel function. See *Frequency Analysis, Modulation and Noise*, by S. Goldman, McGraw-Hill, New York, 1948.

[106] D. C. Erdman, U.S. Pat. 2,593,865, April 22, 1952.

[107] D. C. Erdmann, paper presented to the Society of Nondestructive Testing, Cleveland, Ohio, October 1953.

[108] J. J. Wild and J. M. Reid, *J. Acoust. Soc. Amer.*, *25* (1953), 270. D. Howry, paper presented at *IRE Symposium on Medical Electronics*, New York, November 18, 1953.

laminations, which was scanned by a frequency-modulated flaw-detection system of the kind described above.

It should be noted that the strength of an echo cannot be indicated very accurately on a B-scan, since the dynamic range available in most recording devices is quite limited.[109]   However, for a given position of the crystal probe the received signal can be connected to the vertical scope amplifier to yield the conventional "A-scan," which gives an accurate indication of the pulse height of the echoes.   In some applications, on the other hand, a two dimensional "plan-view" is desired.

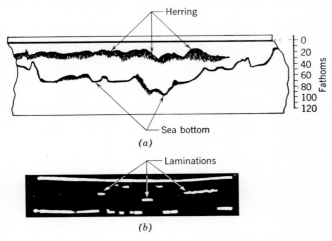

Fig. 8.38.   Examples of B-type presentation. a, Fish location in the ocean (courtesy of SCAM, Paris, France). b, Detection of lamination in a plate (courtesy of Electro Circuits Inc., Pasadena, California).

Such a "P-scan" is obtained by synchronizing the x and y component of the scanning motion of the crystal probe with the x and y deflection, respectively, on the scope.   By suitable gating, only echoes arising from the interior of the test piece will be indicated as bright spots on the scope.   There is, however, no indication of the echo depth in a P-scan.[110]

Factors influencing the resolving power   The depth resolution of pulsed systems is a function of the overall band pass characteristics,

---

[109] The brightness range of the phosphors used in television tubes, as well as the darkness range of the electrosensitive paper in facsimile recorders, are of the order of 10–15 db.

[110] In principle, the ultrasonic plan-view presentation operates just as the so-called PPI-radar system.   In fact, ultrasonic scale models are being used for the training of radar operators.   For details on these techniques see F. J. Larsen, *Electronics, 19* (1946), 126.   C. E. Teeter, *J. Acoust. Soc. Amer., 18* (1946), 448.

including electronic circuits for sending and receiving, transducer and medium. The spectral composition of pulses is discussed in Section 8.9. Short pulses or large amounts of frequency modulation likewise require low Q circuits and strongly damped transducers For a given pass band the depth resolution is determined by the width

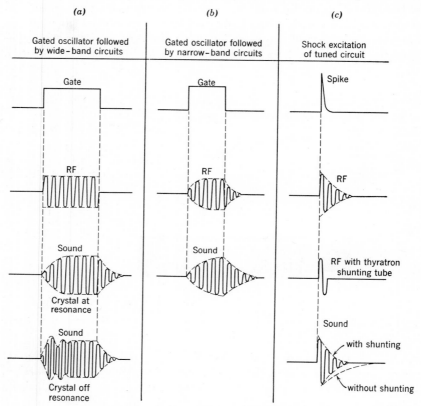

Fig. 8.39.   Three common types of pulsing.

of the propagated pulse, if time delay is measured, or by the sensitivity of the analyzing filter if frequency shift is measured.

Figure 8.39 illustrates some typical shapes of the ultrasonic wave trains which can be generated with three common types of pulsing. Let us first consider square gating pulses as derived, for example, from a multivibrator. In order to retain a square envelope of the gated RF oscillations, low Q electronic circuits must be used between the gated stage and the transducer. A comparison between Fig. 8.39a and 8.39b shows the effects of insufficient damping on the build-up and decay

of the RF pulse.   However, we note that even a perfectly square
driving pulse is finally distorted as a consequence of the limited transducer bandwidth.   This, in fact, constitutes a lower limit for the width
of all pulses generated by gating.

Some improvement can be achieved by shock excitation, as depicted
in Fig. 8.39c.   A strong spike produced, for example, by the discharge
of a condenser through a thyratron, will effectively reduce the build-up
time to a fraction of a quarter cycle of the transducer oscillations.

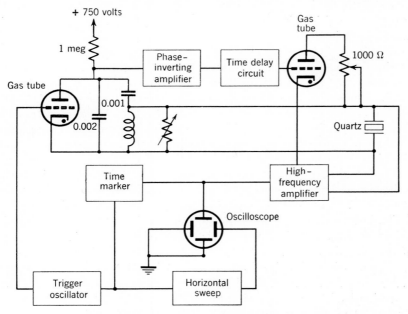

Fig. 8.40.   Circuit for shock excitation (F. A. Firestone).

However, the decay time or ringing of the transducer is still essentially
determined by its mechanical Q which is a function of both the transducer loading and backing.[111]

There are two ways of shock-exciting a crystal transducer: either
the electric spike is directly applied to a crystal operated without
resonant circuit; or the spike is used to shock-excite a resonant circuit
formed by the crystal capacitance and a shunt inductance.   In the
second case, it is suitable to shunt the crystal after a delay of about
1 cycle by means of a second thyratron.   A circuit of this kind, using
two thyratrons, is shown in Fig. 8.40.   We note from Fig. 8.39c

---

[111] For a given transducer the loading can be optimized to some extent by electrical matching, as discussed in Section 4.11.

that the shunting effectively reduces the ringing of the tuned transducer circuit.[112]

So far we have discussed only the factors influencing depth resolution. The lateral resolution which can be achieved by a scanning system depends mainly on the width of the ultrasonic beam. The principles underlying the formation of beamed radiation from a piston source are discussed in Section 3.3. For high lateral resolution a beam characteristic is desired which has both a small angle of divergence of the main lobe and a small beam diameter D, which leads to the two conditions $D \gg \lambda$ and $D < s$, in which λ is the ultrasonic wavelength in the material to be tested and s is the lateral spacing of two objects which are to be resolved. For example, if $s \simeq 1$ cm, D should be approximately 0.5 cm and λ should be of the order of 0.5 mm, corresponding to a frequency of 10 mcps, if the medium is steel. Considering the high attenuation encountered in many solids at these frequencies, we recognize another limitation of ultrasonic flaw detection systems: the higher the desired lateral resolving power, the lower the depth of penetration, owing to the losses associated with the high frequencies.[113]

Mode conversion at boundaries In certain applications the finite spreading of the searching beam leads to several additional difficulties. Consider the detection of flaws in a long cylindrical bar which is accessible only from its end faces, as in the testing of railroad axles. Figure 8.41 illustrates this application for various positions of the transducer on the end face of a bar. Due to beam divergence some part of the longitudinal waves (L) irradiated from the crystal probe are reflected at grazing incidence from the rod boundaries. This reflection leads to a conversion of part of the sound energy into shear waves (S) whose angle of reflection differs considerably from that of the longitudinal waves (see Section 3.5). These shear waves, in turn, will be reflected back and forth between the sides of the rod and at each reflection part of their energy is converted into another longitudinal wave. The result of the repeated reflections and conversions is a multiplicity of pulses, which may obscure the presence of an eventual echo from a small flaw on the final scope presentation.[114]

---

[112] The circuit of Fig. 8.40 and its application to ultrasonic flaw detection was proposed first by F. A. Firestone, U.S. Pat. 2,280,226, April 21, 1942.

[113] The energy returned from a reflecting object imbedded in a test piece also depends on the scattering properties of the object, as shown in Section 3.7.

[114] There is one useful application of this phenomenon for the determination of the velocities of both longitudinal and shear waves by a single measurement in a suitable rod. For details see H. Hughes, *Phys. Rev.*, *75* (1949), 1553, and A. Lutsch, *Z. angew. Phys.*, *4* (1952), 166.

Mode conversion at boundaries between media of different specific impedance is an important phenomenon in seismological applications of sonics.[115]   The amount of energy converted from one wave type to the other depends on the angle of incidence and on the Poisson's ratio of the material.   At certain critical angles the conversion from a shear wave to a compressional wave, or vice versa, may be complete.   For example, a compressional wave in Pyrex glass, incident at a plane glass-air interface, is converted completely into a shear wave if the

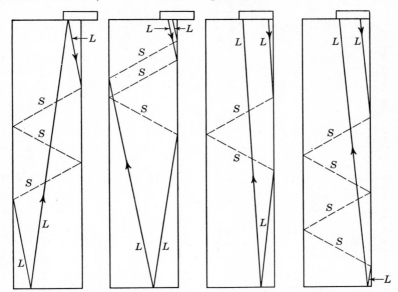

Fig. 8.41.   Formation of subsidiary echoes in a rod.   Longitudinal waves **(L)** are converted at the boundaries into shear waves (S), and vice versa.

angle of incidence is about 45°.   A shear wave in Pyrex glass, on the other hand, is converted completely into a compressional wave if the angle of incidence at the glass-air boundary is 27°, whereas at angles above 40° all the energy is reflected as a shear wave.   It must be noted that complete conversion of energy from one wave type to another is possible only if the Poisson's ratio of the medium is smaller than $\sigma = 0.26$.   This is the case for most glasses (Pyrex: $\sigma = 0.16$), whereas metals and many other solids have higher values of σ (steel: $\sigma = 0.31$).[116]

[115] C. G. Knott, *Phil. Mag.*, *48* (1899), 64.   J. F. Macelwane and F. W. Sohon *Introduction to Theoretical Seismology*, John Wiley & Sons, New York, 1936.

[116] D. Arenberg, *J. Acoust. Soc. Amer.*, *20* (1948), 1.   This paper, dealing with ultrasonic delay lines, gives an excellent survey of mode-conversion phenomena.

Table 8.8 Comparison among Flaw-Detection Methods

	Resonance (Page 343)	CW Transmission (Page 348)	Image Converter (Page 353)	Pulse Echo (Page 384)	X-Ray
Physical basis for detection	Reflection at plane parallel surfaces	Interruption of beam by large flaws	Interruption of beam for large flaws, diffraction for small flaws	Reflection at interfaces, back scattering at inclusions	Differential absorption based on total solid-air contrast
Requirements for coupling to work piece	Access to one side of work only; flat surfaces, direct contact	Access to both sides of work; direct contact or immersion in coupling liquid; critical angles	Access to both sides; immersion in special coupling liquid; good wetting essential	Access to one side of work only; direct contact; clean surfaces for large depths	Access to both sides of work piece; no contact problems
Range of penetration	0.05 to 30 cm in steel, thickness limited by losses and identification of harmonic	Up to 12 m in steel, limited by losses and diffraction	Up to 50 cm in steel; limited by losses and lens aperture	Depth less than 2 cm difficult; upper limit about 10 m in steel at 0.25 mc	Above 2 m only with supervoltage equipment
Field of inspection	Narrow; scanning essential	Narrow; scanning essential	Field diameter 10 to 20 cm	Variability of beam width and angle	Unlimited
Geometrical limitations	Flat plates, sheets or large-diameter pipes; also rails	Simple shapes such as plates and cylinders	Curved pieces difficult due to standing waves	All shapes	All shapes

Resolving power	Limited by beam diameter; sensitive to small separations	For small flaws or large depths limited by diffraction	High laterally, small in depth	High in depth, small laterally	Deep-seated small flaws difficult because resolution depends on contrast
Presentation	Sweep synchronized with frequency modulation; calibration for known materials	Recording of transmitted sound level or meter indication	Two-dimensional screen picture, adjustable in third dimension; direct indication of shape	Display in depth on calibrated range scope, or in depth and width on B-scope; shape identification limited	Shadowgraph on photographic film; no direct indication of depth
Manipulation	No special adjustments; short inspection time; equipment light and portable	Adjustments and evaluation difficult; long inspection time; immersion type equipment rather bulky	Special adjustments; evaluation easy; short inspection time; heavy equipment	Routine adjustments; evaluation moderately difficult; long inspection time, portable equipment	Adjustments difficult; for thick pieces long exposure times; radiation hazards; heavy equipment

The boundary phenomena, outlined above, have found a useful application in the testing of plates and pipe walls. By sending the search beam into the material at a suitable angle, waves of a specified type and direction of propagation can be set up. The required instrumentation is illustrated in schematic form by Fig. 8.42. The crystal probe is coupled to the test piece by means of a solid wedge. Depending on the wedge angle, compressional, shear, or Rayleigh waves may be sent down the plate. It can be seen from Fig. 8.42 that this method is particularly suitable for the detection of radial cracks in pipes and of welded seams which are not directly accessible to the search unit.[117]

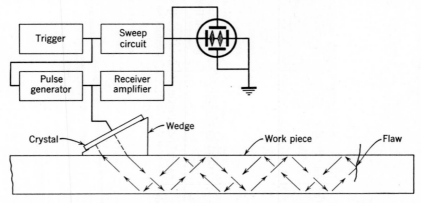

Fig. 8.42.   Beam refraction system for the inspection of plates and pipes (B. Carlin).

An angle unit consisting of a Lucite wedge, a flat quartz disc, and means for connecting a cable to the crystal is shown in Fig. 8.43.

It is not possible to give a complete review of all the possible uses and technical modifications which exist with a method as widely used in industry as the ultrasonic pulse-reflection method.[118] It has appeared to be more important to indicate its physical principles as well as its inherent limitations. To assist the reader in evaluating whether a testing problem may be solved successfully by one of the methods

[117] B. Carlin, U.S. Pat. 2,527,986, issued October 31, 1950. For further refinements of this and other techniques see the review article by F. A. Firestone,"Tricks with the Supersonic Reflectoscope," in the 1948 Fall number of *J. Nondestructive Testing.*

[118] The widely ranging possibilities of the ultrasonic echo method for nondestructive testing are reviewed in the following references: F. A. Firestone, *J. Acoust. Soc. Amer., 17* (1945), 295; R. V. Baud, *Schweiz. Bauztg.* (Zürich), *66,* April 1948; E. G. Stanford, *Nuovo Cimento, 7* (1951), Suppl. 2, p. 446; A. Lutsch, *Arch. Eisenhüttenw., 23* (1952), 57.

Fig. 8.43.   Wedge transducer.   Courtesy of SCAM, Paris, France.

discussed in this chapter, a comparison among the various techniques is given in Table 8.8.   Also, one has to keep in mind that there are other well-established methods, using X-rays, magnetic induction, or beta-radiation, which may be superior for a particular testing problem.

Acoustical Relaxation Mechanisms in Fluids

A.1 General Relations between Macroscopic and Microscopic Properties

The physical properties of any medium may be described either from a macroscopic or from a microscopic point of view. On a macroscopic scale, matter is treated as a continuum which possesses certain properties clearly defined by well-known measuring operations. No knowledge of the internal structure is assumed. Density, for example, can be found by a measurement of mass and by a determination of volume. Similarly, such properties as the thermal expansion coefficient, the compressibility, the viscosity, the surface tension, and the thermal conductivity can be determined for any "lump" of matter by direct measurements of length, mass, time, and temperature. These quantities, in turn, determine the velocity of sound and the absorption of sound which then both appear as macroscopic properties.

The microscopic point of view, on the other hand, is aimed at a detailed knowledge of the internal structure and composition of matter. When one asks what are the forces between atoms and molecules, how they are distributed in space, what energies they possess, and how many degrees of freedom are available, he is entering the realm of the microscopic. Since the molecules and their motions are beyond our direct visual capabilities, the desired information must be obtained indirectly by observations of macroscopic properties. In the following sections we shall show how some microscopic properties can be inferred from sonic measurements.

For example, the velocity of a sound wave is a function of the density and compressibility of the medium. From a static measurement of the isothermal compressibility and from a sonic measurement of the adiabatic compressibility, the ratio of specific heats and the specific heat at constant volume can be determined. These properties in turn, are related to the intermolecular forces, the molecular packing, and the internal degrees of freedom.

Sound absorption in fluids (i.e., both liquids and gases) is determined mainly by viscosity,[1] heat conduction, and molecular effects. The kinetic mechanisms of viscosity and heat conduction are related to the mean free path of the molecules in the case of a gas (see Section 6.3), or the average intermolecular spacing and the binding energies in the case of a liquid.

Sound absorption can be treated phenomenologically as the effect of a time lag between a variation in sound pressure and the associated variation in density in a sound wave. Viscosity, heat conduction, and molecular processes can all be discussed from this unified viewpoint, as indicated in the following sections. The lag between pressure and density can be shown to depend on the time necessary for heat conduction from high- to low-pressure regions in the sound field, or on the time necessary for viscous stresses in the fluid to be equalized, or on the time necessary for molecular energy exchanges to occur. Thus absorption measurements can furnish significant information both for the theory of energy transfer by collision in gases and for the development of concepts to describe the liquid state.

A.2 Phase Lag between Pressure and Density

Let us plot the instantaneous pressure p and volume V of a mass of fluid m in a pV diagram as shown in Fig. A.1. The initial state is point 1, and the final state point 2 is reached along path A. An amount of work W is done, which is given by:

$$W = \int_1^2 p \, dV \qquad (\text{A.1})[2]$$

If the fluid is returned to its initial pressure and volume (point 1) by passing through all the intermediate states lying along path A, an equal and opposite amount of work is done and the *net* work done is zero.

Now suppose the transition from state 1 to state 2 takes place along path B and the return to the initial state is along path C. It is obvious that the integral of $p \, dV$ when following path B does not balance that when traveling along path C. That is, an amount of

---

[1] Experimental values of the sound-absorption coefficient can be made to agree with those calculated on the basis of a viscosity mechanism if the classic hydrodynamic equations of Stokes are modified to include the effects of a compressional viscosity in addition to the ordinary shear viscosity.

[2] The dimension of pressure is newton/m^2, and the dimension of volume is m^3; hence $p \, dV$ is in newtons $\times$ meters = joules.

work has been done which is equal to the area enclosed by the pV loop. This situation arises if pressure and density differ by a phase angle, as illustrated in Fig. A.2. The instantaneous pressure and density are plotted for the case of harmonic time dependence. The

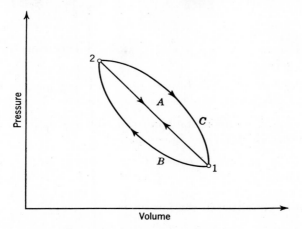

Fig. A.1. pV-loop representing the work done per cycle.

phase difference φ is equal to $2\pi\Delta t/T$, where T is the period of the sound wave.

We consider here the case of a medium with a relatively small attenuation, so that the phase lag φ is small. In such a case, the

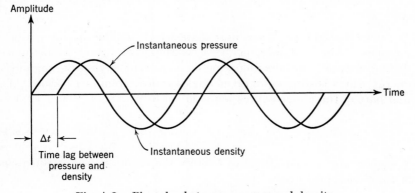

Fig. A.2.   Phase lag between pressure and density.

excess pressure and excess density at a given point in the sound field can be written as

$$p_e = Pe^{j\omega t} \qquad \text{and} \qquad \rho_e = De^{j(\omega t+\varphi)}$$

The total pressure is $p = P_0 + p_e$, where P_0 is the ambient pressure; the total density is $\rho = \rho_0 + \rho_e$, where ρ_0 is the ambient density. Then the change in volume of a small volume V of mass m can be found from

$$V = \frac{m}{\rho} \qquad dV = -\frac{m}{\rho^2}\, d\rho$$

Since ρ_0 is constant, $d\rho = d\rho_e = j\omega\rho_e\, dt$. Substituting these results in eq. A.1 gives

$$W = -\int_0^T (P_0 + Pe^{j\omega t})\,\frac{m}{\rho^2}\, j\omega\rho_e\, dt$$

Since ρ_e is small, we make the approximation $\rho \simeq \rho_0$. Then the work per unit mass which is done in one period is:

$$\frac{W}{m} = -\frac{j\omega De^{j\varphi}}{\rho_0{}^2}\int_0^T [P_0 e^{j\omega t} + Pe^{2j\omega t}]\, dt$$

which can be rewritten in the form:

$$\frac{W}{m} = -j\frac{\omega De^{j\varphi}}{\rho_0{}^2}\int_0^T [P_0 \cos \omega t + P \cos^2 \omega t]\, dt \qquad (A.2)$$

The integral of the first term over one period is zero, but the integral of the second term is $P/2\omega$. Thus eq. A.2 reduces to

$$\frac{W}{m} = -j\frac{DPe^{j\varphi}}{2\rho_0{}^2} \qquad (A.3)$$

We note that the work per unit mass which is done in one period is complex. The real part of W/m is the work which is dissipated during 1 cycle; the imaginary or reactive part gives the amount of energy which is stored and given back to the system in 1 period. The real part of the above expression is given by

$$\mathrm{RE}\left\{-j\frac{DP}{2\rho_0{}^2}(\cos \varphi + j \sin \varphi)\right\} = \frac{DP}{2\rho_0{}^2}\sin \varphi \qquad (A.3a)$$

We may now use eq. 2.28a to express the excess density D in terms of the excess pressure.

$$D/\rho_0 = P/\gamma P_0 = P/\rho_0 c^2$$

With this notation eq. (A.3a) becomes

$$\left(\frac{W}{m}\right)_{\mathrm{RE}} = \frac{1}{2}\left(\frac{P}{\rho_0 c}\right)^2 \sin \varphi = \frac{E_x}{\rho_0}\sin \varphi \qquad (A.4)$$

in which $E_x = P^2/2\rho_0 c^2$ is the energy density of the sound wave at points x, according to eq. 2.51.

The energy lost per cycle   Let us now show how the phase angle φ is related to the linear absorption coefficient α of a plane progressive sound wave.   According to eq. 8.1 we find for the sound pressure:

$$p_e = Pe^{j\omega(t-x/c)}e^{-\alpha x} = Pe^{j\omega t}e^{-j(k-j\alpha)x}$$

for the particle velocity:

$$u = -\frac{1}{j\omega\rho_0}\frac{\partial p_e}{\partial x} = \frac{k-j\alpha}{\omega\rho_0}p_e$$

and for the impedance:

$$Z = \frac{p_e}{u} = \frac{\omega\rho_0}{k-j\alpha} = \rho_0 c\,\frac{1}{1-j(\alpha c/\omega)} = R + jX$$

in which $R = \dfrac{\rho_0 c}{1+(\alpha/k)^2}$ and $X = \rho_0 c\,\dfrac{\alpha/k}{1+(\alpha/k)^2}$

The phase angle of the impedance is identical with the phase angle φ between pressure and density.   It is determined by:

$$\tan\varphi = X/R = \alpha/k = \alpha c/\omega \tag{A.5a}$$

or $$\sin\varphi = \frac{X}{(R^2+X^2)^{1/2}} = \frac{\alpha/k}{(1+\alpha^2/k^2)^{1/2}} \tag{A.5b}$$

Comparing eqs. A.5b and A.4 we note that for small losses ($\alpha/k \ll 1$) the energy dissipated per unit volume and per cycle is simply:

$$H = \rho_0\left(\frac{W}{m}\right)_{RE} \simeq \frac{E_x\alpha}{k} = \frac{1}{2\pi}E_x\alpha\lambda \tag{A.6}$$

i.e., H (in joules/m^3) is proportional to the product of energy density and absorption per wavelength.[3]

We shall see that the phase lag between pressure and density is a

---

[3] The initial temperature rise in degrees per second due to sound absorption in the medium is given by

$$\left(\frac{dT}{dt}\right)_{t=0} = 2\frac{K_h}{\rho_0 C_p}I_x\alpha \tag{A.6a}$$

in which K_h is the mechanical equivalent of heat ($K_h = 2.39 \times 10^{-4}$ kilocal/joule), C_p is the specific heat of the medium, and ρ_0 the density of the medium.   The subscript $t=0$ indicates that eq. A.6a holds for initial conditions only, e.g., at the onset of a sound pulse.   For uses of eq. A.6a see W. J. Fry, *J. Acoust. Soc. Amer.* 25 (1953), 6.

function of frequency, in much the same way as for voltage and current in certain types of electric RC networks. For mechanisms which follow this general type of behavior the term "relaxation" is applied.[4]

A.3 Classical Absorption and Velocity Dispersion

If the excess pressure p_e and excess density ρ_e in the sound wave are in phase, i.e., if no absorption occurs, they can be expressed by a relation

$$p_e = \text{constant} \times \rho_e \qquad (A.7)$$

This is the expression used in a first-order theory of elastic waves in fluids (see Section 2.8). The constant is given by $1/\beta_a\rho_0 = c^2$, where $\beta_a = 1/\gamma P_0$ is the adiabatic compressibility and ρ_0 is the density of the medium.[5]

From a macroscopic point of view, the following three factors may be expected to produce a time lag between pressure and density in a sound wave:[6]

   a. Viscosity.
   b. Heat conduction.
   c. Heat radiation.

The experimental evidence indicates that in most fluids the absorption is caused primarily by viscosity and heat conduction and that the effect of heat radiation is negligible. In liquids, viscosity plays the major role. In gases, on the other hand, viscosity and heat conduction come into play about equally, but they are often overshadowed by molecular phenomena.

---

[4] E. A. Hiedemann and R. D. Spence, *Z. Phys.*, *133* (1952), 109. The term relaxation is used by various authors to include different phenomena. Some apply the term only to the two phenomena of thermal and structural relaxation. In this chapter, the term refers to all processes which result in a lag between pressure and density and therefore also includes viscosity, heat conduction, and heat radiation. Regardless of the terminology used, the basic concept of time-dependent processes causing pressure and density to be out of phase should be kept in mind.

[5] An excellent summary of other acoustical equations of state more complicated than eq. A.7 is given by J. J. Markham, R. T. Beyer, and R. B. Lindsay, *Revs. Mod. Phys.*, *23* (1951), 353.

[6] The theory of sound absorption due to macroscopic effects was fully developed during the classical period of physics. G. G. Stokes discussed the problems of viscosity in *Trans. Cambridge Phil. Soc.*, *8* (1845), 287, and of heat radiation in *Phil. Mag.*, *1* (1851), 305. G. Kirchhoff treated the case of heat conduction in *Poggendorf's Ann. Phys.*, *134* (1868), 177. Absorption caused by these processes is usually referred to as classical absorption.

The importance of viscosity measurements for the process control of certain types of liquids has already been pointed out in Chapter 8. We shall first solve the case of viscous attenuation of a plane wave in some detail. This will illustrate the general way of treating classical absorption. As a next step, the frequency dependence of sound velocity and absorption will be analyzed in terms of an electrical analog which expresses heat transfer in terms of charge transfer. This approach leads to relationships of considerable generality which apply to relaxation of dielectric and paramagnetic dipoles, as in the propagation of electromagnetic waves, as well as to the thermal relaxation which takes place in acoustic waves.

Losses due to viscosity   In place of eq. A.7, the acoustical equation of state is modified to include a term proportional to the time rate of change of density.

$$p_e = \frac{1}{\beta_a} \frac{\rho_e}{\rho_0} + \frac{\zeta}{\rho_0} \frac{d\rho_e}{dt} \qquad (A.7a)$$

in which ζ is a viscosity constant. The stress mechanism inferred by this equation can be visualized with the help of the equivalent circuits shown in Fig. A.3.[7] The total force F is the sum of the forces across the spring and across the dashpot, that is,

in mechanical notation: $F = ax + b\dfrac{dx}{dt}$

$$\qquad\qquad\qquad\qquad\qquad\qquad\qquad\qquad (A.8)$$

in electrical notation: $V = \dfrac{Q}{C} + R\dfrac{dQ}{dt}$

If $F = F_0$ for $t \geq 0$, then $x = F_0(1 - e^{-at/b})/a$. Equation A.8 is formally identical with the acoustical case (eq. A.7a), if these substitutions are made: $F = p_e$, $x = \rho_e/\rho_0$, $a = 1/\beta_a$, $b = \zeta$. When a force "step function" is applied, the resultant displacement in the mechanical circuit does not occur instantaneously, but "follows" slowly. The time constant of this process is simply $\tau = b/a = \zeta\beta_a$, which corresponds to $\tau = RC$ in the electrical analog.

In addition to the acoustical equation of state (A.7a), the equation of motion (see eq. 2.32)

$$\rho_0 \frac{\partial u_x}{\partial t} = -\frac{\partial \rho_e}{\partial x} \qquad (A.9)$$

[7] The analogy chosen in Fig. A.3 corresponds to case I in Fig. 2.2a.

and the continuity equation

$$\rho_0 \frac{\partial u_x}{\partial x} = - \frac{\partial \rho_e}{\partial t} \tag{A.10}$$

are needed to derive the sound-propagation equations.

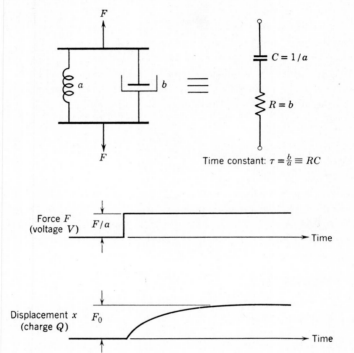

Fig. A.3.   Analog circuits for viscous stress relaxation.

Let us now apply eq. 8.1 to pressure, particle velocity, and excess density.   Substituting the resulting expressions into eqs. A.7a, A.9, and A.10 gives:

$$P - \frac{D}{\rho_0}\left(\frac{1}{\beta_a} + j\omega\zeta\right) = 0 \tag{A.11}$$

$$kP - \rho_0\omega U = 0 \tag{A.12}$$

$$\omega D - k\rho_0 U = 0 \tag{A.13}$$

in which P, U, and D are the amplitudes of pressure, velocity, and density.   These last three equations are homogeneous simultaneous equations of the unknowns P, D, and U. Combining these equations, we arrive at the following necessary condition for a non-trivial solution:

$$k^2 = \frac{\rho_0 \omega^2}{\zeta} \frac{1}{\omega_v + j\omega} = \frac{\rho_0 \omega^2}{\zeta} \frac{\omega_v - j\omega}{\omega_v^2 + \omega^2}$$

in which $\omega_v = 1/\beta_a\zeta = c^2\rho_0/\zeta$ is the reciprocal of the time constant τ defined in Fig. A.3. We now separate k^2 into its real and imaginary parts:

$$k_{\mathrm{RE}}^2 - k_{\mathrm{IM}}^2 = \frac{\rho_0}{\zeta} \frac{\omega^2 \omega_v}{\omega_v^2 + \omega^2} \qquad (\text{A.14})$$

$$2k_{\mathrm{RE}}k_{\mathrm{IM}} = -\frac{\rho_0}{\zeta} \frac{\omega^3}{\omega_v^2 + \omega^2} \qquad (\text{A.15})$$

Equations A.14 and A.15 are then solved for k_{IM} ($= -\alpha$). This gives

$$-\alpha = k_{\mathrm{IM}} = -\omega \left(\frac{\rho_0}{2\zeta\omega_v}\right)^{\frac{1}{2}} \left(\frac{1}{(1 + \omega^2/\omega_v^2)^{\frac{1}{2}}} - \frac{1}{1 + \omega^2/\omega_v^2}\right)^{\frac{1}{2}} \quad (\text{A.16})$$

This rather cumbersome expression can be simplified considerably, provided that $x = \omega^2/\omega_v^2 \ll 1$. In this case, we can use the approximations $1/(1 + x)^{\frac{1}{2}} \simeq 1 - (x/2)$ and $1/(1 + x) \simeq 1 - x$, and the second square root factor of eq. A.16 reduces to $\omega\sqrt{1 - \frac{1}{2}}/\omega_v = \omega/(\omega_v\sqrt{2})$. With $\omega_v = c^2\rho_0/\zeta$ this leads to:

$$\alpha \simeq \frac{1}{2} \frac{\zeta}{\rho_0} \frac{\omega^2}{c^3} \qquad (\text{A.16}a)$$

In order to show that the condition $\omega_v \gg \omega$ is applicable, we must find the magnitude of the constant ζ. As shown in Chapter 8, footnote 44a, the elastic response of matter to the compressions occurring in a plane wave is described by a modulus $c_{11} = \lambda' + 2\mu$. In complete analogy to the elastic behavior we may describe the viscous response of matter to plane compressions by an expression of the form $\eta_{11} = \chi + 2\eta$, where η is the ordinary shear viscosity and χ (quite similar as λ') represents the viscous reaction to all-sided compression if no viscous shear forces were operative. The viscosity constant ζ introduced in eq. A.7a, dealing with plane compressional waves, then is $\zeta = \eta_{11} = \chi + 2\eta$. Further, in analogy to the elastic bulk modulus $K_c = \lambda' + \frac{2}{3}\mu$, one may define a viscous bulk modulus $K_v = \chi + \frac{2}{3}\eta$. In classical theory, it is assumed that there is no viscous reaction to an all-sided compression: $K_v = 0$; hence $\chi = -\frac{2}{3}\eta$ and $\zeta = \frac{4}{3}\eta$. Substituting this result in the above expression for ω_v, we obtain

$$\omega_v = \frac{c^2 \rho_0}{\zeta} = \frac{3\eta c^2 \rho_0}{4} = \frac{3\eta}{4\beta_a} \qquad \text{(A.17)}$$

For example, water has a shear viscosity of $\eta = 1.3 \times 10^{-2}$ poise and $\beta_a = 50 \times 10^{-12}$ (cm^2·dyne^{-1}) so that $\omega_v \approx 10^6$ mcps.[8] This indicates that the condition $\omega \ll \omega_v$ is applicable for all liquids in the observable ultrasonic range, and we obtain

$$\alpha \simeq \frac{2}{3} \frac{\eta}{\rho_0} \frac{\omega^2}{c^3} \qquad \text{(A.18)}$$

Equation A.18 indicates that α/ω^2 should be independent of frequency. Therefore, it is common practice to plot α/f^2 when the attenuation is measured as a function of frequency. If there are mechanisms operating which depend on frequency in some way other than as f^2, they will manifest themselves as a departure of the data from the horizontal line $\alpha/f^2 = $ constant.

Combining eqs. A.18 and A.5, we find that the phase difference φ between pressure and density is given by

$$\tan \varphi = \frac{\alpha\lambda}{2\pi} = \frac{\eta}{\rho_0 c} \frac{4\pi}{3\lambda} \qquad \text{(A.19)}$$

in other words $\qquad \lambda \tan \varphi = $ constant

Empirical evidence reveals that this last result holds for certain liquids, e.g., water, benzene, toluence, carbon tetrachloride, methyl alcohol, within a limited frequency range.[9] Some fluids show $\tan \varphi = $ constant, while others show a maximum of $\alpha\lambda$ at some frequency, above which $(\tan \varphi)/\lambda = $ constant.[10]

The phase velocity of the sound wave is found by solving eqs. A.14 and A.15 for $k_{\text{RE}} = \omega/c$. Considering only phase lags due to viscosity, the velocity is

$$c^2 = \frac{2\zeta(\omega_v{}^2 + \omega^2)}{\rho_0 \omega_v [1 + (1 + \omega^2/\omega_v{}^2)^{\frac{1}{2}}]} \qquad \text{(A.20)}$$

[8] Recent evidence indicates that in some liquids $\zeta > 4/3\eta$; for example in benzene $\zeta \simeq 10^2 \eta$. However, this does not change the validity of the assumption $\omega \ll \omega_v$.

[9] See review in L. Bergmann's book: *Der Ultraschall*, 5th edition, S. Hirzel Verlag, Zürich 1949, p. 332.

[10] See, for example, the discussion of acetic acid by J. Lamb and J. M. Pinkerton, *Proc. Roy. Soc. (London) A, 199* (1949), 144.

Using the same approximations as above, we finally find

$$c^2 \simeq \frac{1}{\beta_a \rho_0} \left(1 + \frac{3\omega^2}{8\omega_v} \right) \qquad (A.21)$$

We note that the velocity becomes dispersive as the frequency approaches ω_v. However, ω/ω_v is very small over the frequency range which is practicably attainable ($f < 10^2$ mcps), so that this dispersion is not measurable and the velocity is essentially constant and equal to $1/\beta_a \rho_0$.

Losses due to heat conduction and radiation It is usual in treatments of sound propagation to consider the adiabatic case. That is, we assume that the successive compressions and rarefactions take place so rapidly that the temperature in a given region changes without heat flow to adjacent regions. It should be recognized, however, that this is an approximation. If some heat does flow from the high- to the low-temperature regions, then a certain amount of acoustical energy is lost each cycle. We have already seen how this loss per cycle can be related to both a phase lag and an acoustical absorption coefficient. At very low frequencies the pressure variations take place so slowly that the temperature can "follow."[11] The temperature of the medium then remains constant and the propagation is spoken of as being isothermal. The adiabatic approximation also fails at very high frequencies (above 10^3 mcps in gases). In this case the wavelength becomes comparable to the mean free path so that enough energy can be exchanged by direct transfer of molecular momentum (heat conduction) to make the propagation isothermal.

Just as energy is lost from the acoustic compressions by heat conduction, so also can it be lost by radiation. Since the compressions are at a slightly higher temperature than their surroundings, their rate of emission of energy according to the Stefan law is greater.[12]

Electrical analog for heat-transfer mechanisms The losses associated with a phase lag in heat transfer, whether by conduction, radiation, or, as discussed in Section A.4, by molecular excitation, can be visualized in terms of an electrical analog.[13] The heat stored in a given volume element following a rapid compression corresponds to an electric charge stored in a condenser. A portion of this heat is immediately available to restore the initial temperature following a subsequent expansion. However, that portion of the heat which

[11] This case is of importance in metals at frequencies of the order of 10 cps. See, for example., C. Zener *Elasticity and Anelasticity of Metals*, Univ. of Chicago Press, Chicago, 1948.

[12] Stefan's law states that the amount of energy radiated is proportional to the fourth power of absolute temperature.

[13] The network used in this discussion was first introduced by P. Debye in 1929 to explain dielectric relaxation phenomena. Its usefulness for elastic relaxation was later demonstrated by J. Frenkel in his book *A Kinetic Theory of Liquids*, Clarendon Press, Oxford, 1946, p. 208.

was lost by external or internal heat transfer requires a certain time to return to the volume element. This corresponds to the electrical case of two condensors in parallel, one of which has a finite time constant $\tau = RC$ for charge or discharge. A circuit of this kind is illustrated in Fig. A.4. For a gas, C_2 represents the adiabatic compressibility and $C_1 + C_2 = C_0$ represents the isothermal compressibility, while R_1 is proportional to a transfer coefficient (of conduction, radiation or molecular excitation).

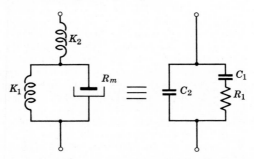

Fig. A.4.   Mechanical equivalent circuit and electrical analog for heat-transfer mechanisms.

Let us now determine the admittance $Y = G + jB$ of this circuit as a function of frequency.

$$Y = j\omega C_2 + \frac{1}{R_1 + 1/j\omega C_1}$$

$$= j\omega \left[C_2 + \frac{C_1}{1 + j\dfrac{\omega}{\omega_r}} \right] \tag{A.22}$$

in which $\omega_r = 1/\tau = 1/R_1 C_1$. Rationalization of eq. (A.22) yields for the conductance

$$G = \omega^2 C_1 \frac{\omega_r}{\omega_r{}^2 + \omega^2} \tag{A.23a}$$

and for the susceptance

$$B = \omega \frac{\omega_r{}^2 C_0 + \omega^2 C_2}{\omega_r{}^2 + \omega^2} \tag{A.23b}$$

The energy lost per cycle is then given by:

$$H = \frac{1}{\omega} \frac{V^2 G}{2} = \frac{V^2 C_1}{2} \frac{\omega \omega_r}{\omega_r{}^2 + \omega^2} \tag{A.24}$$

where V is a driving voltage applied to the terminals of the electrical circuit of Fig. A.4. The energy dissipated in a fluid per unit volume and per cycle was determined in section A.2. Combining eqs. A.6 and A.24 we have

$$H = E_x \alpha \frac{c_0}{\omega} = \frac{V^2 C_1}{2} \frac{\omega \omega_r}{\omega_r^2 + \omega^2}$$

It is reasonable to assume that the analogous electric energy $V^2 C_1 / 2$ is proportional to the acoustic energy density E_x; hence we may set $V^2 C_1 / 2 = \psi E_x$. The sound-absorption coefficient then becomes:

$$\alpha = \frac{\psi}{c_0} \frac{\omega_r}{\omega_r^2 + \omega^2} \omega^2 \qquad (A.25)$$

in which the constant ψ depends on the distribution of energy between C_1 and C_2:

$$\psi = \frac{C_1}{C_1 + C_2} \simeq \frac{\beta_i - \beta_a}{\beta_i}$$

The rate of change with frequency of the energy lost per cycle is found by differentiating eq. A.24 with respect to ω. Setting $dH/d\omega = 0$ we find a peak of absorption per cycle at $\omega = \omega_r$; i.e., the quantity $\alpha\lambda$ has a maximum at $\omega_r = 1/R_1 C_1$.

These results fully represent the frequency dependence of absorption due to heat-transfer mechanisms. The factor $\omega_r \omega^2 / (\omega_r^2 + \omega^2)$ in eq. A.25 is characteristic of all phase-lag mechanisms which exhibit relaxation. For each mechanism the values for ψ and ω_r may be determined by thermodynamic or kinetic theory.[14]

For heat conduction one obtains:

$$\psi = \frac{1}{2} \frac{c}{c_a} (\gamma - 1) \qquad \text{and} \qquad \omega_r = \frac{C_p^2}{V k_h} \qquad (A.26a)$$

and for heat radiation:

$$\psi = \frac{1}{2} \frac{c}{c_a} \left(1 - \frac{1}{\gamma}\right) \qquad \text{and} \qquad \omega_r = \frac{q}{\gamma} \qquad (A.26b)$$

in which molar C_p is the specific heat at constant pressure, k_h the thermal conductivity, V the molar volume, γ the ratio of specific heats, $c_a = (1/\beta_a \rho_0)^{1/2}$, and q is a constant in the Stephan law. The frequency ω_r of relaxation due to heat radiation falls in the infrasonic range

[14] J. J. Markham, R. T. Beyer, and R. B. Lindsay, pp. 367–373, *op. cit.* (see footnote 5).

($\omega_r \simeq 0.002$ cps for air), whereas for heat conduction ω_r is extremely high ($\omega_r \simeq 6 \times 10^3$ mcps for air and 10^{10} mcps for water). For many substances, however, the relaxation frequency ω_r of *molecular* heat exchange (thermal or structural) falls within the observable frequency range.

The expression found above for the susceptance of the analogous relaxation circuit (see Fig. A.4 and eq. A.23b) represents the dynamic compressibility of the medium. The sound velocity is then determined by

$$c^2 = \frac{1}{\rho_0 \beta} = \frac{1}{\rho_0} \frac{\omega^2 + \omega_r^2}{\omega^2 C_2 + \omega_r^2 C_0}$$

Substituting $C_2 = \beta_a$ and $C_0 = \beta_i$ we obtain for both heat conduction and heat radiation

$$c^2 = c_a^2 \frac{\omega^2 + \omega_r^2}{\omega^2 + \gamma \omega_r^2} \tag{A.27}$$

in which $c_a = 1/\beta_a \rho_0$) is the adiabatic sound velocity.

The frequency dependence of α and c derived in this section for different loss mechanisms is represented schematically in Fig. A.5. The effects of viscosity are illustrated in Fig. A.5a, in which the accessible frequency range is also indicated. We note that the velocity increases monotonically with frequency, but this dispersion would become noticeable only at frequencies beyond the attainable range.[15] Likewise, for absorption, a square law holds throughout the accessible frequency range while at extremely high frequencies a square root law would be expected. For heat conduction and radiation (see Fig. A.5b), on the other hand, the absorption per wavelength shows a maximum while the velocity shows dispersion from a low-frequency value c_0 to a high-frequency value $c_\infty = c_a$. This type of frequency dependence of c and α has actually been observed in many fluids. In most cases it is caused by molecular relaxation mechanism which are governed by laws similar to those for heat conduction and radiation.

In general, the magnitudes of the losses from these mechanisms are greatest for viscosity, intermediate for heat conduction, and least for heat radiation. Radiation losses are negligible in most fluids. Viscosity and heat-conduction losses are usually of the same order of magnitude for gases. For most liquids, viscous losses are considerably

---

[15] The highest frequency which has been attained for measuring purposes is about 10^3 mcps, but the generation of ultrasound above 100 mcps becomes increasingly difficult.

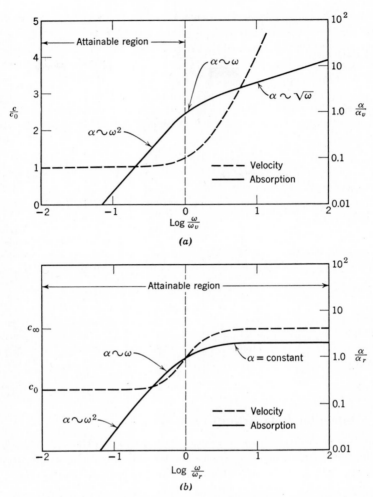

Fig. A.5. Frequency dependence of velocity and absorption for (a) viscous and (b) heat-transfer mechanisms. The velocity in the upper graph is plotted relative to the velocity c_0 at low frequencies. In both graphs the absorption is plotted relative to the absorption at the frequency of relaxation (α_v or α_r, respectively) on a logarithmic scale. At this frequency, the absorption per wavelength $\alpha\lambda = 2\pi\alpha c/\omega$ exhibits a maximum.

greater than conduction losses. A comparison between observed and calculated absorption coefficients (α/f^2) for some important liquids and gases is given in Table A.1. We note that all the liquids listed show much higher absorption than is predicted from classic considerations, with the exception of mercury and castor oil.

Table A.1

All Data for $T = 20°C$ and $P_0 = 1$ atm	Classical Calculation		Total α/f^2 Observed	$\dfrac{\alpha_{obs}}{\alpha_{class}}$
	Heat Conduction α/f^2	Viscosity α/f^2		
Gases	$\times 10^{-13}$	$\times 10^{-13}$	$\times 10^{-13}$	
Argon	0.77	1.08	1.9	0.97
Helium	0.216	0.309	0.545	1.12
Neon	0.75	0.07	5	6.1
Hydrogen	0.052	0.117	peak at 10 mcps	0.97
Oxygen	0.47	1.14	1.57	1.18
Nitrogen	0.39	0.96	1.35	.112
Air	0.38	0.99	2	1.46
Carbon Dioxide	0.31	1.09	peak at 20 kcps	high
Liquids	$\times 10^{-17}$	$\times 10^{-17}$	$\times 10^{-17}$	
Ethyl acetate	0.31	7.95	516	62
Acetone	0.5	6.54	30	4.3
Benzene	0.3	8.36	900	103
m-Xylene	0.24	8.13	78	9.3
Toluene	7.56	0.28	205	20
Water	10^{-2}	8.5	25	3
Castor oil	small	8400	7800	1.17
Mercury	6	small	5.05	1.2

A.4   Molecular Relaxation in Gases

The law of equipartition of energy in a gas states that each mechanical degree of freedom of a gas molecule will carry the same amount of energy, $kT/2$, the total energy of each mole of the gas being

$$U = \frac{NfkT}{2} \qquad (A.28)$$

where N is Avogadro's number,[16] f is the number of degrees of freedom of the molecule, $k = R/N$ is Boltzmann's constant, and T is the absolute temperature.

[16] Avogadro's number N is the number of molecules per mole, while the Loschmidt number L is the number of molecules per unit volume. The relationship between L and N is given by

$$L \frac{\text{molecules}}{\text{cm}^3} \times \frac{1\ \text{cm}^3}{10^{-3}\ \text{l}} \times \frac{22.4\ \text{l}}{\text{mole}} = N = 6.02 \times 10^{23} \frac{\text{molecules}}{\text{mole}}$$

The specific heat at constant volume is defined as

$$C_V = \left(\frac{\partial U}{\partial T}\right)_V$$

which with the use of eq. A.28 becomes

$$C_V = \frac{Nfk}{2} = fR/2 \tag{A.29}$$

where R is the gas constant. Since R is approximately 2 cal/mole, it follows that $C_V \simeq f$ (cal/mole). A monatomic gas has only 3 degrees of freedom, namely, the three $(x, y,$ and $z)$ components of translational motion. Hence $f = 3$, and we obtain for the molar specific heat of a monatomic gas $C_V = 3$ (cal/mole). The specific heat at constant pressure is defined as $C_p = C_V + R$; hence for a monatomic gas $C_p = 3 + 2 = 5$ (cal/mole) and the ratio of specific heats $C_p/C_V = \gamma$ becomes $\gamma = \frac{5}{3}$. As a general rule we find:

$$\gamma = (f + 2)/f \tag{A.30}$$

Hence we obtain $\gamma = \frac{7}{5}$ for diatomic gases which have 2 additional degrees of freedom of rotation, and $\gamma = \frac{4}{3}$ for triatomic gases with 3 rotational degrees of freedom.[17] We note that the specific heat ratio decreases with increasing number of excited degrees of freedom.

The distribution of thermal energy If a sound wave is generated within a polyatomic gas, heat is adiabatically created in the compressional phase of a given volume element. This heat energy will be distributed both in the external translatory degrees of freedom and in the internal ones. The excitation of the latter will take place through collisions and will require a certain amount of time. Therefore, if the sound frequency reaches high values, the time within the compressional half cycles of the wave may become too short for this interchange of energy. This means that the number of active degrees of freedom is reduced and that according to eq. A.30 the specific heat ratio is increased. As a consequence, the sound velocity $c = (P_0\gamma/\rho_0)^{1/2}$ increases. The result is illustrated for carbon dioxide in Fig. A.6.

The velocity dispersion in gases is accompanied by a frequency band of increased absorption $\alpha\lambda$. This absorption may exceed the

---

[17] Although vibrational degrees of freedom are also possible, their contribution is insignificant under static conditions since their full excitation requires high temperatures. They come in to play, however, under the dynamic conditions of acoustics.

value predicted from viscosity and heat conduction by two or three orders of magnitude.

We can visualize the delay of the equalization of energy between different degrees of freedom by examining the behavior of a gas which undergoes a sudden compression, as illustrated in Fig. A.7. The pressure p and volume V, as well as the partition of the total energy E, the external (translational) energy E_e, and the internal (rotational or

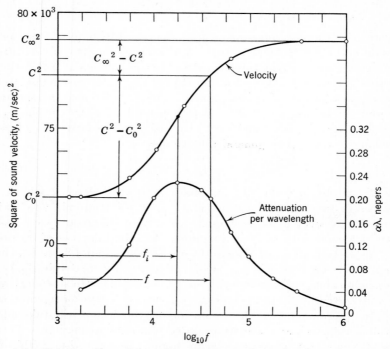

Fig. A.6. Velocity dispersion and concomitant absorption in carbon dioxide (R. W. Leonard).

vibrational) energy E_i are plotted as a function of time. The compression will first increase E_e, which is taken over by the molecules at once. Both pressure and E_e rise to a peak. Now some energy is transferred into vibrational degrees of freedom, and E_i rises exponentially until the condition of equipartition is reached. This causes p and E_e to drop to their equilibrium value. The pressure p of the gas therefore lags behind the change of density (or volume) which the gas undergoes in each compressional cycle.

We note from Fig. A.6 that the sound velocity approaches the values c_0 at low frequencies and c_∞ at high frequencies:

$$c_0 = \left(\frac{P_0\gamma}{\rho_0}\right)^{\frac{1}{2}} \quad \text{and} \quad c_\infty = c_0\left(1 + \frac{\gamma-1}{\gamma}\frac{C_{vi}}{C_{ve}}\right)^{\frac{1}{2}} \quad (A.31)$$

Here C_{vi} is the contribution of the internal degrees of freedom of the molecules to specific heat and C_{ve} represents the external contribu-

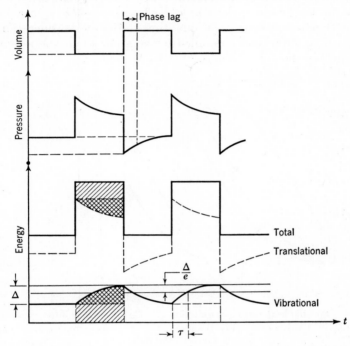

Fig. A.7.   Distribution of energy over translational (external) and vibrational (internal) degrees of freedom.

tion; hence

$$C_{vt} \equiv C_{v\,total} = C_{vi} + C_{ve}$$

With this notation, the above equations can be rewritten as:

$$c_0{}^2 = \frac{P_0}{\rho_0}\left(1 + \frac{R}{C_{vt}}\right) \quad \text{and} \quad c_\infty{}^2 = \frac{P_0}{\rho_0}\left(1 + \frac{R}{C_{ve}}\right) \quad (A.31a)$$

The relaxation time τ of this molecular heat exchange can be determined from the inflection point f_i of the velocity dispersion curve by the relation:

$$\tau = \frac{1}{2\pi f_i}\left(\frac{C_{ve}}{C_{vt}}\right) \quad (A.32)$$

From Fig. A.6 we see that if f and c are corresponding frequencies and velocities anywhere in the dispersion region, then $(f_i/f)^2$ stands in the same ratio as the distances on the ordinate $\dfrac{c_\infty{}^2 - c^2}{c^2 - c_0{}^2}$. Thus f_i can be found from a measurement of any velocity c at a frequency f within the dispersion region ($c_0 < c < c_\infty$), if c_0 and c_∞ are known. If τ has thus been determined, quantum statistical considerations can be applied to obtain more detailed information about the mechanism of energy transfer by collisions.[18]

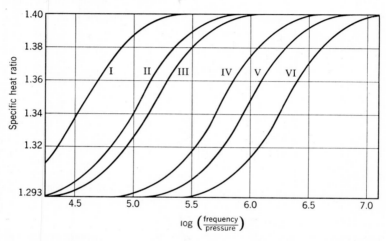

Fig. A.8.   Specific heat ratio as a function of f/P_0 for various impurities added to carbon dioxide (A. Eucken and R. Becker).   Curve I is for pure CO_2; the impurities causing the displacement of this curve to the right are: 5 per cent He in curve II, 11.3 per cent CH_4 in curve III, 5.7 per cent H_2 in curve IV, 12.3 per cent H_2 in curve V, and 2.8 per cent H_2O in curve VI.

These phenomena may lend themselves to gas analytical measurements in chemistry.   It is found that the relaxation frequency depends on temperature, pressure, and composition of the medium.   For example, Fig. A.8 shows the dependence of the specific heat ratio (and hence of sound velocity) on the ratio f/P_0 for various impurities in carbon dioxide.[19]   By incorporating some measuring device such as an interferometer (see Section 8.4), into a monitor or feedback circuit, changes in either sound velocity or absorption can be detected, or even kept within predetermined limits.

[18] H. O. Kneser, *Ergeb. exakt. Naturw.*, *22* (1949), 121.   J. J. Markham, *J. Acoust. Soc. Amer.*, *22* (1950), 628, and *23* (1951), 144.
[19] A. Eucken and R. Becker, *Z. Phys. Chem.*, *27B* (1934), 219.

So far, the industrial possibilities of these analytical techniques, e.g., for the field of chemical engineering, have not been fully realized. However, the study of velocity dispersion in polyatomic fluids has become an important technique of molecular physics. The dependence of sound velocity on both pressure and temperature is of great interest in studies of compressibility and specific heats. It was pointed out in section 8.1 that these quantities are representative of the forces between the molecules and of the energy levels within the molecules. Conclusions with respect to the potential distribution, the nature of bonds, and the energy levels within the molecule can be drawn.[20] In complex molecules a differentiation between particular modes of excitation seems possible, as indicated in Table A.2 for three diatomic and one triatomic gas.

Table A.2

| | Relaxation Frequencies | |
	Vibrational	Rotational
Oxygen	50 cps	53 mcps
Nitrogen	4 cps	240 mcps
Hydrogen	—	10 mcps
Carbon dioxide	20 kcps	—

Physical meaning of relaxation time   We note that the interchange between compressional and rotational energy relaxes at very high frequencies, while for vibrational modes of the gas molecules the interchange proceeds rather slowly. The relaxation constant τ can be visualized as the mean lifetime of an energy quantum which may require a specific number of collisions before it is dissipated. In other words, if the vibrational modes of a gas molecule are fully excited and if the source of energy is then removed, τ is the average time for a single quantum of energy to be dissipated in the process of repeated transfer of internal energy from one molecule to another by inelastic collisions.

Let us consider a two-state model of a gas: the gas is assumed to exist in either the ground state or its first excited vibrational level.[21] A reaction equation can then be set up which determines the equilibrium between normal and excited molecules for a constant number $n = n_1 + n_0$ of molecules involved:

$$-\frac{\partial n_1}{\partial t} = k_{10}n_1 - k_{01}n_0$$

[20] E. G. Richardson, *Nature, 158* (1946), 296, and V. O. Knudsen, *J. Acoust. Soc. Amer., 6* (1935), 199.

[21] A. Einstein, *Trans. Berliner Akad. Wiss.* (1920), 380.

Here n_1 is the number of excited molecules, n_0 is the number of normal molecules, k_{10} is the number of transitions per second from the excited state (1) to the normal state (0) for each molecule, and k_{01} is the number of transitions per second per molecule from the normal state (0) to the excited state (1).[22] This permits a new definition of the relaxation time:

$$\tau = \frac{1}{k_{01} + k_{10}} \tag{A.33}$$

Transitions between states of excitation of individual molecules take place in only one out of a great number of collisions. From k_{10} and

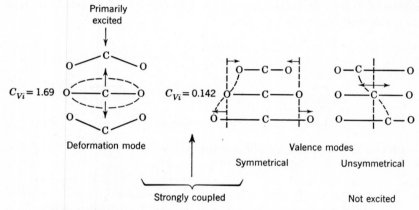

Fig. A.9. Vibrational modes of the carbon dioxide molecule. The deformation mode and the symmetrical valence mode participate in causing thermal relaxation near 20 kcps.

k_{01} the probability of energy transfer for each molecule per collision can be computed. As an example, in carbon dioxide (at 18°C and 760 mm Hg), 670,000 collisions are necessary to form one vibrational quantum from translational energy, while for the transfer in the opposite direction only 51,000 collisions are necessary. The vibrational modes possible in the carbon dioxide molecule are illustrated in Fig. A.9. Their presence can be inferred from infrared spectroscopic data.[23] The experimental results for carbon dioxide suggest that the relaxation mechanism is determined primarily by the reaction constants of the most easily excited deformation mode, although all three

---

[22] See K. F. Herzfeld and J. C. Rice, *Phys. Rev.*, *31* (1928), 691, and D. G. Bourgin, *Phys. Rev.*, *34* (1929), 521.

[23] A. Eucken and L. Küchler, *Phys. Z.*, *39* (1938), 831, and A. Eucken, O. Mücke, and R. Becker, *Z. Phys. Chem.* (*B*) *18* (1932), 167.

modes consume energy, as is borne out by computations of specific heats.[24] This implies some mode coupling within the molecule and shows how far the conclusions from such ultrasonic measurements can be carried.

Influence of impurities So far we have considered only pure gases and vapors. The probability of energy transfer among molecules can be greatly increased by small traces of foreign gases or vapors. Table A.3 gives the average number of collisions necessary for a transfer of energy in three primary gases for various added gases of 1 per cent molar concentration. We note that the addition of argon does not have much influence on the relaxation time, whereas water vapor is very effective in shortening τ, that is, in reducing the number of collisions necessary for energy transfer.

Table A.3   Average Number of Collisions Necessary for Transfer of One Energy Quantum

Added Gas	Primary gas		
	Cl_2	N_2O	CO_2
No added gas	34,000	7,500	50,000
A	32,000	—	47,000
He	900	1,000	2,600
H_2	780	650	300
CO	230	600	—
CH_4	190	840	2,400
NH_3	—	450	—
HCl	120	—	130
H_2O	—	105	40

The results summarized in Table A.3 have received an interesting interpretation.[25] They indicate that the probability of transfer of translational energy into vibrational energy is strongly influenced by chemical affinity between the colliding partners. This does not imply that a chemical reaction takes place; the added gas remains as an impurity, distinct from the primary gas. High chemical affinity does imply, however, that the electron shells of colliding molecules are strongly deformed, and it is this deformation that "couples" the translational energy into vibrational. For example, if a mixture of chlorine and carbon dioxide is irradiated with light, the sound velocity in the mixture is altered. It is known that light exposure changes the

[24] G. G. Sherrat and E. Griffiths, *Proc. Roy. Soc. (London) A, 147* (1934), 504, and *A, 156* (1936), 1051.

[25] J. Franck and A. Eucken, *Z. Phys. Chem. B, 20* (1938), 460, and A. van Itterbeck, P. de Bruyn, and P. Mariens, *Physica, 6* (1939), 511.

chemical reaction level of these gases, so this phenomenon further demonstrates the connection between chemical affinity and transfer probability.

In Fig. A.10 the frequency of maximum absorption in carbon dioxide is plotted as a function of the percentage of various added gases.[26] Using eqs. A.32 and A.33 one can determine from data of this kind the lifetime of a vibration quantum and the number of

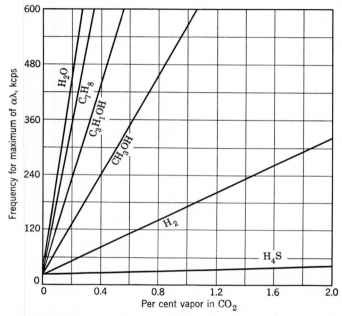

Fig. A.10.   The frequency of maximum absorption in carbon dioxide as influenced by added impurities (V. O. Knudsen and E. Fricke).

collisions necessary for energy transfer.   It turns out that k_{10} is proportional to the percentage of added components.   The factor of proportionality depends on the chemical affinity of the added gas to the principal gas.

Also, k_{10} depends on the pressure and temperature of the gas, being a kinetic quantity.   It is found, for example, that for carbon dioxide the two velocities c_0 and c_∞ both increase with temperature, but that the increase is greater for c_∞ than for c_0.   This means that the inflection point of the dispersion curve shifts to higher frequencies; i.e., the

[26] A. van Itterbeck and P. Mariens, *Physica, 4* (1937), 609, *5* (1938), 153, *7* (1940), 125 and 909.   V. O. Kundsen and E. Fricke, *J. Acoust. Soc. Amer., 12* (1940), 255.

relaxation time becomes shorter as the temperature is increased. For carbon dioxide, a rise in temperature from $-32°C$ to $145°C$ leads to a decrease of the number of collisions necessary for the loss of one vibrational quantum to only one-quarter of the number at $-32°C$.

The characteristic absorption behavior of carbon dioxide suggests an application of sonic analysis in physiology. It has been demonstrated that the absorption in a 60-kcps sound wave transmitted through exhaled air is a function of its carbon dioxide content.[27] Such an instantaneous determination of carbon dioxide yield, which is an important diagnostic quantity in the clinical evaluation of basic metabolism, may have advantages over the present time-consuming methods.[28]

A.5 Structural Aspects of Sound Propagation in Liquids

The properties of matter in the liquid phase are qualitatively described by two characteristics: (1) lack of shear rigidity,[29] in common with gases, and (2) very low compressibility, in common with solids. In other physical properties, such as fusion and solution effects, viscosity, density, and dielectric behavior, liquids partly resemble gases and partly solids.

In the transition from the solid phase to the gaseous phase the liquid phase appears in a relatively small temperature range.   Solids exist over a temperature range from absolute zero to about 10^2–10^3 degrees Kelvin. Gases exist from about $100°K$ to many millions of degrees. Between these two extremes the liquid state occupies a region which is often less than $100°$ wide. At temperatures and pressures above the critical point, the liquid phase does not exist at all.

Thus the liquid phase might be considered as a narrow transition zone between solids and gases.   At low temperatures near the freezing point the structural concepts of the solid phase are applicable, while at high temperatures near the boiling point the statistical concepts of the kinetic theory of gases are more useful.   Both of these approaches, however, are only approximations to more accurate descriptions of the liquid phase.[30]

[27] W. D. Keidel, *Nuovo Cimento*, *5* (1950), Suppl. 2, 610.

[28] S. J. Haldane, *Methods of Air Analysis*, Griffin and Co., London, 1920.

[29] This is true only in a first approximation.   Second-order phenomena like vortex formation, streaming, and drag forces (see Section 6.6) are dependent on the presence of viscous shear stresses.   See, for example, P. J. Westervelt, *J. Acoust. Soc. Amer.*, *25* (1953), 60, and W. L. Nyborg, *J. Acoust. Soc. Amer.*, *25* (1953), 68.

[30] H. Born and H. S. Green, *A General Kinetic Theory of Liquids*, Cambridge University Press, 1949.   H. S. Green, *The Molecular Theory of Fluids*, Interscience, New York, 1952.

The packing of matter   The microscopic arrangement of ions, atoms, or molecules in a macroscopic lump of matter is called the packing, which may take place in varying degree of order or regularity. A gas is commonly described as structureless since the molecules are moving with high velocity and hence have no fixed relationship to other molecules. The statistical distribution of velocities is well known, and there is a mean separation of the molecules at any instant. We showed in Section 6.3 that the average separation of molecules is given by the mean free path, the average distance traveled by a molecule between two collisions.

In solids, on the other hand, the packing occurs in well-defined configurations since the molecules are essentially fixed in space and vibrate about equilibrium positions. Contributions from the fields of crystallography and X-ray, and electron and neutron diffraction have resulted in a precise knowledge of the geometrical structure of most solids. The structure of a solid is specified by completely different physical quantities than those used to describe gases. A structural arrangement of high regularity can be described by indicating how the molecules are distributed around the points of various types of space lattices.[31]   In such a case one speaks of long-range order, because the appearance of the solid structure is the same from any lattice point, regardless of its position. A liquid, on the other hand, is characterized by a short-range order. In the immediate neighborhood of a given molecule some degree of order is noticeable in the packing, but the local structure is not repeated regularly as the distance from a given point is increased.

The different types of packing are illustrated in Fig. A.11 and A.12, in which the radial distribution function $dN/dr = 4\pi r^2 \rho(r)$ is plotted versus radial distance. This function represents the number of molecules, atoms, or ions in a spherical shell of radius r, thickness dr and local density $\rho(r)$. In an ideal solid lattice at zero absolute temperature, which is illustrated by the solid lines in Fig. A.11, the molecules are located only at certain fixed distances. In real solids at elevated temperatures, however, the molecules perform thermal vibrations about their equilibrium positions, and there may be small irregularities in the lattice dimensions. Therefore, there is a broadening of the distribution function as indicated by the dashed line in Fig. A.11.

The distribution for a liquid is indicated by the solid line in Fig. A.12. The occurrence of the peaks shows that some regularity of

[31] See C. S. Barrett *Structure of Metals* Chapter 2, McGraw-Hill, New York, 1943, and C. Kittel *Introduction to Solid State Physics*, Chapter 1, John Wiley & Sons, New York, 1953.

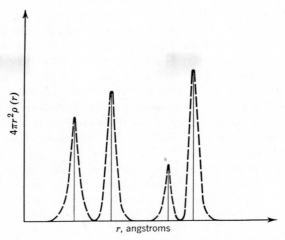

Fig. A.11. Density distribution function in a typical solid. The distribution indicated by the line spectrum (solid vertical lines) corresponds to zero absolute temperature. At elevated temperatures a band spectrum (dashed curve) is obtained.

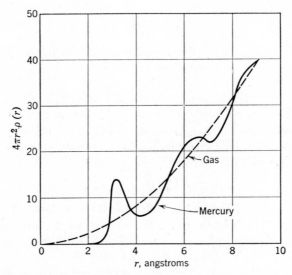

Fig. A.12. The distribution function in liquid mercury as determined by X-ray analysis (N. S. Gingrich).

structure is present in liquids. It is also apparent that the evidence of an ordered structure is blurred out as the distance from any lattice point increases. The parabolic dependence of dN/dr which results at larger distances closely resembles the distribution function for gases which is indicated in Fig. A.12 by a dashed line. In gases, $\rho(r)$ is independent of distance and hence $dN/dr = $ constant $\times r^2$. The solid curve in Fig. A.12 represents the distribution function of liquid mercury as determined by an X-ray diffraction method.[32]

The concept of packing leads to the definition of three different kinds of volume for a liquid. One is the macroscopic volume $V = M/\rho$, which is obtained by a measurement of the spatial extent of a liquid mass. Dividing the molar volume by Avogadro's number one obtains the volume of the unit cell which contains 1 molecule:

$$V_1 = V/N = M/\rho N \tag{A.34}$$

The unit cell volume, however, is only partly occupied by its allocated molecule, whose volume V_m is usually much smaller than V_1. Hence the difference $V_1 - V_m$ is actually a free volume unoccupied by matter. For one mole of matter and molecules of approximately spherical shape we may then define two additional volumes:

1. The molecular volume:

$$V_0 = NV_m \simeq N\tfrac{4}{3}\pi R^3 \tag{A.35}$$

which is the volume actually occupied by matter in space.

2. The available or free volume:

$$V_a = N(V_1 - V_m) = \frac{M}{\rho} - N\tfrac{4}{3}\pi R^3 \tag{A.36}$$

which corresponds to the spaces unoccupied by matter. The ratio of the molar volume to the molecular volume expresses the degree of packing, or packing factor

$$s = V_0/V = V_m/V_1 \tag{A.37}$$

which is the main determining factor for the compressibility of a fluid (see Table 8.1). We are now able to analyze the propagation of a sound wave through a loosely packed medium ($s < 1$) in terms of a simple model which pictures the molecules as rigid billiard balls.[33] Let the average distance between the centers of the molecules be L

[32] N. S. Gingrich, *Rev. Mod. Phys.*, *15* (1943), 90.

[33] L. Tonks, *Phys. Rev.*, *50* (1936), 955. H. Eyring and J. O. Hirschfelder, *J. Phys. Chem.*, *41* (1937), 249. J. F. Kincaid and H. Eyring, *J. Chem. Phys.*, *5* (1937), 587, and *6* (1938), 620. C. Kittel, *J. Chem. Phys.*, *14* (1946), 614.

and the free path length between their surfaces be L_f. The mechanical momentum of a sound wave is transferred from one molecule to the next with the gas kinetic velocity which from eq. 6.2 is $v_m = (3P_0/\rho)^{1/2}$. Since the molecules are assumed to be rigid they must travel only the fraction L_f/L of any distance over which momentum is transmitted. A part of the path of the sound wave is thus short circuited by the molecule; i.e., in the time internal Δt between two collisions the molecules have traveled a distance $L_f = v_m \, \Delta t$, but the momentum is transferred over a greater distance $L = c_{\text{liq}} \, \Delta t$. Equating these two expressions we obtain for the velocity of sound in a liquid

$$c_{\text{liq}} = \frac{L}{L_f} v_m = \frac{L}{L_f} (3P_0/\rho)^{1/2} \simeq \frac{L}{L_f} \left(\frac{3}{\gamma_{\text{gas}}} \right)^{1/2} c_{\text{gas}} \qquad (A.38)$$

The distances L and L_f are directly related to the free volume V_a and the molar volume V, and it can be shown that for relatively dense packing $(L > L_f)$

$$\frac{L}{L_f} \simeq 3 \frac{V}{V_a} \simeq \frac{3}{1 - s}$$

Using $\gamma \simeq 1.4$ we may now rewrite eq. A.38 in the form

$$c_{\text{liq}} \simeq 4.3 \frac{c_{\text{gas}}}{1 - s} \qquad (A.38a)$$

which establishes the importance of the packing factor s for the sound propagation of liquids. Experimentally it is found that c_{liq} is of the order of five to ten times the velocity in the vapor at the same temperature. This allows us to estimate the magnitude of the packing factor s, which is found to be between 0.15 and 0.55.

Physically, the packing of the molecules will affect both the compressibility and the density of a liquid. However, we note from eq. A.37 that an increase in density need not influence the packing as long as the molecular volume remains the same. If we build additional atomic constituents into a complex molecule without changing its size, the compressibility of the liquid will not be affected. In turn, an additional atom may increase the size of the molecule considerably without a large increase of density, but with a great reduction of the free volume. This is the case, for example, for the saturated hydrocarbons listed in Table A.4.

We note that the addition of CH_2 components changes the density only slightly, but reduces the compressibility by large amounts. The measured sound velocities therefore reveal a large influence of the length or shape of the molecules on the degree of packing. For instance, if in the benzene ring (C_6H_6) one H atom is replaced by NO_2, giving nitrobenzene, the effective volume of the molecule is increased, which causes an increase in sound velocity from 1326 m/sec to 1473 m/sec (at 20°C).

Effects due to association   Structural arrangement is influenced not only by the shape of the molecules, but also by their mutual interaction. In particular, electric dipole moments affect the compressibility since the resulting electric forces pull the molecules into tighter packing. This effect, called association, is characteristic of a class of liquids showing pronounced structural properties. The establishment of molecular order by association is counteracted by thermal agitation. In an associated liquid one may expect the ratio dV/dp in a sound wave to increase as the temperature is lowered. A compression will then lead to a more orderly alignment of adjacent molecules, which requires less space than a random packing. Since the compressibility β_a is defined as $-(dV/dp)/V$, the sound velocity $c = (1/\beta_a\rho_0)^{1/2}$ will become smaller as the temperature decreases. An example of a highly associated liquid is water whose sound velocity increases from 1422 m/sec at 0°C to 1557 m/sec at 74°C.[34]

Table A.4   Sound-Propagation Constants in Saturated Hydrocarbons at 20°C

Substance		Density (kg/m^3)		Velocity (m/sec)	Compressibility (m^2/newton)	
Pentane	C_5H_{12}	0.621		1008	158.4	
Hexane	C_6H_{14}	0.654		1083	130.4	
Heptane	C_7H_{16}	0.684	$\times 10^3$	1162	108.0	$\times 10^{-11}$
Octane	C_8H_{18}	0.703		1197	99.3	
Nonane	C_9H_{20}	0.738		1248	87.0	

For non-associated liquids, on the other hand, the following empirical relationship holds over a wide temperature range:[35]

$$c^{1/3}\frac{M}{\rho} = \text{constant} \qquad (A.39)$$

in which M is the molecular weight and ρ the density. Measurements of the dependence of sound velocity on temperature will thus furnish information on the amount of association present in a liquid. The constant in eq. A.39 is also related to other characteristic constants of liquids, such as the boiling point, the critical point, and the optical index of refraction. This is not surprising since all of them are related to the cohesion forces between the molecules and the degree of their packing.[36]

The conclusions which can be drawn from our simple model of a liquid composed of rigid balls of matter which are packed in a char-

[34] G. W. Willard, *J. Acoust. Soc. Amer.*, *19* (1947), 235.

[35] M. R. Rao, *J. Chem. Phys.*, *9* (1941), 682. R. T. Lagemann and W. S. Dunbar, *J. Phys. Chem.*, *49* (1945), 428. K. Altenburg, *Kolloid Z.*, *117* (1950), 153.

[36] A. Weissler, *J. Am. Chem. Soc.*, *71* (1949), 1272.

acteristic way may be stated as follows: the time required for the transfer of momentum from molecule to molecule in the sound wave is directly proportional to the mass of the molecules and the distances between the molecules, and it is inversely proportional to the molecular volume. Of these three causes for a change in sound velocity, the latter two are of primary importance.

Correlation with van der Waals' equation of state The kinetic model of a liquid discussed above allows us to use van der Waals' equation of state to describe the behavior of the liquid. This is a fundamental equation of state for fluids which accounts for the phenomena of condensation and evaporation which are characteristic of the transition between gaseous and liquid phase.

In van der Waals' equation, the simple gas law $PV = RT$ is extended to include the influence of intermolecular attraction and the effect of finite size of the molecules. The pressure is increased by a term a/v^2 and the "available" volume is decreased by an amount $b \simeq 4V_0 \simeq 4sV$, yielding the equation:

$$\left(P + \frac{a}{V^2}\right)(V - b) = RT \qquad (A.40)$$

One may thus combine eqs. A.40 and A.38 to obtain a new functional relationship $c_{\text{liq}} = c(\gamma, M, \rho, s)$ for the sound velocity in liquids.[37]

Measurements of sound velocity thus allow us to calculate accurate values for s and the molecular radius $R_m = \left(\frac{3}{4\pi} \frac{sV}{N}\right)^{1/3}$. The results check very well with optical refraction measurements[38] and with thermodynamic measurements at the critical point of the liquid.[39] For example, the molecular radius of benzene at 20°C evaluated from sonic measurements is 2.01×10^{-8} cm, from optical measurements 2.16×10^{-8} cm, and from a determination of the critical point 2.18×10^{-8} cm.

[37] W. Schaafs, *Ergeb. exakt. Naturw.*, *25* (1951), 110.

[38] The refraction of light depends on the total molecular volume present in a macroscopic quantity of matter. It is related to the molecular packing by the relationship

$$\frac{n^2 - 1}{n^2 + 2} = \frac{4\pi}{3} R_m{}^3 \frac{N\rho}{M} = s$$

in which n is the optical index of refraction.

[39] If T_c and p_c are the temperature and pressure at the critical point, one obtains:

$$b = \frac{RT_c}{8p_c} = 4sV$$

Let us now return to eq. A.37 for the packing factor.   The molecular Volume $V_m = sV_1$ can be assumed to be the sum of the volumes of all the atoms which make up the molecule, that is:

$$V_m = \sum_i (zA)_i$$

in which A is the atomic volume, z is the number of atoms of the same kind, and i is the number of kinds of atoms present in the molecule. In seeking a simple relationship between the sound velocity c_{liq} and the packing factor in a liquid, one may plot the product $c_{liq}V$ versus

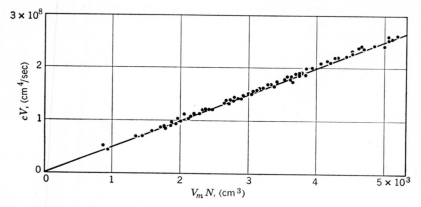

Fig. A.13.   The dependence of sound velocity on molecular packing for 92 hydrocarbon liquids (W. Schaaffs).   The product of sound velocity c and molar volume V is plotted versus the product of molecular volume V_m (as determined from the atomic constituents) and Avogadro's number N; note that $V_mN = sV$.

V_mN.   The rather striking result is shown in Fig. A.13 for 92 different aliphatic hydrocarbon compounds containing C, H, O, N, and Cl atoms.   We can thus conclude that for each organic homologous series a simple relationship exists between c_{liq} and s of the form

$$c_{liq} = Ws \qquad\qquad (A.41)$$

in which W is for each series a constant which depends on the efficiency of momentum transfer by collision between molecules.[40]   These relationships lead to the expectation that accurate measurements of

[40] For a more detailed discussion of the relationships between sound velocity and chemical constitution see W. Schaaffs, Z. phys. Chem., *194* (1944), 28–50 and 66–85; *195* (1944), 170–178; *196* (1951), 397–426.

sound velocity by use of the techniques discussed in Chapter 8 may become a valuable tool for chemical analysis.[40a]

Lattice theories of the liquid state   The distinctive feature of all lattice theories of the liquid state is that they require each molecule to be more or less bound to one position in space.   This is in opposition to the viewpoint of the gas-kinetic theories where the molecule has almost complete freedom of motion.   Once a molecule is restricted to a relatively small volume, the analysis can be simplified considerably since, in a first approximation, only the nearest neighbor need be considered.   Further, the concept of "holes" or vacant sites in the lattice is required to account for the fluidity of liquids.

Let us assume that the difference between the volume of a liquid and the volume of closest packing, $V - V_0$, is due to the presence of holes, all of equal size Δv.[41]   The number of holes N_H is a small fraction of the total number N of molecules present and is given by

$$N_H = Ne^{-U/kT} \qquad (A.42)$$

where k is the Boltzmann constant, T the temperature, and U the activation energy, i.e., the amount of work necessary to remove a molecule from a lattice position.   Then

$$V - V_0 = N \,\Delta v e^{-U/kT} \qquad (A.43)$$

If we write $n = N/V_0$ and $U = U_0 + p \,\Delta v$, then

$$V = V_0[1 + n \,\Delta v e^{-(U_0 + p\Delta v)/kT}] \qquad (A.44)$$

in which p is the external pressure on the liquid and U_0 is the amount of work necessary to form a hole when $p = 0$.   Equation (A.44) is an equation of state relating the volume, pressure, and temperature of a liquid.   It allows one to determine the compressibility and various other thermodynamic functions of interest.   For example, the isothermal compressibility is

$$\beta_i = -\frac{1}{V_0}\left(\frac{\partial V}{\partial p}\right)_T = \frac{V - V_0}{V_0}\frac{\Delta v}{kT} \qquad (A.45)$$

From eq. A.45 and $\beta_i/\beta_a = \gamma$, we obtain for the velocity of sound

$$c^2 = \gamma/\rho\beta_i = \frac{\gamma kT e^{U/kT}}{\rho n \,(\Delta v)^2} \qquad (A.46)$$

which accounts for the temperature dependence of sound velocity.

[40a] T. Karpovich, paper *P9* presented at the 47th meeting of the *Acoust. Soc. of Amer.*, New York, June 25, 1954.

[41] J. Frenkel, *Kinetic Theory of Liquids*, Oxford University Press, 1946, p. 174ff. J. S. Rowlinson and C. F. Curtiss, *J. Chem. Phys.*, *19* (1951), 1519.

Equations A.45 and A.46 illustrate the connection between the macroscopically observed sound velocity and the microscopic properties of the liquid, i.e., the molecular volume V_0, the activation energy U, and the volume of a hole, Δv.

Structural mechanisms of the sound absorption in liquids This concept of a "quasi-crystalline" structure of liquids is supported by evidence from X-ray diffraction patterns obtained in liquids[42] (see Fig. A.12). The lattice theory of the liquid state assumes that the compressibility is due to two components: the increase in potential energy when the distance between molecules is decreased, and a change in the degree of local order in the arrangement of the particles. The latter means that the arrangement is more compact when the liquid is compressed and that a more open distribution is formed upon expansion. In a sound wave of periodically alternating compression and expansion, a constant rearrangement of the particles, or in other words redistribution of their mutual orientation, or degree of dissociation or association, takes place.

These processes, which require a certain activation energy, will occur with a finite speed; therefore a phase lag between the change in degree of local order and the variation of pressure must be expected. Such an order-disorder relaxation in liquids implies the occurrence of both a velocity dispersion and a non-classical absorption. In some instances, an intramolecular relaxation of the type observed in gases (See section A.4) may also contribute to the absorption in liquids.[43]

The order-disorder relaxation suggested above is equivalent to the presence of a compressional viscosity χ in the liquid, in addition to the ordinary shear viscosity whose acoustic consequences are discussed in Section A.3. In such a case, the viscosity coefficient in eq. A.16 must be written as $\zeta = \chi + 2\eta$ according to the reasoning presented in Section A.3. The compressional viscosity in light liquids may be determined by measurements of ultrasonic streaming.[44]

[42] G. W. Stewart, *Phys. Rev.*, *37* (1931), 9; *35* (1930), 726; *31* (1928), 174; *32* (1928), 153. G. W. Stewart and R. M. Morrow, *Phys. Rev.*, *30* (1927), 232. G. W. Stewart and E. W. Skinner, *Phys. Rev.*, *31* (1928), 1. R. M. Morrow, *Phys. Rev.*, *31* (1928), 10.

[43] A thermal relaxation can be ruled out, at least for water. In water at 4°C both the temperature expansion coefficient and the quantity $(C_p - C_V)$ vanish. The sound wave thus proceeds isothermally without alternate heating and cooling, and there is no occasion for the population of internal vibrational states of the molecules to change. Hence, there cannot be any attenuation caused by a delay in thermal equilibrium and the observed non-classical absorption must be attributed to structural effects.

[44] Streaming is caused by radiation pressure in an absorbing liquid, in which there is an exponential drop of energy density along the axis of an ultrasonic beam

The ratio $\alpha_{exp}/\alpha_{class}$ can be used for a classification of liquids on the basis of structural behavior, as given in Table A.5.[45]

Table A.5   Acoustic Classification of Liquids

Class	Absorption Properties	α_{exp}/α_{cl}	Temperature Dependence of α	Type of Liquid	Examples
AI	Anomalous	3–1500	Positive; $\alpha_{exp}/\alpha_{class}$ varies with temperature	Unassociated polyatomic	Carbon disulphide, benzene, carbon tetrachloride
AII	Anomalous	1.5–3	Negative; $\alpha_{exp}/\alpha_{class}$ virtually independent of temperature	Associated polyatomic	Water, alcohols
AIII	Anomalous	5–5000	Depends critically on temperature	Organic acids esters	Acetic and formic acid, ethyl acetate
NI	Normal	1	Positive	Monatomic, diatomic	Helium; mercury; liquid oxygen
NII	Nearly normal	~1	Negative; $\alpha_{exp}/\alpha_{class}$ varies with temperature and may even become 1	Associated, polyatomic	Glycerin; castor oil; highly viscous liquids

Phase-change phenomena   We have previously noted that a liquid in some respects resembles a solid while in others it behaves more like a gas. It is then reasonable to assume that these similarities will be most apparent for liquid states in the neighborhood of the respective phase transition point. At the temperature at which a phase change occurs, there are discontinuities in the thermodynamic properties of a medium, such as the thermal expansion coefficient and the specific heat. Since sound propagation is also a function of these properties, we can expect that a sonic analysis of a medium undergoing a phase change will yield useful information on its internal structural parameters and on the characteristics of the phase transition itself.[46]

In some substances there is a decrease in sound velocity, by a factor of about 5,

---

(see Table 2.1). The resulting d-c motion of the liquid is determined by the equilibrium between a driving force proportional to $\alpha = \alpha(\chi, \eta)$ and a retarding force proportional to η. The equilibrium conditions have been worked out by C. Eckart, *Phys. Rev.*, *73* (1948), 68, and have been verified experimentally by L. N. Liebermann, *J. Acoust. Soc. Amer.*, *20* (1948), 868, and *Phys. Rev.*, *75* (1949), 1415. See also S. M. Karim and L. Rosenhead, *Rev. Mod. Phys.*, *24* (1952), 108.

[45] J. M. M. Pinkerton, *Proc. Phys. Soc. (London) B*, *62*, (1949), 129. J. J. Markham, R. T. Beyer, and R. B. Lindsay, *Rev. Mod. Phys.*, *23* (1951), 353.

[46] S. J. Lukasik, Master's thesis, Massachusetts Institute of Technology, Physics Dept., June 1953. J. R. Pellam and C. F. Squire, *Phys. Rev.*, *72* (1947), 1245.

when the substance passes from the solid to the liquid state.   This decrease results from the disappearance of long-range order.   Sound velocities in gases are smaller than the corresponding velocities in liquids by a factor of about 3.   Here the phase change brings about the disappearance of the remaining short-range order of the liquid.   As the structure becomes more open, the compressibility increases and the velocity of sound decreases.   In turn, the perturbations in pressure and temperature which occur in a sound wave may have an effect on the time rate of the phase change.   Thus details of the order-disorder transition of melting or of the inverse process of crystallization can be studied.   Measurements of sound velocity and sound absorption, and their pressure and temperature coefficients, may prove particularly useful for analysis of phase transitions which take place during polymerization of plastics, in thixotropic changes of colloidal systems, and in the solidification of amorphous substances.[47]

Near the transition point the effect of statistical fluctuations is significant; i.e., the instantaneous local deviations from the mean become important.   It appears, for example, that small regions of the second phase are formed slightly before the temperature of the transition point is actually reached.   These deviations cause anomalous behavior of the specific heat.[48]

A.6   Sound Propagation in Fluid Mixtures and Solutions

So far we have discussed sound propagation only for pure liquids, and its bearing upon the theories of viscosity, relaxation, and liquid structure.   Valuable information can also be obtained from studies of such systems as liquid mixtures, electrolytic solutions, and chemically active media.   A brief review of some experimental results and theoretical concepts will conclude this appendix.[49]

For the sound velocity in mixtures of two different liquids one might expect a simple rule such as

$$M_1 c_1 + M_2 c_2 = (M_1 + M_2) c_{12} \qquad (A.47)$$

where M_1 and M_2 are the molecular weights of the two components and c_{12} the sound velocity of the mixture.   However, since the compressibility of a liquid is primarily a function of the degree of packing and only to a lesser extent of the molecular mass, liquid mixtures actually show a more complex behavior.   Two typical examples are

[47] G. A. Sofer and E. A. Hauser, *J. Polymer Sci.*, *8* (1952), 611.   W. P. Mason and H. J. McSkimmin, *Bell System Tech. J.*, *31* (1952), 122.   J. D. Ferry, L. D. Grandine, and E. R. Fitzgerald, *J. Appl. Phys.*, *24* (1953), 911.   Y. Wada and S. Shimbo, *J. Acoust. Soc. Amer.*, *25* (1953), 594.

[48] A. R. Ubbelohde, *Trans. Faraday Soc.*, *34* (1938), 292.   P. G. Strelkov and W. P. Gatchkoosky, *Physik. Z. Sowjetunion*, *12* (1937), 58.

[49] See, for example, "Symposium on Acoustics in Chemistry," reports published in *J. Acoust. Soc. Amer.*, *25* (1953), 443–490.   A survey of the electrochemical effects of ultrasound is presented in this series by E. Yeager and F. Hovorka, p. 443.

illustrated in Fig. A.14, namely, a mixture of benzene with carbon tetrachloride and of ethyl alcohol with water. The solid curves represent experimental data, and these deviate considerably from the predictions of eq. A.47 as indicated by the dashed curves. In water and ethyl alcohol, which are both dipole liquids and therefore tend toward association, a decreased compressibility is observed. This suggests

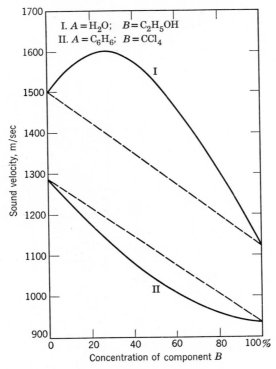

Fig. A.14. Sound velocity in two typical liquid mixtures as a function of concentration (R. Parshad).

that the degree of association is reduced by mixing. In benzene and carbon tetrachloride, which have no dipole moment, an increased compressibility is found.[50]

In liquid mixtures whose compressibility is controlled by association, the influence of temperature on the sound velocity depends on the mixture ratio. For example, pure water below 74°C has a positive temperature coefficient, but in a mixture consisting of 18

[50] O. Nomoto, *J. Phys. Soc.* (Japan), *8* (1953), 553. D. Sette, *Ricerca Sci.* (Italy), *19* (1949), 1338. R. Parshad, *T. Chem. Phys.*, *15* (1947), 418.

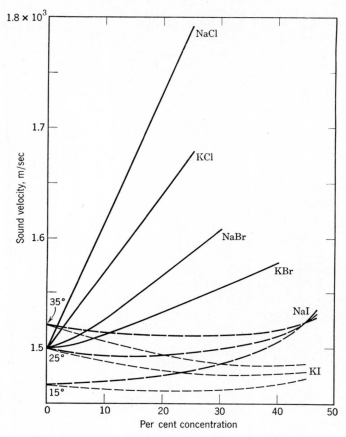

Fig. A.15. The effect of solvent concentration on sound velocity (E. B. Freyer, *J. Amer. Chem. Soc.*, *53* (1931), 1313).

per cent ethyl alcohol and water the sound velocity is independent of temperature over a range from 5° to 45°C.[51]

It has been found that the compressibilities of solutions in water decrease with concentration according to the relation

$$\beta = \beta_0 + Ac + Bc^{3/2} \qquad (A.48)$$

where β_0 is the compressibility of the solvent, c is the molar concentration of the solute, and A and B are constants depending on the

[51] Such a liquid has found useful applications in ultrasonic delay lines. See, for example, *Massachusetts Institute of Technology Radiation Laboratory Series*, *20* (1949), Chapter 12, p. 482.

molar volume of the electrolyte.   This behavior is shown in Fig. A.15. The decrease of compressibility in the presence of ions has been explained as follows: Each ion sets up an electric field which exerts a local electrostatic pressure within the water of the order of 10^4 atm. This high internal pressure leads to a closer packing of the water molecules, in much the same way as by application of high external pressures.[52]

Relaxation in chemically reacting media   A relatively high sound absorption is observed in sea water at frequencies of the order of 10^5 cps.   This absorption can be attributed primarily to the presence of a minute concentration (0.02 moles/l) of dissolved magnesium sulfate.[53]   To explain this effect, we consider a volume of a substance containing two chemical components in reaction equilibrium.   If the equilibrium constant of the chemical reaction is pressure dependent, an instantaneous decrease in volume will produce a higher initial pressure than a slow reduction of volume.   Hence, the compressibility is found to depend *on the rate* of the compression or dilation, in the manner indicated in Fig. A.7.

One consequence of this behavior is the formation of a loop in the pV diagram (see Section A.2).   The associated losses follow the relation:

$$\alpha\lambda = \frac{A\omega c}{1 + \omega^2\tau^2} \tag{A.49}$$

in which A is a characteristic constant of the substance which depends on compressibility.   The absorption maximum occurs at the frequency $\omega = 1/\tau$, which is determined by the reaction time constant τ. As demonstrated above in Fig. A.4 such a fluid will exhibit two compressibilities: a static equilibrium compressibility, and a dynamic compressibility whose value depends on the compression rate, and which approaches a limiting value at high rates of compression.   In electrolytic solutions the frequency of relaxation depends on the cation, as shown in Table A.6 for various sulfates.

The phenomena reviewed in this section suggest the possibility of determining the reaction rates of rapid chemical processes by suitable

---

[52] For example, at a hydrostatic pressure of 6000 atm the sound velocity in water at 30°C is increased by a factor of 1.553 and the compressibility is increased by a factor of 2.8.   See P. Biquard, *Rev. acoustique, 8* (1939), 130, and G. Holton, *Phys. Rev., 73* (1948), 543.

[53] L. N. Liebermann, *J. Acoust. Soc. Amer., 20* (1948), 868.   G. Kurtze and K. Tamm, *Acustica, Akust. Beih. 3* (1953), 33.   A. Weissler, *J. Acoust. Soc. Amer., 25* (1953), 651.

Table A.6   Dependence of the Relaxation Frequency in Sulphate Solutions on the Cation

Substance	$1/\tau$ (kcps)	Substance	$1/\tau$ (kcps)
$BeSO_4$	<1	$CoSO_4$	4×10^2
$NiSO_4$	10	$MnSO_4$	3×10^3
$MgSO_4$	1.3×10^2	$ZnSO_4$	$>10^5$
$MgSO_3$	1.8×10^2	$CuSO_4$	$>10^5$

measurements.[54]   For example, the explosive reactions occurring in gasoline engines have been analyzed by ultrasonic pulses propagated through the combustion chamber.[55]

[54] L. N. Liebermann, *Phys. Rev.*, *76* (1949), 1520.   M. Leontovich, *J. Exptl. Theoret. Phys.* (U.S.S.R.), *8* (1938), 40.

[55] T. P. Rona, Master's Thesis, Massachusetts Institute of Technology, Department of Electrical Engineering, submitted on May 25, 1953.

AUTHOR INDEX

441

SUBJECT INDEX